Eileen Foster

$8.95

The SCIENCE *and* PRACTICE

of

IRIDOLOGY

A SYSTEM OF ANALYZING AND CARING FOR
THE BODY THROUGH THE USE OF
DRUGLESS AND NATURE-
CURE METHODS

●

ILLUSTRATED

By

BERNARD JENSEN, D. C., N. D.

Lecturer and Teacher of the Art of Right Living

PRIVATE PRACTICE SINCE 1929; SANITARIUM PRACTICE
SINCE 1931; INSTRUCTOR IN IRIDOLOGY TO THE
PROFESSION SINCE 1935; FOUNDER OF HIDDEN VALLEY
HEALTH RANCH, ESCONDIDO, CALIFORNIA; AUTHOR
OF "THE JOY OF LIVING AND HOW TO ATTAIN IT,"
"VITAL FOODS FOR TOTAL HEALTH," "LIVING LOVELIER,"
"YOU CAN FEEL WONDERFUL — ENJOY IT NOW,"
AND "YOU CAN MASTER DISEASE."

Published By
BERNARD JENSEN, D.C., N.D.
Route 6, Box 811, Escondido, California 92025

The information and precepts set forth in this publication are designed for research and application by practitioners of the healing arts.

Possession of this publication does not authorize use of the information contained therein in contravention of federal, state, and other laws regulating the healing arts.

PRINTED IN UNITED STATES OF AMERICA
SECOND PRINTING, 1964
THIRD PRINTING, 1970
FOURTH PRINTING, 1973
FIFTH PRINTING & COPYRIGHT, 1974

TO MY SON, DAVID

IT WAS AT THE BEGINNING
OF HIS LIFE THAT I RECEIVED
MY FIRST INSPIRATION TO
GIVE LIFE TO THIS WORK.

FOREWORD

By way of definition, iridology is a science whereby the doctor or operator can tell from the markings or signs in the iris of the eye the reflex condition of the various organs of the body. In other words, it is the science of determining acute, sub-acute, chronic, and destructive stages in the affected organs of the body through their corresponding areas in the iris. Drug deposits, inherent weaknesses and living habits of the patient are also revealed in the iris of the eye.

Many authors use the term "Iridiagnosis" or "Irisdiagnosis," but I prefer to use "Iridology" because I feel the science is not the last word in determining the diagnosis of a patient according to the generally accepted methods. It reveals inherent characteristics of the tissues in an organ. It shows tissue changes resulting from proper or improper treatment. It is a check-up on both the patient and the doctor as to whether the patient is improving. It is a diagnosis that works hand in hand with natural habits of living which build health and eradicate disease.

This book is presented with the idea of enabling the reader to learn how to apply the science of iridology. It is written to bring this subject up to date and make it applicable to the ever-changing system of healing that has been developed, and to make this science conform to the changes in our civilized methods, our occupations, our city life, our drugs, and to the other types of diagnosing in use today.

You will find in this book many developments that have not been presented in the iridology books of the past twenty or thirty years. The writer does not pretend to know it all, however, and suggests that you study the material with an open mind, after which you may go as far as you please, either to prove or disprove it.

Judging from the type of inquiry which I receive from time to time, I believe that some information in connection with my own start in this work may be worth mentioning here. In the first place, I found it difficult to find a course of study on iridology in any school, but my interest was so aroused by the little knowledge gained through studying with the few doctors practicing iridology that I was determined to learn more.

Twice I closed my office—the first time for nearly a year and the second time for over six months—to study iridology and its related sciences. In my travels I spent a great deal of time studying the theoretical and practical work, and in most cases the time and money spent were sacrificed as I learned much that I had to weed out and discard later. As an example, some instructors offered to teach me how to determine pregnancy, and other natural phenomena

If it can be done, I have yet to be shown. Only what I found to be worthwhile is included in this book.

A considerable sum was spent on cameras alone so that the eyes could be photographed in such a way as to prove that iridology merits classification as an exact science. Many X-ray photographs and many blood tests were taken to prove to myself that the iris was either reliable or not in revealing body and tissue responses.

It would be impossible to compile this material in a manner whereby one could know all that is necessary about iridology, without touching upon its related sciences. I suggest, therefore, that you read the book as a whole, bearing in mind that the index will be complete enough to enable you to refer to passages and paragraphs which you want to emphasize or review.

Bernard Jensen

ABOUT THE AUTHOR

The author was born in Stockton, California, in 1908. As the result of a decision to enter upon a course of study which would enable him and his family to live healthfully, he attended the West Coast Chiropractic College, graduating in 1929. Though much illness had prevailed in his family, he had no idea of becoming a doctor until his interest became so intense in this field that full time was devoted to learning how to become well and how to maintain a good standard of health.

He went to New York, studied with Dr. Benedict Lust, and worked at his sanitarium in Butler, New Jersey. In his studies he became well acquainted with Dr. Tilden and with Dr. Kellogg of Battle Creek fame. His travels took him throughout the country, studying groups of people. Of particular interest to him were those in Baja, California (Lower California), in Mexico, and in Canada where he studied natural Indian life and the Dukaboors, a Russian vegetarian colony. His interest in human nature attracted him to such training courses as "Personology," which includes vocational guidance, marriage counseling, and human behavior problems. He is a certified analyst from the Personology Foundation. His most recent study has been at the Pacific College of Naturopathic Physicians.

While traveling in Europe and visiting many of the spas there, Doctor Jensen observed the methods of the nature cure sanitariums and learned much about the old nature cure water treatments.

Always uppermost in the doctor's mind has been his interest in iridology, and he has conferred with many teachers and practitioners in this field both in this country and abroad.

In his research he spent considerable time working with cameras and experimenting with color, and he has made diagnoses from at least 300,000 eyes. His work has developed into a practice of preventive therapeutics, teaching people how to gain and how to maintain good health. His sanitarium practice has given him the privilege of observing his own methods at work. His experiences have been brought forth in this volume to be used as practical material by those who would like to learn more for the higher good of man in a much neglected field.

ABOUT THE BOOK

This book is compiled for the sole purpose of acquainting you with an extraordinary science of analyzing human ailments. The science of iridology has not been presented too well in this country, and most of us who have the knowledge had to dig it out from the few books so far written and learn from teachers inadequately equipped to teach. Furthermore, the teaching of this science definitely has been neglected. This book has been written with one idea: to teach those who have the desire to learn this subject as simply and as clearly as possible.

We have dealt very little with non-essentials, but have dealt lavishly, and perhaps redundantly, with those portions of the subject which we feel are important to impress upon you. We have chosen the simplest ideas to approach the subject in the simplest manner, and we have used as many kinds of charts and illustrations as possible to better present the subject from all views. Some of you are more color-minded than others; some of you will see the chemical side of the science first; others of you will want the mechanical interpretation first.

However, it is well to look at the whole program and learn what you can by seeing the whole picture first from both the philosophical and theoretical standpoints. The book is planned in such a way that you can refer back to any particular portion you wish, and we have tried to give you the correlating ideas between the usual way of diagnosing and treating and that of the Science of Iridology. The entire subject of course is not covered in this volume; there are books yet to be written on iris studies which are still in the experimental stage. We only hope that this book serves as your beginning in a useful field and helps you get practical instruction.

This is the first time iridology has been presented with the aid of the photographic medium. Our unique photography and art work bring the science of analyzing through the iris up to date in its approach. Photography has made it possible to teach it in a simpler and more complete manner. Whereas previously we had to rely upon incorrect and incomplete drawings, now, through our persistent and persevering efforts and over eighteen years of study, we give you the true reproduction of the iris and its manifestations. We have diagnosed approximately 150,000 patients and have taken thousands of colored photographs in order to present our subject in an understandable light.

To master this science will require careful attention to details, never-ending patience, and keen insight for developing the ability to find first causes.

The presentation of this book on the subject of iridology is humbly made to the profession, with due recognition of the arduous efforts of our pioneers in this work. First steps are always the hardest, and so in this book, as in previous efforts, there may appear evidences of faltering. Such evidences must, of course, be used as a basis for discussion and not criticism, so that by intelligent and sincere cooperation the, as yet hidden, benefits of iridology may be brought to light for the general good.

The historical and anatomical factors presented are not complete. The historical information, though of good preparatory value, must be viewed as of passing interest; anatomical considerations must be subjected to further intensive laboratory and clinical research. A later edition will cover these two items more fully.

We acknowledge indebtedness for pioneer work in this field to

Ignatz von Peczely	J. Haskell Kritzer
Nils Liljequist	R. M. McLain
Henry E. Lane	F. W. Collins
Henry Lindlahr	Peter Johannes Thiel
	Marko J. Petinak

"If any man can convince me and bring home to me that I do not think or act aright, gladly will I change; for I search after truth, by which man never yet was harmed. But he is harmed who abideth on still in his deception and ignorance."

—Marcus Aurelius Antoninus

INTRODUCTION

Modern practice is proving to us more conclusively every day that man, in his complex structure, is very incompletely understood in spite of our advances in science. Certainly we are becoming increasingly aware that a faulty premise underlies a method which must first determine the name of a disease, classify it according to its symptomatology, and then treat it on the basis of the symptoms. This method of diagnosis, when finished, deals with effects only; and in describing and naming a million and one symptoms from the few basic causes of disease, a complex procedure is established.

There are many who try to study iridology with a skeptical mind. All new things that are given to us are accepted with a certain amount of skepticism by those who seem to be grounded in a system that is satisfactory for the moment. However, all systems are changing today and there is no reason why we should be bound to any one train of thought without investigating something new, without realizing that possibly there is more to be known than that which we have learned even in the finest colleges in the land.

Statistics have shown that the Mayo Brothers Clinic has been in the past, only 42% correct in their diagnoses. In the June, 1929 issue of the FORUM, Mr. T. Swann Harding writes:

"As a matter of fact, I heard Dr. Charles Mayo make a proud boast before a surgical congress in Washington, D. C., in 1927. He boasted that the Mayo Clinic had attained the phenomenal record of fifty per cent correct diagnoses. This included, of course, autopsies upon patients who had died, but whose ailment the clinic had diagnosed correctly. It is probably a high mark for all time. Certainly few would contend that the snap diagnosis of the average general practitioner working alone is right in more than one case out of five."

Since the Mayo Clinic treats in accordance with its diagnoses, its treatments must therefore have been only 42%, or as Dr. Charles Mayo stated, 50% correct. If Mayo Brothers, who have the finest institution to work with, were only, at tops, fifty per cent correct, how correct, even now, could the less skilled doctors be with their inferior equipment for both diagnosis and treatment?

A low percentage of correct medical diagnoses also has been revealed by Dr. John Cabot of Harvard University. The shame in all this is the fact that before allopaths can treat, they must decide upon their diagnoses. Since they treat in accordance with their diagnoses, may we not conclude that their treatments must therefore still be only forty to fifty percent correct? No wonder there are so many doctor-shoppers today.

There is no doubt that disease is just as baffling to the doctor today as it was back in the 1800's, regardless of the new "wonder" drugs and the numerous doctors who are seeking cures for the many diseases that are increasing so rapidly today. We are developing many new kinds of diseases and symptoms that we never before had. These symptoms, to which are attached new disease names, are the outgrowth of the suppression of inflammations that have arisen in the body through civilized living conditions. New diagnostic methods are needed to determine the causes underlying these symptoms.

It required a spectrographic analysis of one patient in a Los Angeles hospital to determine that it was arsenic poisoning causing symptoms of appendicitis. How many doctors have spectrographic diagnostic instruments in their offices, and how many appendicitis operations are performed in the wrong diagnosis of such cases? Certainly, with all that is happening in the human body, more reliable diagnostic methods are needed when looking for the patient's trouble.

The percentage of incorrect diagnosing is almost as great today as it was back in 1927 due to the increase in disease symptoms. This increase, together with the additional combinations of X-Ray, radium, sulfa drugs and more refined foods, makes it difficult to diagnose accurately. Symptoms developed today are entirely different from symptoms developed from the canned foods, white flour and quinine of the 1920's. Changes in living habits also change the manifestations of the various symptoms of disease.

In approaching the study of iridology, it might be well to be open-minded and investigate what is brought to you by one who once was a skeptic himself. I have taken it upon myself to prove iridology as thoroughly as possible in my own way, and I believe that anyone who endeavors to get what is worthwhile out of this science will feel rewarded. There is a place for iridology, but at the start we acknowledge that it is not all-inclusive. It has a definite place when we are interested in preventive medicine; when we are interested in teaching people how to live correctly.

Most doctors are kept busy these days thinking up names for new disease manifestations which are being developed constantly because civilization is making many changes in man's habits, environment and family life. He lives indoors more than ever, has to breathe more carbon monoxide gas than he did twenty years ago, and he is subject to powerful electrical influences. The noise of the city, the rapid pace of factory life, etc., all take a toll of health and vitality. Thus, new symptoms are bound to develop, but no matter how numerous these become, we still have only the same number of body organs in which diseases can settle. No matter how our habits of living may be altered, the same organs will still be affected.

Of course, the ways in which the organs may be affected occur in a variety of combinations, each combination having its separate symptoms. But rather than have an unlimited number of names to designate these symptoms, is it not better to employ a method whereby we can directly find the cause, regardless of the name? Many symptoms appear in the patient with nerve tension; a deficiency of minerals and vitamins will also create additional symptoms. But why have names for all the symptoms when there is a means of determining the source of the nerve tension as well as the chemical imbalance of the tissues? From the diagnostician's standpoint, there are claimed to be some 38,000 diseases yet four general classifications sum them up:

1. Chemical: Toxemia, infections, chemical imbalance.

2. Mechanical: Spinal lesions, trauma, pressure.

3. Psycho-somatic: Incoordination between the mental and physical.

4. Environmental: Atmosphere, occupation, social factors, etc.

Iridology is of more value to the doctor in his relationship to the patient than any other analysis I know. Through most forms of diagnosis it is difficult to determine tissue changes as they occur in the various parts of the body. In this science we have a method of studying the actual tissue change. We have an opportunity of seeing by an external sign the internal organs change to a better state of health. The real value of iridology is due to the fact that we have a direct check on the patient. We can tell whether he is improving in health, or if his condition is becoming worse. We also have a check on the doctor, as to whether he is giving the proper advice to the patient. When the patient is following his advice and there are no changes for the better, something must be wrong. We have a check on the doctor's knowledge, the type of patient with whom he is dealing, the patient's inherent qualities, and we know the possibilities for the patient's recovery.

A true doctor must be a blessing to patients, not only for this moment, but in years to come.

In iridology, the important fundamental is the appearance in the iris of signs that new tissue is replacing old tissue. Who would not exchange an old body for a new one?

Having studied this particular method of analysis for eighteen years, we feel there is no reason for any condemnation of iridology. We have heard many practitioners express an opinion or condemn it after only thumbing through a book for perhaps ten minutes, but these remarks do not alter the findings of one who has spent years trying to fathom this science. Iridology can be used in conjunction with any other form of analysis and diagnosis in helping a patient to a better state of health.

This form of analysis is developed through natural therapeutic methods rather than from the medical point of view. The person who spends any time in studying this method will find there is still more to know, for iridology is not by any means a finished science. We know there is more truth to be found in the eyes than can ever be interpreted by the iridologist examining them.

Iridology has many advantages over any other form of diagnosis: The iridologist can determine the inherent structure and the working capacity of an organ, can detect environmental strain, and can tell whether a person is anemic and in what stage the anemia exists, although the exact blood count cannot be determined from the iris of the eye. He can determine the constructive ability of the blood, not from the blood count, but from the standpoint of ability to circulate the amount of blood needed for the proper repair of body organs. He can determine the nerve force, the responsive healing power of tissue, and the inherent ability to circulate the blood. This latter is just as important in the repair of tissue as the blood count. There are patients with a good blood count who are very sick,

and others with a low blood count who feel well. Pressure symptoms, which may be of a mechanical nature such as prolapsus or ptosis, can also be determined.

The iris of the eye can show acute, subacute, chronic, and destructive stages in the body. Many other factors are also revealed, such as organic and functional changes, inherent weaknesses, and how we respond to our environment with the body we possess. It foretells the development of many conditions long before they have manifested into disease symptoms. It reveals the suppression of disease through mal-treatment, such as the administration of drugs, which is not the right way to correct any condition. It indicates when tissue is not being replenished and rejuvenated. When symptoms disappear, most of us say we are well, but the body may be far from well.

It is impossible to tell from the eyes what germ life exists in the body, but when tissues have degenerated to the stage where germ life exists in various parts of the body, it will be reflected in the iris. In most of such cases, other forms of diagnosis should also be used.

Since in the last twenty years man has developed nutritional diseases, nervous disorders and similar troubles, having entirely different symptoms than ever before known, let us remember that these merely represent different combinations of causes manifesting in the same organs of the body. Let us determine the nature and the degree of the congestion, place the patient in the proper environment chemically and mechanically, and watch for changes. If the patient is abiding by laws of health, his irises will indicate that he is, and if the doctor is giving proper treatment and guidance, the patient's irises will show healing signs. All this can be determined through iris analysis. As already pointed out, iridology is a good check on both doctor and patient.

This system of analysis makes apparent the need for application of all the healing arts, and the doctor who understands it must be so broad and rounded out in his understanding that he is able to use all forms of healing in order to better help his patient. For example, surgery may be unavoidable in certain advanced cases, although for those who will cooperate with natural methods, surgery usually can be avoided.

Through iridology patients can be warned in time for prevention of disease. Today there is a challenge that never has existed before for the doctor who uses natural methods.

THE SCIENCE AND PRACTICE OF IRIDOLOGY

CONTENTS

Foreword
About The Author
About The Book
Introduction

PART I

INTRODUCTION TO THE SCIENCE OF IRIDOLOGY

PART II

INSTRUCTION IN METHODS OF APPLICATION

PART III

INTERPRETATION OF IRIS MANIFESTATIONS

PART IV

PICTORIAL SECTION

PART V

CASE HISTORIES

PART VI

ADVANCED RESEARCH IN IRIDOLOGY

Part I

INTRODUCTION
to the
SCIENCE of IRIDOLOGY

1

HISTORICAL HIGHLIGHTS

He that hath a truth and keeps it,
Keeps what not to him belongs.
But performs a selfish action,
And a fellow mortal wrongs.

—Andrew Jackson Davis

Most of the text books on iridology give a rather thorough outline of the stages and development of the science, so we will go into this only briefly. Whether the history is true or not is no reflection on the science as it is being developed today. The account of the original discovery runs something like this: Dr. Ignatz von Peczely of Egervar, near Budapest, Hungary, discovered nature's record in the eye quite by accident when only a boy of ten years. While playing with an owl, he happened to break one of its legs. He also happened to notice the appearance of a dark stripe in the lower region of the iris of the bird, and later found that this darkened area corresponded to the location of the broken leg. Eventually this black streak became a tiny black spot, around which were white lines and shading. This incident made a lasting impression upon the mind of the future doctor, and when working later in the college hospital in surgical wards, he had a good opportunity to observe the eyes of patients after accidents and before and after operations. In this manner he was enabled to construct the first chart of the iris.

As far as we know, Doctor von Peczely did not follow up the relations suggested by the changes in the iris of the owl until about 1861, when he was treating his very sick mother. At the age of 36 he became interested in medicine and studied first in Budapest in 1862. In 1864 he went on to Vienna. In 1866 he started practicing in Budapest, and published his first book on the iris, "Discovery in the Realm of Nature and Art of Healing." This work was made known in Germany by August Zoeppritz. Dr. Emil Schlegel of Tuebingen published a book on the results of von Peczely's work.

There was also a Swedish homeopath, Nils Liljequist, who discovered and improved many of the methods of iris diagnosis and brought this work to America. His writings were translated into two volumes called "Diagnosis from the Eye."

It is interesting to note that although these men lived many miles apart and did not know each other, they wrote similar books at the same time, even writing alike word for word in many instances.

Today, after many years of research work by prominent doctors, most of them medical men, all organs of the body have been represented in charts developed through the efforts of these various doctors. Dr. Henry Edward Lane, a native of Austria, came to this country and taught iridology to Dr. Henry Lindlahr of Chicago. Doctor Lane wrote the first iridology book published in this country, entitled "Iridology, the Diagnosis from the Eye." This book was copyrighted and is in the Congressional Library in Washington. The sixth edition was published in 1904. Doctor Lindlahr, as Doctor Lane's student, gave iridology serious study and applied it in his work in natural therapeutics. He wrote a very valuable reference book entitled "Iris Diagnosis," which is Volume VI of his library on nature cure. Doctor Lindlahr was the one who favored the regime of bringing back the acute conditions which began every chronic condition in the body. This retracing method is thoroughly discussed in later chapters on healing crises.

It was Dr. Nils Liljequist who discovered, through the effects of vaccines and drugs such as quinine and iodine, that certain color changes and markings eventually appear in the irises of patients who take drugs. In his own words he says:

"In my thirteenth or fourteenth year I was vaccinated the second time. Being formerly hale and hearty, I now became sickly; first the lymph glands of my neck began to swell, then I was taken ill with malaria, vehement cough, influenza, polyps appeared in the nose, terrible pains in the bones of the legs,—and all that in the course of a year after the vaccination. Physicians were consulted for years. They always prescribed iodine to besmear the swollen glands, quinine for malaria, and used the tongs to remove the polyps which, however, reappeared every year. Thus years passed by. In the meantime I noticed how the color of. my eyes changed more and more, and when twenty years of age I brought forth my discovery: 'Quinine and iodine change the color of the iris; formerly I had blue eyes, now they are greenish with red spots in them.' Nevertheless, I continued taking medicine, in spite of the warning of Dr. T., a homeopath and then a teacher at the Helsingborg gymnasium. He even offered me homeopathic remedies and let me try small granules of sugar. But why didn't I accept his kind offer? I often regretted it, but

then my sound judgment was disturbed by a newspaper article which wholly ridiculed homeopathy. I took the same standpoint which the Royal Swedish Board of Medicine still takes in the year 1893 and believed that homeopathic medicine contained nothing but 'sugar, starch, and water.' Besides I desired to become a physician myself and did not care to promote the 'silly teachings' of homeopathy. But the longer and the more I suffered, the more vanished my admiration for the sacrificing, philanthropic vocation of the physician, and finally I lost my liking for it altogether.

"When I came to the city of Lund in 1871, I consulted there new physicians, hoping they would prescribe for me some better mixtures; but I was disappointed. I continually got quinine and iodine with the addition of iron which should help my exhausted stomach. I began to protest, but the physician declared that it would mean my death if I stop taking quinine. As I did not like to die quite so young, I strictly followed his advice. Sometimes I got up to three grams of quinine per dosis. Thus I spent six of the best years of my life on the sick-bed. Oh! If I had only conformed myself to suffer from malaria, I should have felt well at least some time in my life, as the fever does not appear daily during the whole year. But on account of the quinine and iodine dosing I had been constantly sick since my seventeenth year; every day vehement headache, especially in the forenoon, heaviness and dullness above the eyes, ringing in the ears,—all symptoms of quinine poisoning.

"Finally in my thirtieth year I arrived at the conviction that there must be other methods to acquire health, and other remedies besides those which I had taken. Professor Jaeger's work *Die Neural-Analyse* convinced me of the truth and excellence of homeopathy, and in the year 1882 I became my own physician, and I did not get . any worse on that account. On the contrary, in spite of having suffered from malaria for seventeen years, and in spite of the immense quantities of quinine and iodine which I had swallowed, I am now at 45 years of age quite a healthy man, full of love and vigor for work."

Other scientists also have used and contributed to this science. For example, Peter Johannes Thiel of Germany is considered one of the great iridologists of the day. Dr. J. Haskell Kritzer has written a very splendid textbook called "Iris Diagnosis and Guide in Treatment." Dr. Marko J. Petinak and Dr. F. W. Collins have contributed valuable charts. Probably the greatest recent contributor to the development of iridology in this country is Dr. R. M. McLain of Oakland, California, who has been teaching this science for many years.

In the past the provisions for learning iridology have been very limited. Very few schools and colleges have taught it. Most of the men who know this science have had to learn it by their own efforts. It has been my endeavor to correlate and to bring together into a volume all published material, to include my years of experience, and to present material which will teach this science logically, giving practical explanations and a practical foundation upon which to base conclusions.

2

THE PHILOSOPHICAL PHASE

Sit down before a fact as a little child, be prepared to give up every preconceived notion, follow humbly wherever and to whatever abysses nature leads, or you shall learn nothing.

—Thomas Huxley

In order to determine abnormalities in the body and to make use of the iris findings, there is a definite philosophy which must be understood and applied. In order to understand the science of iridology, it is necessary to be in accord with the philosophy that goes with it. What more need a doctor know than the location of the inflammation in the body, the stage it is in, how it arrived there, how to free the body of it, and most of all, *when* you have freed it? The person who believes sulfa drugs will cure a disease, would be likely to disregard the significance of the alterations which will be recorded in the iris as a result of administration of these drugs. A workable philosophy will help us to understand that the "eyes are the windows of the soul." Truly, they bear witness to the workings and conditions of every organ of the body.

To know this science completely would be impossible. The honest iridologist realizes that more Truth is recorded in the eyes than he is capable of analyzing. When we see evidences in the eyes of improved conditions, we are reminded of the quotation from the Bible, "The light of the body is the eye; if therefore thine eye be single, thy whole body shall be full of light. But if thine eye be evil, thy whole body shall be full of darkness." I remember one of my old teachers telling me that the white

areas in the iris are likened to the angels of heaven, while the dark or black areas are compared to the devil of hell.

The perfect eye shows no flaws,—no holes, no inherent weaknesses, no distortion of fibres, no deposits, and is a perfect color, either blue or brown. The ordinary diagnostician, not knowing what the appearance of the perfect eye is, would be unable to understand, and probably unwilling to believe, that any variation from this perfection is a sign of lowered function, a condition of dis-ease or dis-harmony. One who analyzes from the standpoint of the cause and effect relations in natural law, will be able not only to recognize the disorders which are represented in the iris, but will recognize the progress of correction, and will observe and follow the healing signs as they become manifest in the iris. This person will be aware that a sound philosophy is connected with the science of iridology.

Doctors employing natural methods of healing know that health is affected by habitual diet, and that the body must live by what it gets through its environment. Man molds himself in accordance with whatever he feeds his body (the solids and liquids taken into his stomach), by the air that comes to his lungs, by the luminous ether that comes to the skin and the eyes, and by the vibrations that are around him, which are food for his "feeling" body. In order for man's health to be maintained, his food must be properly balanced, and if there is radical departure from that upon which he was meant to live, that which God created for him, he develops a state of inharmony, discord, and disease. We know that a horse fed too much alfalfa will have diarrhea and will not be able to work properly, and if given too many oats will become overheated.

Why should we expect disease to accompany old age? Why not be young at fifty, sixty, or even seventy? Why not be limber, active, and able to walk around and enjoy life? We build up eating habits in our early years, take drugs and other remedies that develop chronic diseases, and we do nothing about learning to take the proper care of ourselves.

It is not pleasant for the well person to have so many sick people around. Many patients are desirous of doing the right thing, so it is time they are taught "how to live." Although man has changed it considerably, the Garden of Eden is still here. Few dare to tell the truth because of the fear of consequences.

There is not all the freedom of thought in the healing arts that there should be, and if there is to be true healing in the future, there must be more harmony among the practitioners. That healing group which does the most fighting within itself will die through its own disunity. Much is criticized about the methods being used today, so true healing must assert and prove itself. People live in more fear today than ever and there is so much in the "feeling" world regarding illness—cancer, for example—that once a person has it, he considers himself doomed, makes his will and gives up. A person who has high blood pressure or a stroke feels finished. The healing arts as practiced today do not offer much to soothe the ailing mind.

The true healing art is one in which we teach a patient to change his living habits to conform to natural laws so that instead of having to rebuild a sick body, he can *prevent* disease in the first place. One of my greatest criticisms of present-day healing methods is that serious conditions are allowed to develop before corrective measures are taken. Do you not agree that a poor policy was employed when you find cancer or arthritis in a patient, and *know* that he lived it, ate it, breathed it, and had it coming on for twenty or thirty years? Consider the patient who has lived on devitalized flour products and vitamin-B-less products for many years, which definitely cause heart trouble, who comes to the doctor with heart failure. The doctor probably starts giving him vitamin B. Why not natural foods in the first place? Then he would not have developed the heart trouble. If the doctor consulted could have foretold what was ahead for the patient, as is possible in the use of iridology, and had given warning instead of allowing the patient's difficulty to develop, he would have been in the field of preventive therapeutics. I am sure that is what the average patient wants. To prevent disease in the first place is the goal.

We cannot do much about the past, but what a tremendous job for the future! There is no use going to the food processors and complaining that their numerous varieties of devitalized goodies are depleting the vitality of the American people; telling Breakfast Cereal Companies that they have cheated the American people of vitamins and minerals needed for good health by advertising and selling "foodless foods" for half a century. Do you know that their reply would be: "This is what people want, and we serve the people."

There is so much mystery surrounding all the different forms of healing today that people are held in ignorance, and when they go to a doctor, nine times out of ten they get into the wrong hands. The person who has fallen or twisted his body needs mechanical help, as performed by the osteopath, chiropractor, mechano-therapist, and others. If he went to a dietitian, he would be in the wrong hands. The same person could develop stomach trouble from eating coffee and doughnuts, and would be in the wrong hands if he sought cure through a practitioner who employed only mechanical methods, medical aid, water treatments, or spiritual endeavors. Before he could get well he would need dietetic or chemical procedures and a teacher of right living to change his habits. In my busy office, seventy-five per cent of the patients are doctor-shoppers, looking for a "cure," looking for a doctor, not for a specialist in one kind of healing.

Patients have little knowledge of their bodies. When they get into trouble they do not know whom to consult. The numerous divisions of our healing arts have developed because doctors are not doctors—they are specialists. The average eye, ear, nose and throat specialist, for example, does very little to correct the spine, the colon, or the diet; the surgeon does very little to investigate the cause underlying a diseased condition upon which he is going to operate. We have cult after cult developing as specialists—all the way from nudists to mental therapists. Some think diet accomplishes everything; others believe that a little water on the abdomen would cure every disease from fallen arches to festered eyebrows. So there is a lot of work to do in the healing profession, whether it be in the natural healing art or others.

The person who studies iridology and the philosophy that goes with it will find where the real doctor is, where the causes of dis-ease must be looked for; where the "cure" comes from, and what methods are necessary for removal of the condition revealed.

I believe the reason diagnosing conditions from the iris of the eye has met with so much rejection and criticism is that many who have taken up this form of analysis and diagnosis have attempted to use it as those who try palm reading for predicting the future. Those who really are interested in knowing a fundamental means of determining pathological readings in the body certainly should undertake the study of iridology.

Iridology is still a new science; there are many changes to be made. But there is something basic behind it that deals with the physiological and pathological changes in the body. When we begin to see how the history of the patient coincides with the findings in the iris of the eye, the true meaning of these findings is revealed to us and the value of iridology as a form of analysis is understood.

Even the most competent and reputable physician knows that addition of a valuable technique is always an asset to him. And certainly iridology can be of much value to the surgeon, for through it he can determine the difference between the true and the false appendix inflammation; he would have something at his command that would be invaluable. We all are familiar with patients who do not feel much better after a serious operation and who require many months to recuperate. There are definite reasons for these conditions, and we want to find a method for preventing them.

It would indeed be a wonderful thing if we could amalgamate the healing arts and agree without prejudice. One field could help the other instead of working against one another as in the past. All the nature cure books and books on iridology seem to criticize the medical art for its use of surgery, vaccines, drugs and injections. I believe they can accomplish their goal without using the above methods. This kind of criticism has developed out of differences of opinion, and sometimes these differences have gone to the extreme and harsh statements have been made, reflecting undue criticism on the entire profession.

It is lamentable to see hatred between the physicians and surgeons and those in the natural healing art. We find that truly great physicians agree with nature cure methods.

3

THE THEORETICAL PHASE

Custom is the plague of wise men and the idol of fools.
—Proverb

In studying iridology, it will soon be apparent that it is a science of symbology that actually records itself in the iris fibres. When we have a reflex condition from any organ of the body referred to the iris of the eye and presenting a certain expression, certainly we do not see the organ itself, but an area in the iris corresponding to that organ. A fever is a reflected condition; the body's reaction to some internal or organic cause such as an infection in some organ. Eczema of the skin or a rash is only a symbol of the real cause, and is a referred condition from some internal part of the body. Liver spots appear on the skin as a referred condition. Pain can also be a symbol. For example, a pain in a woman's heel may denote an ovarian disorder, but you do not diagnose the heel itself to determine the condition of the ovary. Dr. Henry Edward Lane brings this out well in his book, "The Diagnosis from the Eye," when he says:

"It has been said that the eye is the mirror of the soul, and that it discloses the different mental and physical conditions of the body: we generally speak of the 'vivid clear eye' of the well man, of the 'anguishing, glaring eye' of the consumptive, of the 'expressionless eye' in typhoid fever and especially insanity (a contraction of the pupil in regular intervals is noticed during the delirium in typhoid fever), of the 'broken eye' of the dead-sick. The enlargement of the pupil indicates the presence of spool-worms; a small inequality of the pupils with the inclination to enlargement is found in those suffering from tuberculosis; various nervous diseases are disclosed by the decreased mobility of the pupil; frequent disturbances of the sight are pointing to diseases of the kidneys (diabetes), as does also the falling out of the eye-lashes. The inward growing of the eye-lashes discloses scrofula, and reddened eyes female diseases; Basedow's disease of the kidneys brings the eyes out of their holes; a swelling of the eyelids makes us suspect trichinosis, etc., etc.

"In a book probably 300 years old I found the following instruction: 'Shepherds judge the diseases of their sheep by the lines (falsely called *radii solares*) and other signs of the eye. In man, signs near the iris indicate diseases of the lungs and chest, also cough. If children have sound flesh in the inner angles of the eye, it means health; if these angles lie deep and are devoid of flesh, it means disease or death. If the white of the eye is turning into blue and is veined, it indicates diseases of the sexual organs,' —and so on in a really interesting manner."

Let us continue with our examples of symbology. When we analyze the iris of the eye, it is possible to determine the condition of the liver by reflex markings found in the corresponding fibres of the iris. Let it be understood that we are not looking at the liver, but simply determining its condition from the corresponding reflex area in the iris. Thoughts and emotions influence the body and their effects can be seen in the iris of the eye. From the iris we can readily determine inflammation and the

9

stage of the inflammation,—whether it be acute, sub-acute, chronic or destructive,— by shadings which range all the way from very bright white to white, light gray, dark gray and on through to black.

No other science tells so accurately the progress from acute to chronic states, or indicates the retracing process often re ferred to as the "healing crisis."

I am willing to put iridology to the most severe tests. During the eighteen years in which I have been studying and applying this science, I have not been trying to fool myself. Though I will admit I am an ideal-ist, I believe in practical results. My work must speak for itself, as it were. While I am convinced beyond the shadow of a doubt of the information expounded in this vol-ume, I sincerely believe I am only touching the surface of this great science. If such a wonderful structure as the body can be perfectly conceived and constructed, surely it can be maintained in perfect health. This is my firm belief.

While we regard our civilized methods of living as responsible for most present-day diseases, rather than attempt to cast out all of the ideas which evolve with civilization, we should bring about reform in those factors which are causing ill health. For example, we could reduce some of the city noise, establish more favorable working con-ditions for employees,—such as better re-flecting surfaces and lighting facilities,— abandon coal tar smoke in the cities, serve better school lunches, teach the natural care of the body in schools and colleges, and teach a philosophy to better equip us to cope with the complexities of modern life. We could have better restaurants by having laws against serving arthritis-causing diets, gas-producing lunches, and belch-provoking desserts. We could establish camps just out-side of cities; health camps that would not serve hot dogs and soda pop which break down the human system as fast as the clean air, rest and sunshine build it up. We could start our day earlier so that people could follow the sun cycle more closely and get to bed as near time of sundown as possible.

We could establish a city board of health consisting of health-minded scientists whose training would enable them to devise meth-ods for preventing or minimizing health hazards. As an example of a desirable de-vice, an extension might be designed for the mufflers on automobiles which would change the poisonous carbon monoxide gas to invig-orating ozone or carbon of a non-toxic type. They might render innocuous industrial fumes which are eating holes in people's lungs. An arrangement might even be made whereby workers who handle such sub-stances as dyes would be protected against absorbing toxic dosages, and so prevent such occurrences as the one in Kansas City where a number of women developed a serious skin disease from handling blue denim over-alls. I do not know whether men and women who smoke and drink could be con-trolled, but the public could be educated by not allowing advertisers to make mislead-ing statements. A statement constantly drummed into the ears of the public, such as the one that 4007 doctors approve of a certain cigarette as being kinder to your throat, is bound eventually to become ac-cepted by the subconscious mind of the unenlightened.

Our clothing, the quality of the news-paper we read, the colors in buildings—all should be checked—for these are an impor-tant part of our environment. Such matters as clothing styles which interfere with pro-per elimination through the skin, irritating reflections due to shiny paper, glaring build-ing walls constantly before us,—serious causes of unnecessary expenditure of ner-vous energy,—could be watched by doctors' associations. Surely the fashion designer should endeavor to meet demands for cloth-ing which would not be detrimental to health, the paper manufacturer should see the desirability of producing paper which would not injure eyesight, and the contrac-tor should want to build structures which would improve living conditions.

These are a few ideas to think about. It is time we get back to nature before nature demands it.

I do not like at all the "cure" idea which some patients and doctors have. Most of my patients say they would have done something about their condition before coming to me if they had only known what to do. It is difficult to build up a broken down body, but it is simple to keep a well body healthy. The main duty of doctors should be to prevent disease. Even though they are able to accomplish a great deal with disease-ridden bodies, they must fail when it is too late. Many a doctor has sent a bill to the patient's widow for curing her husband until he died.

Prevention is the supreme goal.

The medical pharmacopoeia changes every few years its list of drugs for disease. The allopaths are finding what they have given in the past to be a failure, otherwise there need be no changes. Is there anything to prove that what they are doing now will not be considered a failure five years from now? Since the sulfa drugs came in, thousands of drugs have been pushed back on the druggist's shelf. Doctor and layman alike are looking for a panacea for our ills. If we could only realize that we are responsible for our own tensions, strains, and disorders, we would become aware of the means whereby we could correct our evaluations, substitute good habits for bad, and learn the requirements for regeneration.

In the past, people have done what they loved to do. To give up that which they love is the hardest thing in the world. Many persons, for example, say they would rather die than give up their coffee. Knowing this, doctors as a rule pamper the patient's appetite rather than insist upon what is good for him. Few patients realize their ill health is due, at least in part, to their indiscretions. Let us not make it too easy for people to do the wrong thing.

If you agree that a preponderance of devitalized foods in the diet will result in tissue degeneration which will be reflected in the fibres of the iris, then you will see a relationship between unnatural living habits and the phenomena expressed in the iris. If you believe there is something to living correctly and that the body will adjust itself

to more normal living habits, then you will be able to interpret the philosophy expressed through the markings in the iris. On the other hand, if you believe you can produce a perfect body by living on coffee and doughnuts, pickles and ice cream, then no matter what changes occur in the iris, you will accept the appearance of such signs without considering the conditions which they signify according to this science.

Diseases are on the increase today. Heart disease, cancer, diabetes, tuberculosis, and insanity, are overtaking us at a very rapid rate. Nutritional diseases are so prevalent that they are now recognized by everyone, yet what do we find being done about improving the foods on the grocer's shelf? The American Medical Association approves of foods on the basis of their being disease-free and germ-free, disregarding the lack of natural values. It seems as though they are aprroving of everything from pasteurized milk, which is lacking in mineral content and proven to be deficient and disease-producing from a nutritive standpoint, to cream-of-grain, which is far from being the "cream." Their stamp of approval on these foods is a stamp of ignorance as far as that which is supposed to sustain man is concerned. If they would attempt to control *how foods should be grown and in what kind of soil* and prevent devitalizing processes, then they would be remedying the source of a great many of our diseases and they would be getting at the basic causes.

If they would encourage scientists to develop more natural means of preserving our fruits and vegetables we would have better foods and consequently better bodies. To begin with, if they would insist upon retaining all the natural vitamins that are found in these foods, we would have less heart troubles, cancers, and other diseases today. The removal of natural vitamins and the addition of synthetic chemicals in an attempt to make up for the loss certainly must not have the approval of the Creator for such procedures disturb the natural balance and harmony of His creations.

FIG. 1. Live food produces a full shovel and feeds the whole body. With this full measure of health you are not going around half-starved, with half the tensile strength in your bones, with only half your muscular capacity when needed, or with depleted nerve functions and poor elimination because of "hidden hunger."

Doctors are not wholly at fault, due to the fact that the demands of the people control the situation. The president of a flour concern at one time made the statement that he was no longer interested in trying to provide a natural whole-grain product because the people did not want to buy it when it was offered. He said thousands of dollars were spent to educate the people to whole wheat flour and other whole wheat products, but the public's demand for white flour was not altered thereby. This shows the ignorance of the public. People do not even know what is good for them. This is due to faulty education somewhere; someone has fallen down on the job.

A company that puts out 88 varieties of stomach-ache is not feeding the public the best health products possible. They probably pay their chef more than is received by the president of the United States in order to get their soups and other products to taste good and to meet the demands of the public. I am sure they would give the people what they should have if the people only knew what to demand and knew what was good for them.

Experiments show that coal tar products produce cancers in rats and guinea pigs, yet about ninety percent of cough syrups and most of the cold remedies are made from coal tar products. Practically all patent headache remedies contain these coal tar ingredients, approved and prescribed by some medical doctors. Thus they may be creating cancer conditions by their own treatments while still expensively searching for methods which may cure cancer.

In this study of iridology and its related sciences, we will give little attention to the names of disease conditions. Instead we will tell you where inflammation is in the body and the stage of the inflammation; that is, whether it is in the acute, sub-acute, chronic, or destructive stage. We will tell you how the inflammation got there and whether you eliminated it or not under treatment.

If the proper treatment is administered, healing signs will develop in the iris.

One reason why some persons condemn and depreciate this method of diagnosis is that they have not spent enough time and effort to know that gold is there for the digging. The mere perusal of this book will not enable the reader to recognize all the truth represented in the iris or the good that can come from diagnosis through the iris unless he spends at least three months diligently and sincerely working with this form of analysis. Whenever anyone, whether doctor or layman, tells me he thinks there is nothing to it, I make it a practice to ask first if he has studied iridology and whether he has spent more than three months with it. Invariably I find that those who have condemned it never have spent more than ten minutes or so reading about the subject. Surely this form of diagnosis could not come down through the ages and be used by the most successful nature cure men and not have merit. The strange thing about this form of diagnosis is that it was discovered by medical doctors, and every medical doctor who has ever used it gave up many of his medical remedies and turned to nature cure methods for healing.

Iridology needs no psychological means to prove itself. Many times the conditions revealed in the iris today will not be apparent in the body for years to come, but time will inevitably show the analysis to be correct. Let me add that in iridology we often hear about someone who has made a phenomenal diagnosis, but I do not consider any diagnosis in this science to be phenomenal at all. To be able to tell where abnormal conditions are by this means is not at all unusual.

And now I ask you, "What more do you want?" Iridology serves to check up on the patient, and at the same time gives a good check on the doctor. I present my work gladly and freely, knowing what it has accomplished.

4

THEORY IN APPLICATION

The primary factor in bringing about scientific discovery is not necessity or individual genius but the relentless pressure of accumulating knowledge.

—Aaron J. Ihde

Let us spend a little time developing the basis underlying iridology so that we can see the application of the philosophy to the practical work. More of the practical phases will be taken up in the chapter, "Technique In Iris Reading."

The iris of the eye is so constructed that the layers, lying on top of one another, represent a variety of shadings all the way from an extreme white to a dark black. The white represents the acute stage of dis-ease, the acid stage, while the black represents the extreme chronic stage. Every disease in its course of development—from the cold right on through the different catarrhal manifestations and eliminations to the condition called asthma, which is considered a chronic disease,—is represented in these shadings as follows: white for acute, light gray for sub-acute, dark gray for chronic, and black for the destructive or last stages of disease.

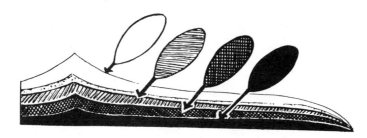

FIG. 2. This chart illustrates the four layers of the iris, each shaded differently. The acute stage is shown in the top layer. These shadings, as seen in the iris, represent the stages of inflammation.

15

If a sign of inflammation occurs in any one section of the iris, it may appear as a small cut in a pie or a portion taken out of a wheel, and may be a reflex area representing some part of the body.

If there is a chronic inflammation or a toxic settlement in, say, the thyroid gland, the iris area may appear a dark gray color. This dark gray condition is produced reflexly in the iris of the eye in the organ area representing the thyroid gland. As you progress, you will learn from your charts where the thyroid gland area is located in the iris, and if this is dark gray, you will know what is going on in the thyroid gland.

In the accompanying illustration of a section of the iris of the eye, we show a dark black spot, which may indicate a chronic settlement of toxic material in the bowel area.

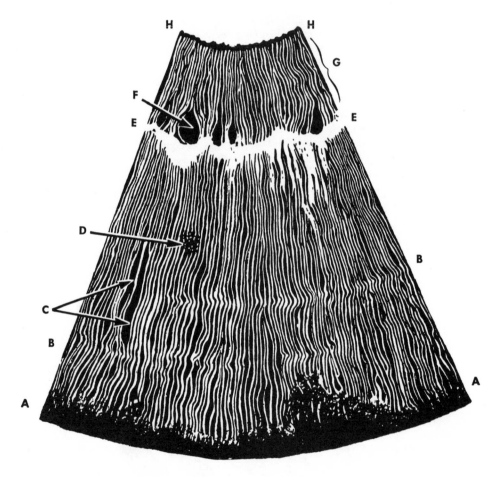

FIG. 3.   Section of an iris

A. Scurf rim.

B. Nerve or cramp rings.

C. Inherent weakness.

D. Psora—Broken fibres demonstrating destruction of tissue. Can be cancer sign.

E. Autonomic Nerve Wreath.

F. Toxic settlement in bowel or Bowel Pocket.

G. Gastro-intestinal area.

H. Pupil area margin.

FIG. 4. These illustrations approximate the appearance of the various degrees of inflammation. The white represents the acute; the light gray the sub-acute; the dark gray, the chronic; and the black, the destructive stage. We produce chronic conditions through our habits. When suppressed, acute conditions first become sub-acute and finally chronic in nature. These conditions are evidenced by discolorations in the iris as indicated in the above diagram.

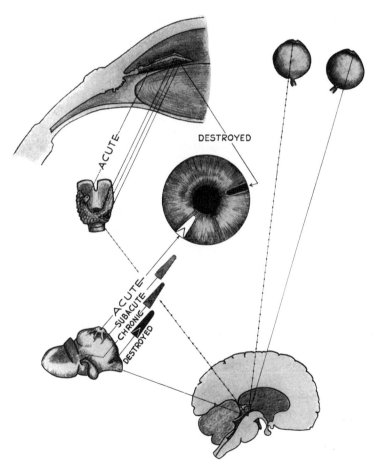

FIG. 5. This chart indicates the location of the areas of inflammation, acute, sub-acute, chronic and degenerative. From each section a rate of vibration or a nerve impulse is carried to the brain area, registering a picture and transmitting it to the iris of the eye. Acute areas show up very white, while more advanced stages grow darker until the black, which indicates the destructive stage of degenerated tissue, appears. This demonstrates hypoactive and hyperactive conditions.

Some of the lines may be separated and allow part of the dark pigment underneath to show. This signifies weak tissue structure and an inherent weakness in that particular area. Broken fibres indicate degeneration in the corresponding tissues. When nerve fibres are pulling up or drawing together in any one spot, we refer to them as cramp rings.

The outside rim of the iris in any one organ area may be very dark, showing that the skin covering that area is very inactive and that toxic material has settled there. Uneliminated fatigue acids and uric acid may have settled there.

The signs of these acids may appear in the varying shades from the white of the acute to the very dark of the chronic. By these signs we determine how acute is the inflammation, where the inflammation is, and we can watch it increase or disappear, according to the person's living habits. The accompanying diagram illustrates this condition, and the explanation under it gives you a philosophy to follow regarding the relationship of the iris to the rest of the body. We know that all we do is recorded in the mind and also that the mind has records of every disease, habit, etc. These are reflected directly through the nervous system to the iris of the eye.

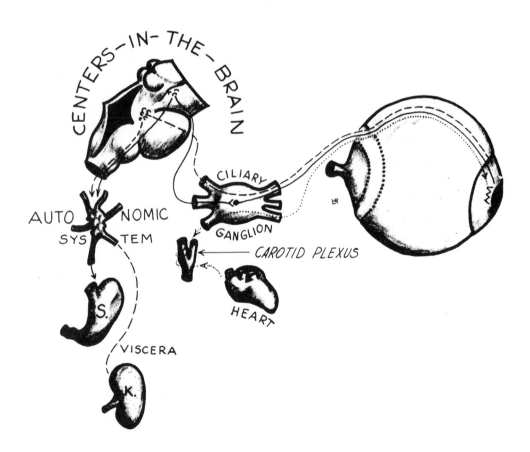

FIG. 6. This diagram illustrates the functional activity of the heart, sending vibratory impulses, by way of the ciliary ganglion, directly to the heart area of the iris. Similarly, the kidney could be responsible for nerve tension reflex signs in the iris, as could also the stomach or the thyroid gland.

The person who knows the nature of tissue reactions, can tell what is going on in the different organs of the body from the iris.

The following advertisement of the Upjohn Company, Kalamazoo, Michigan, calls to public attention the fact that the eyes reveal bodily conditions. (Time Magazine, 11-29-48). "What Your Eyes May Tell About Events Ahead:"

"To any medical man your eyes are a remarkably sensitive barometer by which he can often predict conditions which may affect you months or even years from now. It is not at all unusual for him to recognize disorders of the blood, the circulation, the kidneys, the glands, or the nerves just by examining your eyes. Did you ever know, for example, that the first signs of high blood pressure may appear in the eyes? Advance information given by the eyes can often avoid a serious or a prolonged illness. That is why a really thorough physical check-up should include examination of your eyes. It is almost uncanny what can turn up—even such facts as whether or not you are getting enough vitamins. When you think about your eyes in this new way—as a means of staying well—you will have them looked at regularly instead of waiting until they bother you. Your Doctor."

5

COMPARISON OF DIAGNOSTIC METHODS

*Nothing has such power to broaden the mind as the ability
to investigate systematically and truly all that comes under
thy observation in life.*

—*Marcus Aurelius Antoninus*

Whether a diagnostic examination deals with effects or causes, we should recognize what is behind that which we see. In all the different forms of diagnosis we have today, including chiropractic, osteopathic, and medical, not everything is mechanical, chemical, mental, or just a matter of bad diet. In nearly all the healing arts, we are dealing today with effects. The doctor must know there is a chemical, an electrical and a mental influence. He must know in his diagnosis that the body is made up of physical substance, mental material and spiritual essence.

If causes are lying latent behind every effect in the body, the doctor who is making the diagnosis should picture the entire body; should take into consideration every possible influence in these causes and effects. The patient whose body is suffering from lack of a proper amount of sodium probably will have a sour stomach. A psychiatrist would be fighting a losing battle trying to develop sweet thoughts in the mind of the patient with a sour stomach. A person with dyspepsia, colitis, extreme aches and pains, is unable to sit down and reasonably work out his problem from a mental standpoint. It is all right to assure him that God is good and all is well, but he should change his diet too.

I have seen mental conditions change to peace and harmony through corrective diet.

The most desirable foods in the world, however, may rot in the stomach of one who is mentally perturbed. The body-mind relationship cannot be separated.

Only iridology is capable of directing attention to impending conditions; only iridology reveals and evaluates inherent weaknesses. Suppose we are examining a pocket in the bowel. Its existence can be determined by X-ray, but is that pocket from an excess amount of gas, or is it a local condition? Is it an inherent condition, or has this weakness been developed over a period of years? Iridology can answer these questions while an X-ray picture cannot. Whether inherent weakness is involved in the condition can be determined by whether the fibres in the iris are close or spread apart. When tissue is weak, the fibres appear loose-knit, like the weave of gunny sack material, while the fibres representing strong tissue, with strong, recuperative powers, will appear as closely woven silk.

If the tissue of an organ has become like gunny sacking and cannot withstand pressure, it must be considered a weak organ, whether it be due to the inelasticity of the arteries or to the fact that the arteries have accumulated toxic material over a period of years. Possibly the combination of these things can bring on a stroke much earlier in some people than in others. Very few persons can stand a blood pressure as high

21

as 320 systolic, yet a person with a pressure of only 180 could have a stroke more readily than one with a pressure of 320. We must recognize the combination that will cause this extreme blood pressure and which may fool the average doctor in his diagnosis. If there is an inherent weakness in the bowel area producing a toxic condition, and toxic absorption brought on the high blood pressure, we invariably find a stroke affecting the right side.

We have a blood pressure center, or an "egotistic center," which can be overworked by bragging and extreme intensity in any expression, such as forwardness, too much leadership, trying to break down fears or overcome handicaps. With all these mental blocks added to the stress of the average day's work, the blood pressure is burdened by mental tension rather than by toxic accumulation. In this particular type of case a stroke will affect the left side. Of all the cases of stroke I have treated, eight out of ten were affected on the right side of the body, which tell us that the left side of the brain was affected—from a toxic condition set up in the descending colon. This is verified in a later chapter when we discuss reflex conditions or causes of certain diseases, and how they produce the effects that many doctors are diagnosing today.

We must consider the ninety odd areas of the iris and the parts of the body which they represent, as an entity.

We must not content ourselves with naming a disease after one symptom, as it takes more than one organ to produce a symptom in a particular individual. The combination of inherent weaknesses which will produce arthritis in one person may come from a pancreatic weakness or a weakened bowel structure, while in another person an inherent weakness of the thyroid gland, or an over-active thyroid gland, will produce the same arthritic symptoms. Arthritis may develop from a break-down of the parathyroid gland or a combination of heart troubles whereby the circulation is impaired. Arthritis may also occur in a person with a very acid stomach which has burned out

the sodium to such an extent that the calcium cannot be kept in solution. A patient may have had an accident to the bony structure of the body which has so impaired circulation that the proper amount of sodium cannot reach the injured part because of scar tissue, and so an arthritic condition develops. Can we say that the arthritic patient needs a mental treatment, a pill, or an adjustment? Arthritis is only the name of an *effect,* it does not deal with the basic *cause* we may find in the patient.

Based upon facts which I have already mentioned, I do not believe that symptomatology will provide the diagnostician with enough material from which to plan treatment. Therefore I believe that the man who diagnoses a case should never be allowed to treat it. The crime of many operations—the crime of many of our treatments today—comes from the fact that the man who diagnoses the case treats it according to his own personal ideas. There should be a separation in this respect. There should be a check-up of each form of diagnosis, one with another, so that if certain treatment is indicated by the diagnosis, the patient has the privilege of starting with any form of treatment he desires. As an example, if in the chiropractic consultation it was suggested that the patient would most likely get well through chiropractic adjustments rather than through the surgery indicated by the surgical diagnosis, I think this should be given a trial. If chiropractic treatments fail, then surgery could be resorted to. If a patient undergoes a surgical operation when chiropractic treatments could have helped his condition, it is too late to do anything about it after the operation.

What form of chemical analysis will tell that one side of the body is functioning faster than the other? What form of mechanical analysis would tell us that possibly we have moods developing from a binarius difficulty that may come from our parentage? How many times can analysis of these moods be exactly the same when these moods are developed in cycles according to age, to the foods eaten, or to the mental pressure under which the patient has lived? Perhaps the disturbance began with some internal conflict.

What form of analysis can determine all these factors? What system of diagnosis is so complete that through it the doctor can tell that a certain patient needs intensive self-expression and that another needs to go off by himself? What form of analysis, whether chemical or mechanical, can suggest what pill to use, or that an unhappy person who is dealing with inanimate objects should be dealing with people in order to be happy? The analysis is not complete unless we use *all forms of analysis together.*

The following quotations prove that diagnosing in the past has been inadequate in serving the patient or indicating to the doctor the information needed to aid the patient:

"Professor Drummond, President, British Medical Association—Diagnosis was incorrect in 80 per cent of cases shown by post mortem examination.

"Dr. Cabot—50 per cent of diagnoses made at Massachusetts General Hospital were wrong as shown by post mortem examination.

"Dr. Sir James McKenzie, St. Andrews Clinic—Not more than ten per cent of the diagnoses were correct, the other 90 per cent were mere guesses."

While the old-fashioned osteopath can help greatly by stimulating circulation through the joints and other parts of the body, and the chiropractor may open up the nerve channels to the various organs of the body, we know that the dietitian also has his place in making the proper chemical changes in the body. He knows that lack of iodine produces rough skin and dry hair; that silicon is necessary in skin disorders, etc. Is it logical just to attach a name to a disease and give the treatment supposed to correct the condition? Let us say that the disorder is of the skin, and an indicated sulphur salve is used. It will drive the skin

disorder back into the body. What is needed is analysis of the body chemistry, and in this the natural dietitian is best qualified.

As we have said, all forms of diagnosis should be considered in getting at the basis of the patient's trouble. We may even include the metaphysical and the clairvoyant; or we may depend upon the memory of the patient; or a diagnosis may even be made under hypnotic control.

In connection with the latter, many developments can be revealed in a hypnotic diagnosis that probably could not be in any other way. For example, a patient was brought to me who had a mental fixation due to a thyroid disturbance. Several psychiatrists had worked with this case, but it had proved very difficult from a psychological standpoint. Under hypnotic suggestion, we were able to bring back something that the memory had filed away. It was revealed that when the patient, now a woman of thirty, was a child of six, she had a severe case of scarlet fever. The fever raged in the girl's body to such an extent that much of her hair fell out. Fearing the loss of all her hair, her mother cut the remainder before she returned to school. The result of this was that from the time her hair was cut, the patient had difficulty in school. She developed an aversion to a certain teacher of arithmetic, and in future years, everything that had to do with arithmetic was a problem to her. In relating this experience, she remembered all the details and after a certain amount of grilling we witnessed an extreme crying spell. After we thus broke down this fixation and the patient realized the cause of her condition, we were able to bring about a healing crisis through a right-living program. Changing the hate into love for her past teacher was also part of the therapy which eventually got results.

To a degree, the chemical laboratory is excellent for diagnosing kidney disorders, but if the kidneys are not throwing off certain acids, and an appreciable amount of these acids are settling and possibly forming stones, how can anyone conclude from a urinalysis that the kidneys are all right? We should not wait until a stone forms before we start working on the kidneys.

Another important thing to consider in comparative diagnosis is that many of the diseases diagnosed are not actually in the locality which is causing the trouble. For example, a soreness palpated in the heel can be a reflex set up by an ovarian condition. A pain in the calf of the leg can be a reflex emanating from the prostate gland. The iris can show reflex conditions from stomach trouble or a mastoid condition. The cause of discomfort felt in the forehead area can be in the descending colon. The right ear may cause symptoms which are reflected in the hepatic flexure. We should consider all symptoms, from which we name a disease, to have their origin in some other part of the body. Treat the real cause rather than the symptom.

There is much comment today about electronic diagnosis. It has its value and may become one of the greatest of all forms of diagnosis. I believe, however, that much is yet to be learned, for at the present time a great deal is misunderstood in electronic diagnosing, as in other forms of diagnosis. Everything in life has its own vibratory effect. Chemicals have their rate of speed. Colors have vibratory rates. Each disease manifestation also has its vibratory rate. This has been proven so many times there should be no doubt that a condition such as tuberculosis can be diagnosed electronically. Some beautiful experiments were performed with the old Abrams form of diagnosis, and much of this work can be used today in comparative diagnosis.

The chemical diagnosis of fingernails, skin, breath, the different sounds of the body, all tell us things that other forms of diagnosis fail to disclose. There is "type" diagnosis, by means of which we can predict that certain types of individuals can develop certain diseases—such as tuberculosis and mental disorders—easier than others. From the chemical type of diagnosing we can determine the status of the body chemistry, which should be balanced by dietary instructions.

Another form of diagnosis, developed in England, is study of the human aura, and this procedure is the subject of a wonderful book written by Dr. Walter J. Kilner. This work was carried out in the St. Thomas hospital in London, England. He demonstrated that by looking at a person placed against a dark background through certain colored glasses,—which probably are made from potassium cyanide glass,—the diagnostician can determine from the aura of that person various types of incipient diseases and conditions long before they are apparent in the physical body.

In considering the forms of diagnosis generally used along with iridology, we must consider the mental faculties that can be expressed in and around the eye. The irises do not tell whether we are honest or dishonest; they do not reveal whether we are guilty or not guilty; but they definitely can express such faculties as our capacity to love, our mood swings, and poor judgment. We can even see a casualty syndrome developing. The white of the eye may be changed to a blue color showing venous congestion, or it may turn yellow showing gall bladder and liver congestion. From examination of the retina the oculist can detect diabetes, syphilis, strokes, nerve pressures, and tumors, but this has nothing to do with iridology except that it is another form of diagnosis which may be used along with iridology.

When we speak of the eye as being the "window of the soul," we suggest that through this window we can observe the constant development of the soul. It expresses the degree of physical, mental and spiritual control we have over the body. An old soul can take a poor body and live in health and happiness. A young soul can take a good body, lose everything that is in life for him, and quickly run it into the grave. The development of the soul does not determine what type of body you have. Your body has been given to you to show what you can do with it. The most advanced soul in India may have to live on the poorest of foods, yet he has perfect control over his emotions and can take the poorest body and produce the greatest amount of good with the least amount of effort.

The iridology form of analysis includes every organ of the body in the colored portion of the iris. An orderly chart shows areas corresponding to every organ in the body. The chart in the front of this book, as well as other charts, have the organs listed. All authorities agree that the upper part of the iris deals with the brain while the lower part deals with the lower extremities. We find that Mendel's law of heredity is perfectly borne out through the irises. All of our inherited characteristics as far back as our great great grandfathers and great great grandmothers are recorded in the iris.

No two persons in the world, not even twins, have eyes alike, with exact markings or the same characteristics. If photographed by the police department, the eye would prove to be of greater help for identification purposes than finger-printing. When photography is developed to a more perfect science, I believe the eye can be used to a far greater extent by the police department than any other means of identification now in use. The ruffian might destroy the markings in the skin on his fingers, but he would not put his eyes out. Regardless of how much a body may be mutilated, the basic foundation of the eye will always remain the same.

Iridology can convince us that we are only as strong as our weakest organ. The strong organs take care of themselves and outlast the weaker. All of us have inherent weaknesses. But if we would properly strengthen the weaker organs, they might outlast the stronger ones. When revealing to the patient what his greatest weaknesses are, he should be told too what his proper environment should be, the right job for him, and how his thinking processes could be governed. He should even be given the proper philosophy, if necessary, to show him the right way to perfect health and how to keep it. An understanding of the

reflex organ areas found within the iris, which the doctor can interpret for the patient, will help that patient keep in better health. The majority of persons who go to a doctor realize that had they known better they would not be in the condition in which they find themselves.

I have never seen a completely well person. In fact, I do not think there is a perfectly well person on the face of the earth. This is a broad statement for many persons say they are feeling fine, but they have hemorrhoids, difficulty in breathing, prolapsus, or other conditions they do not complain of or perhaps do not know about. When a person reaches the complaining stage, that is a difficult time to start taking care of the ailment. Many forms of diagnosis are dependent upon what germ life exists, and its existence in the body usually indicates a bad state of deterioration. Disease germs are nature's undertakers. We should have a form of diagnosis that can determine danger signs early in life and long before we reach the complaining stage. To give a man a perfect bill of health, only to find two or three days later that he died of heart trouble or some other weakness that could not be determined through any one diagnosis, seems proof enough that all forms of diagnosis must be enlisted to make certain of helping a patient. Future diagnosticians should be more interested in what constitutes a perfect body and not wait until a disease appears.

In iridology we do not determine disease names from the iris, but we do recognize toxins,—whether they are developed through the intestinal tract, or as nerve acids, catarrhal discharges, excess fatigue acid, or carbonic acid. These toxins are the breeding ground for the various kinds of germ life. If all toxic acids, gases, and accumulated pus are eliminated from the body, and a clean body is the end product, how many disease germs would stay and how little work would the doctors have to do in diagnosing and treating?

An outstanding advantage of iridology over the average diagnosis is that the trouble can be looked for externally. If we employed all forms of laboratory, chemical, and other analyses in use today to get a complete picture, a patient would be required to spend five to six weeks in the process. Iridology reveals immediately in which part of the body the trouble exists and the condition of the organ affected. We can then corroborate what we find in the iris with other types of diagnosis. Many times we have determined the problem by this means before any other form of diagnosis could substantiate our claims. Over a period of years I had verified, by X-ray or chemical analysis, the abnormal conditions which I saw indicated in the iris. For instance, in spite of a normal blood count reading, some particular organ might be anemic due to pressure. The blood calcium may be normal, but what about the amount of vitamin D or sodium for balance to keep it in solution? There is much more to be found out than what laboratory tests reveal.

As an example, I cite the case of a gentleman at Lake Tahoe. We told him he had kidney disturbance and that he had better take care of it. He said, "No, I think you are wrong because I have a very heavy insurance policy and I am checked regularly every six months." This man was wealthy and carried heavy insurance policies. I insisted that if he did not take care of himself, in a year's time he would have a serious kidney disturbance. Diagnosing from the iris, this could have been nephritis, albumen, or it could be several other different things. Eleven months later I received a telegram from this gentleman saying, "Your diagnosis was correct. They have found albumen in the urine. I am flying from Montana to see you right away." What a great advantage it is to be able to recognize the beginning of such conditions, and then do something about it to keep in good health.

Iridology can diagnose a patient for the doctor if he has a perfect colored photograph showing three-dimensional depth of the patient's eye. The patient need not be present. This diagnosis is not a psychic one, though many patients who have been diagnosed in this manner cannot understand

how the diagnosis can be so infallible. It is astounding only because other diagnoses have failed to such an extent. It was Will Rogers who said: "We have good doctors back in Oklahoma; they call them horse doctors. They can't ask any questions. They have to find out by themselves what is wrong."

In using iridology you need ask no questions yet you can tell where pain is, what stage it is in, how it got there, and when it is gone. It is a diagnosis that can completely check on what the patient's activities have been and what he is doing while under the doctor's care. And, most important, it determines whether the doctor is caring for the patient properly while under his supervision.

Although I firmly believe that iridology should be considered as one of the most essential diagnoses, I repeat that along with it we should employ every other form of analysis that might result in help for the patient.

Since the healing crisis many times is misunderstood, we place here a chart which may help you to understand what is going on in the body during the retracing process. We start in at the age of two with the acute condition represented in white. At the age of eleven the condition develops into the sub-acute stage, represented in gray. The darker gray represents a chronic state of affairs at the age of twenty-eight. The very dark gray at thirty-six is the sub-chronic stage. After the age of thirty-six, the darkest stage is complete degeneration. We show here how disease is developed, how the accumulated effects produce certain symptoms in the body, and how the reversal process brings back the troubles of the past.

This clearly shows that we should be interested in the patient rather than in the disease. We do not know what the patient will do for himself. A "cure" of disease is dependent upon the cleansing of the body tissue; replacing old tissue with new. The

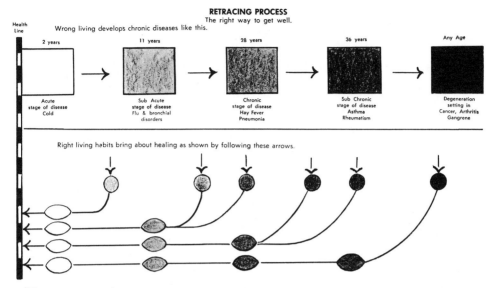

RETRACING PROCESS
The right way to get well.

Health Line

Wrong living develops chronic diseases like this.

| 2 years | 11 years | 28 years | 36 years | Any Age |

| Acute stage of disease Cold | Sub Acute stage of disease Flu & bronchial disorders | Chronic stage of disease Hay Fever Pneumonia | Sub Chronic stage of disease Asthma Rheumatism | Degeneration setting in Cancer, Arthritis Gangrene |

Right living habits bring about healing as shown by following these arrows.

FIG. 7. According to Hering's Law of Cure, symptoms should disappear from above downward, from within outward, and in the reverse order of their coming.

chart indicates the need for cleansing crises to bring white healing lines within the black areas shown in the iris.

It is a wonderful thing to see in this work how we can reverse the processes of disease and bring the patient back to a better health state. We are interested in using any treatment regime which will release the patient from the grip of disease and its symptoms. We must reverse the process. We have had

case after case which started with a cold, that settled in the bronchial tubes, developed into 'flu, and finally ended with pneumonia. Some children's diseases, such as measles, mumps, and scarlet fever, develop into a toxic thyroid. Hay fever always precedes asthma, and when the patient finally comes to us, the asthma has developed into arthritis. In the reversal of this chronic disease process, past diseases develop just the same as they were previously developed.

FIG. 8. The accompanying illustration was made by an artist friend of mine. The reason for his making this drawing is rather interesting. One day as we were standing over the drafting board on which he had been working, I chanced to look into his eyes and told him that he had evidently had some recent stomach trouble; that in fact, I surmised he might even have a stomach ulcer. My friend was startled by what I told him, and I remember his saying he thought his coat covered that condition. He was puzzled as to how I could see this since it was a deep secret between him and his doctor, so I explained that I determined the condition from markings in the iris of his eye. He became very much interested in this work and later made up this little symbolic picture of the iris, showing the general areas of various organs. While it is not true to scale, I have used it as a symbol of my work in iridology.

Monk's 'Dead-Eye Diagnoses' Draw Swarms of Patients to Door

Rich and Poor from 5 Nations Flock for Advice, Treatment

BY CHARLES FERNANDEZ

Daily News Foreign Service

BOGOTA, Colombia--Ailing mankind never ceases to pray for the miraculous.

That's largely why, rightly or not, the self-tutored "Miracle Monk" of Colombia has made legend of his "dead-eye diagnoses."

The lame and the halt, the rich and the poor, from five countries--Colombia, Venezuela, Ecuador, Panama, Peru--have been swarming to his door for 10 years with the fanatic zeal of repentant sinners hitting the sawdust trail. Even a few Americans have consulted him.

His practice assumed such fantastic proportions that organized medicine stepped in a couple of years ago to try to stop him. But the public outcry was deafening, and the monk won.

Moves Continuously From Town to Town

Today he moves continually from town to town without advance fanfare to keep the sick from stampeding his humble quarters.

Small, bespectacled Tomas Rodriguez--a 43-year-old Augustine monk known far and wide simply as "El Lego" (the lay brother)--says there's nothing miraculous about his work.

But the simplicity of his diagnoses and herb prescriptions has captured mortal minds ever ready to put faith in unfathomable talent. El Lego asks for no symptoms, checks no pulses, listens to no heartbeats. He simply looks into a patient's eyes through a small magnifying glass. And that's all.

Eye-Peering Tells Past, Present Ills

The eye-peering reveals to him not only what's wrong with the patient but what ailed him in the past.

"The iris of the eye," he explains with mystic softness, "reflects all parts and organs of the body."

To illustrate, he broke out the book that first started him to legendary fame in 1939. In it a Chilean physician, Dr. Manuel Lezaeta Acharan, reviewed the "Theory of Irisology."

Two illustrations--looking something like those charts put out by politicians to show where your tax dollar goes--indicated what particular part of the iris supposedly mirrors what particular part of the anatomy.

El Lego says he followed through on the theory, reading all he could find on the subject, and discovered that "it really works."

His Name Spread Throughout Land

His "dead-eye diagnoses," bulwarking years of self-study in anatomy and herb cures, soon spread his name throughout the country.

Brother Tomas practically was born into the Catholic order of St. Augustine, named for the 4th century saint who is known as "the doctor of the church." His farming father was field overseer for the famed monastery, Desierto de la Candelaria, near Cali, Colombia.

As a boy he showed a talent for the care of the sick and a hunger for medical knowledge. In the monastery he got the chance both to employ his talent and to appease his hunger.

He read avidly on herb cures and was fascinated particularly be ancient works in the library of the 450-year-old monastery. His basic knowledge of anatomy he got out of a book by the 18th century Spanish doctor, Martin Martinez--a work El Lego says he "wouldn't trade for any other."

Tries Out Theory On His Brothers

His hunt for ancient and forgotten lore led him to the iris theory in a treatise printed in 1939. He tried it out on the brothers, and his fame soon spread.

Three years ago fabled El Lego came to the Augustine colony in Bogota.

Hundreds--on stretchers, on crutches, in rags, in sartorial splendor--lined up for blocks.

Alarmed, organized medicine labeled him a quack, a charlatan, a fake, and demanded that he be stopped from practicing without a license.

Orthodox diagnosticians knew there was nothing new to examination of the iris.

Because that part of the eye provides the only window through which they can see the blood vessels, physicians often peer at the iris to countercheck other findings in the diagnosis of brain tumor, brain hemorrhage, syphilis, nephritis and arterio-sclerosis.

Scoff at Ability To Diagnose Ills

But to pretend to diagnose all ills merely by looking at the iris is preposterous, they scoffed.

Whether El Lego should get a green or a red light became a national issue. Cabinet ministers were divided. The people were stirred to fever pitch. The Augustines hired lawyers to defend their medic.

When the smoke cleared, El Lego was still in business. Noted author German Arciniegas, then minister of education, signed a diploma giving him the right to practice.

Today El Lego proudly points to not one but two certificates framed on the wall of his cubbyhole proclaiming him a recognized homeopath.

"Many of the poor people think Brother Tomas is a miracle monk," says Spanish-born Father Eugenio Ayape, superior of the Bogota colony. "But his work is no miracle; it's purely scientific. He is not given to magic.

Monastery Must Keep Him Hidden

"His is really a singular case. We have to keep him somewhat hidden, or the people would make this look like an ancient Roman festival."

The padre says El Lego's clientele includes not only the common people but archbishops, ministers, diplomats.

"Graduate doctors have gone to Brother Tomas without identifying themselves," relates Father Ayape, "and later they have come to me to say his diagnoses are really amazing."

When Father Ayape ushered me into the inner sanctum, El Lego, his small, Indian-like face beaming under his Augustine crew cut, offered to give me a fast check.

He took one large magnifying glass in his left hand to spot the sunlight, and through a smaller glass in his right hand he looked me in the eyes.

Tells Reporter His Findings

Slowly, almost inaudibly, he announced his findings. The newspaperman, he said, has minor kidney trouble and stomach hypertension.

And a touch of bronchitis. He got a gold star there. Rather hesitantly, as if thinking out loud, he concluded that I'd had some trouble with my right leg. He was close on that one. It really had been my right foot: a badly bruised metatarsus arch during boyhood.

Later, an American friend who is a veteran medical researcher advised me with a laugh, "Don't bet too strongly on that diagnosis."

But he wasn't completely shrugging off El Lego and his ilk, either.

Can't Completely Ignore Them

"You can't completely ignore these fellows," he added. "Don't forget the first positive cure we found --quinine--came from the Indians in Peru. And one big reason you seldom see a gray-haired Indian in these countries--unless he's very old--is they eat a lot of green hot peppers, which contain p-amino benzoic acid, an anti-gray hair factor.

"In medical research today we've just about reached the point where we can throw away the microscope. Biochemistry, in my opinion, is the new field.

"These medicine men, without knowing how or why, have stumbled onto some of the answers. We can learn some things from them, but that does not mean they have all the answers--not by a long shot."

FIG. 9.   This article appeared in a Chicago daily newspaper in 1949.

6

THE THEORY OF THE HEALING CRISIS

*All cure starts from within out and from the head down
and in reverse order as the symptoms have appeared.*
—*Hering's Law of Cure*

In dealing with the healing crisis we can take up only the theoretical side because first we must have had a certain amount of practical study and application of this science in order to understand the crisis and the iris changes. In our philosophy we do not rely upon the name of a disease to signify the cause or the treatment. We deal with the body in its entirety. We must make a start in finding the causes and must have a philosophy to follow as we proceed in our iris work.

In the next few chapters we will go into iris color and shadings and how these variations are found to correspond with different diseases and symptoms. For instance, starting with a cold, which is one of the first eliminative processes of the body, we find that the cold symptom reflects in the iris as a very light whitish shading of the fibres, quite devoid of the pigment found in the deeper layers of the iris. As the subacute stage develops, the white becomes gray and the fibre you are watching in the iris recedes. As this condition develops into one more chronic, we find that the gray fibre becomes darker and almost black and recedes to a place where only the pigments beneath are showing through. Just as we watch this condition develop in the iris as disease progresses in the body, we can also watch the condition in reverse as good health returns.

Watch the alterations in these dark holes or dark sections in the iris as the patient follows right living methods. Watch the little gray and white lines reappear. Finally, the white appears again in the iris as it was in the original acute stage. Thus this reversal process can be clearly followed in all its stages. Observing iris changes is one of the finest means of watching this reversal process take place in the body through reflex actions. Through this reflecting mirror on the outside of the body we can watch recuperation take place. As the skin becomes cleared, we can see that condition taking place by changes in the iris of the eye. We can also watch kidney changes and bone changes reflexly in the iris. There is a thrill to the doctor interested in this work in thus witnessing the recovery of his patient. Changing from disease to health brings color changes in the fibres.

While I was studying and observing some of the work of Henry Lindlahr, I did not fully appreciate the value of the healing crisis until I actually saw it working in my own practice. Also, you have to see the healing crisis work under your own care, watch it develop before your very eyes, to really value iris analysis. One of the first cases brought to me some years ago so impressed me that to this day the healing crisis is the most interesting part of my practice. The patient was a lady, of perhaps 65, who came into my office because she had two boils under one of her arms. She had been having them treated under what is known as orthodox medicine today. They had been lanced repeatedly over a period of years with no results. Remembering that disease is impossible in a clean body, I started a cleansing process, and in two months, these boils were eliminated and no others appeared. Approximately three months later, however, this lady broke out with two more boils on the breast. Upon questioning, I found she had had two boils on the breast two years before. This was my first lesson in the retracing of disease in that this was her first process to reappear, but these breast boils had been her last disease process treated before the boils appeared under the arm. In my striving for a "cure," I had no particular treatment for the boils, other than that of cleansing the body. I made sure that the blood stream was purified and that all the blood necessary reached the parts affected. Within a very short time—a week or so—the boils cleared up completely. During this time I saw that the patient reduced her food intake and rested sufficiently.

For about a month and a half this patient enjoyed average good health, but at the end of this time she came to my office assisted by two men, hardly able to walk. Her first remark was, "I have my old rheumatism back again—the same thing I had ten years ago. I thought I came here to get well, but now look at me!" I told her I had handled other cases successfully and felt I could do the same with her case through right living methods; that there was no reason why she should not carry on with right living habits as she was doing and see what would happen in the next few days. This crisis or elimination process lasted only three days. It was hard to believe that such a severe retracing process would occur, but after the third day this lady had no return of her rheumatism and was able to go about her work without any difficulty whatever. Is it possible for a person to have such extreme pains, such extreme discomfort, and yet have them leave so completely and suddenly? Sometimes the patient's pain during the healing crisis is of greater severity than while he is building the chronic disease. I distinctly remember how very happy she was in overcoming this problem. She came

in to tell me how wonderful she felt and how spryly she could get about.

This was not the end of the case, however. A month or month and a half later the lady came in with a discharge from the ears. I did not mention above that she was suffering from deafness. I had accepted this merely as part of her old age. After about a week of this discharge from the ears, the patient recovered her hearing, and recovered it to such an extent that she was disturbed by the ticking of the clock in her bedroom at night. It kept her awake. This was the first time she had heard a clock in twenty years!

Viewing this case in the "order reversed," as Hering puts it, we note that she had the first boil about two years previously, her rheumatism about ten years, then finally her deafness which began with a discharge about twenty years ago. I watched this internal law work perfectly in the body and I had the wonderful science of iridology to predict these crises as they were evidenced by certain color changes in the fibres of the iris.

The good iridologist is able to predict whether a person can get well and what processes he will have to go through in getting well, by watching these fibres reappear in their natural order. Many times he is misunderstood by those not acquainted with this science. They know so little about it that they accuse one of predicting things to come in an unorthodox way.

I do not believe an iridologist can predict death from the eyes nor do I believe the life span can be told from the eyes. So much depends upon the patient's way of living. To offset what has been said against iridology, it is well that we emphasize the truth that lies within it. If this science did not follow natural law, there would be reasons for regarding it as a science of man-made folly or ideas, but I have found it to fall in perfectly with every means used in the natural healing art.

I should like to describe some examples of healing crises that have come under my care in order to bring out a lesson. Bear in mind that the unusual does not happen in every case. While these cases may seem unusual to you, anyone who is using this science has had the same experience, for I am not alone in what I say as far as these healing crises are concerned.

One of my most unusual cases was a lady who had been crying intermittently for a period of two months. She had sought relief without avail. Now what would you do if the patient said she had tried chiropractic, had tried medicine, had tried the different types of healing, and no one semed to get to the cause of her trouble? The first thing I suggested was a fast. There was no use trying to use more chiropractic or any other systems of healing, but to try what we know to be one of the first fundamental laws: make a chemical change through fasting. This was brought about by reducing the amount of toxic material in the body by purifying the blood stream, and by making sure more blood was rushed to every organ of the body.

After fasting for fourteen days this lady was completely free of her symptoms. She developed a wonderful outlook on life and started to build a better body from the diet care and teaching we were giving her. After about a month of this right-living process, however, she had a return of her crying and developed a fever. It was an unbelievable thing, but her whole head became infested with lice. Certainly there was nothing in my treatment which was conducive to the development of head lice! Where did they come from?

In questioning this patient we found that when she was a child in Kentucky she had had head lice, and that kerosene had been used to destroy them. I am sure the condition was thus suppressed and lay dormant beneath the scalp, and then years later it took the eliminative process to really clean it out. In this way was the cause of her distressing symptom uncovered. I believe the crying spells were a chronic condition, developed over a period of years of breaking down body energy to such an extent

that it took a healing crisis to bring about a complete elimination of the symptoms. We took care of the reappearance of head lice in a natural way, by fasting, cutting down on food, resting, and using a natural wash for the hair.

Another case was a lady whose iris analysis showed a great deal of sulphur settled in the brain area. We told her she would probably have a sulphur elimination. Usually sulphur works out through the skin in some form of a rash, pimple or boil. This came to pass, through an eliminative process. The patient's gray hair turned absolutely yellow as this sulphur was eliminated through the scalp. It even turned yellow the water in which she washed her hair. The strange thing about this case is that she developed considerable diarrhea and bowel trouble. It was hard for her to remember this particular trouble in the past, but when she was a child her grandmother had given her sulphur and molasses as a spring tonic. In the eliminative process her gray hair turned back to its natural black color in a couple of months.

It is wonderful how a doctor observing the iris can check on himself and follow his patient's progress in the healing crisis. Patient and doctor should work together for one common result—healing. I use the iris analysis to check up and see whether I am giving the patient the proper advice and the proper guidance. It is difficult to carry the patient through this nature cure regime and make him understand that the "reverse order" is going to take place and old symptoms be brought back. We can use iridology to tell a patient he will have a bronchial tube eliminative process or that he will have a bowel eliminative process. It is well to obtain past history from the patient to see how chronic disease developed and how the various stages reflect themselves in the iris.

To watch these regenerative processes gives the doctor an added interest in his work; gives him something that goes beyond just trying to find a push-button method of treatment: One patient has asthma, give him this remedy; another has hay fever, give him that remedy; another has colitis, give him some remedy. It is best to see the individual as a whole and recognize that every disease can affect many organs, some more than others. There are never two symptoms exactly alike. Iridology gives the doctor an opportunity to use his delving-into propensities and gives him the privilege of solving problems with a sense of satisfaction in accomplishment, especially if the patient is desirous of working toward his own higher good.

Another crisis we wish to mention is that of a Santa Monica gentleman. He had a high fever for three days, with a great deal of weakness and emaciation. I advised rest, a diet program, and natural treatments. Over a period of a month, this man improved and left his bed. Then he developed another fever which ran for a period of four days. He had all the symptoms of malaria. I found in rechecking that he had had malaria four or five times while he was in the tropics. After this crisis he got his old strength back again, regained his weight, and felt fine.

A case which required considerable time for healing through the cleansing crisis was that of a young man with an ulcer of the stomach. He had lost considerable weight and was very thin, and wanted to know how he could gain his weight back. I told him he probably would not gain any weight until after he had gone through the crisis. I explained that the average person develops a crisis within three months, and that probably he could expect one after the third month. In this case, however, the crisis did not come for a whole year. He used to joke with me about it and said he wondered whether he must wait the rest of his life in order to gain a little bit of weight. One morning about two o'clock he called frantically because he was disturbed by the fever he had. When I saw him I knew he had finally come to the crisis I had promised him. It was quite severe, lasting over a period of three days, running into delirium, very high fever, extreme

headache, and extreme pains in the head around the ears. He then remembered having had this exact condition one time on a trip to Alaska. Nothing much was done while on the trip except that drugs were administered. He was now tasting the same drugs in the eliminative process. After the crisis this man gained fifteen pounds and again felt wonderful.

Still another crisis was brought about with water treatments in a patient at the sanitarium. We used cold water and the heat of the sun to bring about body reactions. It was amazing to see how within a couple of weeks this patient erupted nearly ninety boils. This was not a comfortable procedure by any means and the patient violently objected to the eliminative process. Although it was not the easiest thing to go through at the time, it was a blessing to his body. The toxic material within the body had to be eliminated. Certainly we should regard this elimination of latent waste settlement as one of the most wonderful things that could ever happen.

The above cases should be proof enough that the patient brings back old diseases in the healing process. You can predict this reverse order in your analysis, which is your proof in both the diagnosis and the treatment. Many eliminative processes will bring back old troubles in such a way that it inspires one to live an entirely different life. I believe as the Bible tells us: "We suffer the sins of our flesh." Troubles brought back inspire us to resolve that we are finished with the old way of living. We go on to a better day; we want to live a better life.

We cannot put a new foundation in the body without first cleansing the body, a process not always comfortable. We work for the crisis in our practice because we realize it is among the greatest methods for cleansing the body, getting rid of chronic disease, and restoring good health. We may never attain the perfect health goal but in the reversal process, brought about through better food, and a more suitable climate and environment, new tissue replaces the old.

And this remarkable process you see going on in the iris as new fibres fill in the dark holes. It is like knitting a new pair of socks out of an old pair. The new lines we see appearing represent new tissue.

Some doctors maintain that it is not necessary to have the healing crisis in order to get well. I would not want anyone to have a healing crisis of my own making, but it is nature's way. It is the body itself that has the make-up and the materials that produce a crisis. This capacity is found in everyone. Anyone can have a crisis at any age, though the young person will have the crisis much more quickly than those of advanced years. It requires energy to have a crisis; it takes activity of blood cells, and power of tissue structure. It takes a reserve to go through a healing crisis, and the body will not produce a crisis unless it is able to go through with it. It is as natural a process as the sun rising in the morning, a Godly process. If you want a clean body and wish to get as close to a "cure" as possible, go through the healing crisis.

An interesting case was that of a lady we treated over a period of a month. Her attitude, after taking some classes in spiritual psychology, was that God would heal her of everything and that it would not be necessary to continue taking treatments. She said that all she would have to do was wait on God and the "cure." Now I definitely believe in aligning ourselves with the God Power through prayer, but I believe too that since He has given us "dominion over every living thing that moveth upon the earth," we should do our part to be in harmony with the Laws.

This patient requested an iris examination to determine her physical condition. I assured her that the healing was progressing satisfactorily, that the healing signs were appearing, and that within a very short time she should experience a healing crisis. When she inquired what kind of crisis it would be, I predicted that she probably would have a very severe cold and diarrhea. Her unusual reply was that she believed herself

already to be healed and disease-free, and therefore, need not expect any further reactions or difficulty. I did not reply other than to say that she would have a cold within a very short time.

Within a week she telephoned me and said, "You are right. I have one of the worst colds I have ever had, but what I cannot understand is, although you promised me this cold, why should this come about when I have worked it out in a spiritual way?" I explained that this also was a Godly process, that it was a process working with the laws of nature which are the laws of God, and that it was beyond my control either to produce or to stop a crisis which came as a part of a right-living program. I further explained that the healing crisis differs from the disease crisis in that it is a blessing and not a curse to the body, and told her that she deserved it because she wanted to do the right thing to get well.

I would advise the person who wants to see if there is anything to iridology not to come to any definite conclusions until he has spent at least three months with this form of analysis. Anyone who has spent three months working conscientiously with this science, watching signs change in the iris, especially watching the development of white lines and white fibres in the dark areas, and seeing during the patient's crisis the white or high point of manifestation within the iris, certainly will begin at least to respect this science. It seems that those who are using iridology and who really believe in it, believe only after a good deal of hard work and detailed study, and then they tend to become silent about it due to the fact that others cannot see what they see and they know it.

After we have dealt with the structure of the iris and its recording of organic conditions in the body, we will again take up the healing crisis, as this chapter is more on the philosophical side. Later we will take up the more practical side of producing and developing the healing crisis.

THE WHEEL OF LIFE

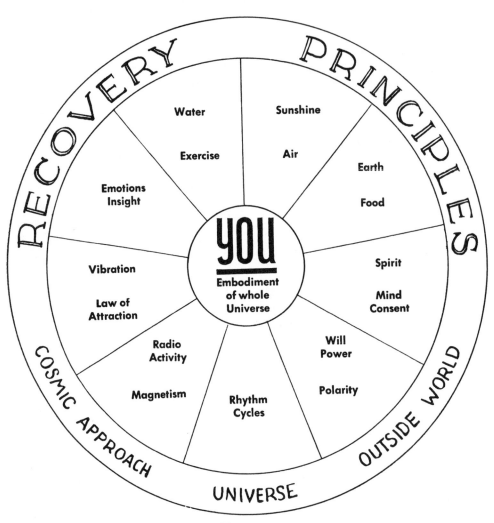

Fig. 10.

It is difficult for the average person and for the average doctor to tell the difference between the healing crisis and a disease process. Though usually the manifestations are similar, a healing crisis is brought about through an accumulation of health in the body, and the active healing power carries the person through. It is difficult to accept the fact that a healing crisis comes right after a patient is feeling his best. Invariably a patient says, "I have never felt so well in my life." This is the time you can usually expect the crisis and is the time when the crisis can do its best work.

It takes energy to eliminate wastes, to go through these eruptions, whether boils, rashes, or pimples. It is only through the ascendancy of an inherent power to eliminate that we can accomplish what we do in a healing crisis. During the healing crisis the patient's bowel movements usually are better regulated than they are during a disease crisis. We can usually tell the difference in this way, and of course, the difference is made evident by the use of the science of iridology.

Do you remember as a child that whenever a disease crisis developed in the body the first thing mother or grandmother did was give a laxative or an enema? We find that during the healing crisis no enemas or laxatives are indicated. Nothing is indicated. The body itself is doing its greatest work—a life-preserving job. It is getting rid of the old and allowing the new to come in and take its place. What better thing could happen than to have a new body take the place of the old one?

One crisis is not always enough for a complete "cure." The person in a chronic state, who has gone through many disease processes in his life, must go through these disease processes again in the reverse order in which they occurred. As I said before, we prepare for a better body by building good health, and we must not conclude the process before its natural completion. We can only reach good health by going through these crises. Lindlahr tells us that good health can be accomplished through these healing crises, by nature's cleansing and healing activities in the form of inflammatory and feverish processes. Anything short of this is merely preliminary improvement. Just living correctly is not enough for the "cure." It is like training for the fight, but it is not the fight itself. We find that any healing system which assists nature in removing the old encumbrances that have been lying latent in the body is to the body's advantage; that which only changes acute inflammatory processes and interferes with the healing efforts of the body, merely changes these processes into chronic and destructive diseases. It is marvelous to see how all the natural healing arts agree and how this same cleansing process operates successfully for all of those who are interested in allowing nature to take its natural course.

We find that the chiropractor brings about many of these crises through his so-called retracing process. No matter how it is accomplished, we must bring about a crisis and retracing in the whole body as well as in the individual organs. Specific treatments can help to bring this about, chemically or mechanically. We can have a full set of crises and we can bring a complete development of new tissue to all organs of the body. Even homeopathy works for these healing crises. No matter what system we use, if we can possibly bring about these healing crises, we are working for the patient's higher good.

In looking over the whole process, consider that disease is an eliminative activity of the body. If we believe that the body is consistently trying to remain well, we believe that even the process of disease is an eliminative process; and we should do little to interfere because the body is fighting for supremacy over the disease. It is well to know that even disease can be looked upon as a "cure" by allowing it to run its course and by giving the body every opportunity to recover of its own accord.

Many changes are coming about in the healing art today. While in the past it was considered dangerous to have a fever, and anything to get rid of the fever was considered sound practice, now we find it helpful to induce fever. For the past twenty years we have been producing fevers naturally through the healing crisis. It is the natural process to produce a crisis and a fever to get rid of accumulated toxic wastes that have settled in the body. Many of the schools of thought who formerly advocated suppressing fever, are today changing their ideas and are using fevers as a help towards getting a person well. Injections which produce artificial fevers in the body are given to cure certain mental disorders. Fever treatments are now available in hospitals. It seems that with all these changes natural healing will soon be considered right. But what suffering mankind has to go through before the truth can be recognized.

7

HOW DISEASE BECOMES CHRONIC

*Inflammation is a reconstructive process and should not be
suppressed. Every acute disease is a result of a cleansing
and healing effort of nature.*

—Henry Lindlahr

When we look at the body, it may seem to be as senseless as wood; it cannot make suggestions or ask for anything except through pain or symptoms. But even psychologists admit that there is such a thing as cell intelligence. To the doctor treating a body and observing changes, the latter seem as though speaking a language of the flesh—the language of cell life. The law of change is constantly going on in every organ and every cell of the body, and must be answered. Cell life molds itself from the very air we breathe, the food we eat, the thoughts and feelings we entertain, and the home life we habitually live. Today we are subjected to living habits which force cell changes that produce our chronic diseases. Our living habits produce the kind of body we have, and this body in turn is responsible for the effects in health or disease.

Many changes in the healing systems have taken place due to the fact that at one time sanitary conditions had to be considered above all else. Plagues of the past were due to filth and lack of sewage disposal in cities. We know through experiments and experiences that we can develop most types of disease to which man may be heir through eating devitalized foods. Every disease from which we suffer today can be traced back to some chemical imbalance within the body.

In developing our theory on chronic stages of disease as seen in the iris, iridology brings out the fact that chronic diseases are developed over a period of time. This has been proven through all nature-cure sciences, including homeopathy, osteopathy, chiropractic, and naturopathy. Nature is interested in giving us at birth as disease-free a body as possible, but our living habits and our abuse of the body through life produce chronic diseases. The proof that chronic diseases are developed will be more comprehensively shown to you in the chapter on The Healing Crisis In Practice.

When the health standard is lowered and the body becomes enervated, as is so aptly explained in Dr. George Weger's book, "The Genesis and Control of Disease," the body is unable to resist and does not have the power to overcome the natural attraction to germ life. One may then develop a symptom called a cold. A cold is the beginning of all chronic disease. It is the first link in the long chain of increasingly serious symptoms. We do not take care of the cold the way nature intended us to, by resting and going with as little food as possible. Instead we stuff with so-called "nourishing food that will keep up one's strength" and with various advertised cold "remedies." We "have a job to do," so we carry on and do not give the body the opportunity to recuperate. We distribute our energies in various directions, and feed the body for stimulative purposes, to carry on

37

the job. This is the first step that starts the suppression which later produces a latent condition from the cold. A cold is a natural eliminative process.

The word catarrh, which condition exists in the body as a result of a cold, is a derivative of an old Greek word meaning "I flow." If material in the body is working itself out in any discharge whatsoever, this should be allowed to proceed to the complete cleansing point. Cleansing, itself, is part of the "cure." Nature is producing this cure and should never be interfered with. Today the prevalent practice is to stop this discharge. In so doing, nature's process of elimination is interfered with, and suppression is the result. Consequently, instead of having a clean body, we go on feeling merely fairly well with only the degree of health in which most people are living today. This is not a complete health state; many of us are only half alive.

Then out of a clear blue sky, we develop 'flu. Where did it come from? Many persons accept the idea that cold air or a draft causes 'flu; few realize it is brought on through bad living habits. Well, if the disease has developed, what are we going to do about it? We treat it. What treatment are we going to use? Are we going to do what the body demands, or are we going to act according to our education? Are we going to develop a better body through elimination and right living, or are we going to suppress this disease and develop a more chronic condition? Every known kind of treatment has been administered to the influenza patient instead of giving instructions to merely go to bed, fast, and rest it out.

When combating a cold or influenza, the body needs every bit of its recuperative power to overcome the disease. It must draw upon stored-up energy. We subtract from our potential power by not resting, and we overfeed the body because we are not accustomed to waiting until we become hungry. Even when ill, we eat to keep from getting hungry. Our habits of living have become so distorted that we no longer follow the body's cravings and real needs. Doing what is customary or what we have been taught, may not be the right way. We overcome the 'flu, possibly in two days or maybe we were able to "knock it out" in even one day with some nostrum advertised on the radio. People run after so-called cures, not realizing that the 'flu in itself is a natural eliminative process, a safety valve which the body opened of its own accord. The body needed the opportunity for a natural process to take place. We often fail to realize that the body seeks to maintain itself through the law of preservation; that it works to preserve itself constantly, in order to regenerate and rejuvenate itself as long as possible.

When we are inexperienced in the healing processes, yet have "knocked out" the 'flu in the average manner, we may think we really have something to brag about to our friends. We took care of it by some "quick cure" remedy we saw advertised and the next morning we were completely "well." The valve that was opened by the body to allow perfect elimination to take place, has now been closed. That which should have been eliminated was retained within the body. The body's reserve power was sufficient to handle only one condition at a time, and the energy that should have been used for healing was dissipated in the suppressive processes of treatment. Assuming that we are "well" now, we continue existence, below par, still not having learned how to live.

A little later, we develop a cough, possibly a fever, and in a day or so a bronchial disturbance; and the first thing we know we have to give up work because of a catarrhal elimination through the bronchial tubes. Refusing to let this get us down, we seek treatment for it. We start doctoring again. We find a patent medicine that claims to take care of this condition. Stubbornly the body tries to bring on elimination. Even fever is developed to aid in the elimination. But instead of allowing the fever to run its course, we look for some remedy to try to "knock out" the fever

If we only realize it, the fever is a natural process coming to our rescue to burn up the toxic material that has begun to settle in the body.

Though we are now able to control the fever through a "quick-cure" remedy or some radical treatment, this is very hard on the body. We get over our immediate problem all right, but every night in the cool damp of the evening, we develop a wheezing. Why should we have wheezing when we have been so well all our lives, outside of a cold or 'flu or a little bronchial trouble? Few ever stop to think that the body is moulded by the habits of the individual. If you look back you will recall that you treated these symptoms I have mentioned, and now they have developed into the first symptom of a chronic condition —hay fever, the follow-up of the wheezing.

What do the inexperienced do about the hay fever? You may use one of the hay fever remedies: nose drops, eye drops, or certain types of cigarettes to control it. You may treat it for years, inhibiting the eliminative processes of the body, consistently damming up every channel, and keeping inside what the body wanted to throw out. In working against the body's cleansing processes, you work against one of the greatest laws we have: *Disease is handled from within out!* Cleansing *always* proceeds from within outward.

It is not natural or necessary to have the various expressions of disease. They are the consequence of wrong living habits, and when they become apparent they should be given a chance to eliminate themselves. If you become constipated, do not use liver pills; if you have gas, do not use some gas remedy; if you have belching along with it, do not use an alkalizer of some kind. If you have an idea that some pollen is causing the trouble, do not take injections or an allergy treatment. If you find you can handle only certain foods, do not go on a diet of devitalized, processed foods that are not natural, for you are then compromising and resorting to a doctoring program, a "patch-up" program.

As a consequence of these suppressions, the hay fever finally develops into asthma. Where did this asthma come from? Did it come from some outside source? All of you who have asthma—look back. Have you had hay fever previously? Look back further. Have you had bronchial disorders, pneumonia, bronchitis? Look back still further. No doubt you had the 'flu and some fever when you were a child. A cold started this vicious chain. Did you treat that cold with a suppressive remedy? If so, you should be able to see how a chronic disease was developed over a period of years. The process is a consequence of not following natural laws of the body; not allowing it to restore itself by way of the healing crisis and the reversal process of "cure." Let the body bring about the kind of cure it requires.

Disease does not invade the body. It is through lowered energy that we develop symptomatic diseases that may settle in any organ—particularly in the organ with an inherent weakness. Catarrhal discharges that should be worked out naturally through the nose, skin, eyes, and other eliminative channels, when suppressed, will be driven back and cause symptoms in the inherently weak organs. The reason disease can develop in weak organs is that they do not have the resistance to throw off the toxic material settling in the body. Strong organs and weak organs differ extremely with respect to their functioning ability. The weak organs manifest disease to such an extent that we are constantly treating them. They are constantly worked on to such an exent that the resisting power cannot throw off any latent toxic material settled there and a more chronic disease may develop—such as cancer, arthritis, tuberculosis. Whereas about twenty-five years ago only one out of twenty-five persons had cancer, today, one out of every eight has this disease. It should be noted that although we have found ways to overcome symptomatic disease, we are developing more chronic diseases than ever before.

Of course fear and nervousness have their place in the development of chronic diseases. It certainly is not to our advantage to hear someone on the radio tell us that one out of every eight has cancer, and suggest, "You may be next!" There are many persons with small fatty tumors, growths, warts, or insignificant blemishes who might suspect these as being cancerous after hearing these words. They live in a state of accepting fear thoughts, and "that which they feared finally comes upon them." During the last twenty years of my practice I have observed a change in the type of patients I have been treating. Patients come into the office today in a frightened state of mind. With a combination of mental stress and physical difficulties, they have a double problem with which to cope; and so does the doctor. Most doctors regard conditions which are predominantly physical as simple to handle compared to those which have become complicated with dis-ease of the mind.

As we develop our theory throughout this book you will become aware of the fact that every moment of life has an effect on every cell of the body. Certainly when drugs are used to suppress disease symptoms, they produce harmful effects in the body— in fact, the very chronic diseases we are fighting today. If anyone asked his family doctor whether the drugs, injections, shots or vaccinations used to cure any disease— and I mean to stipulate the word *cure* —would absolutely cure a condition for which they were administered, I am sure the doctor would not guarantee a cure. He probably would state that some relief could be expected and that certain diseases might be prevented, but he could not promise that certain others would not be developed.

The accompanying reproduction of a report from the New York Associated Press states that the cause of psychoses is laid to the bromides taken into the body.

Notice at the end of this article that the doctors say these bromides appear to produce "much chronic ill health." To this we add that not only do bromides produce chronic ailments, but all drugs.

It is necessary to give serious consideration to what goes into the body, whether through the skin as an injection or through the mouth in the form of unnatural foods. This material is carried by the blood and lymph to the various organs, and finally becomes a part of the human working tissue. I do not understand how anyone can expect meals consisting of such lifeless products as coffee and doughnuts to produce a good working body. And how can we expect the body to function perfectly with drugs making up a part of its tissues?

The patent medicines in the modern drug store and the radio advertisements lauding the virtues of such remedies actually have been instrumental in causing the development of a good many of our chronic diseases today.

Here is an excerpt from a letter sent me by one of my patients:

"Dear Dr. Jensen: In April 1946, I had a bad cold which was accompanied by a cough. I had seen "C———" advertised a great deal so finally decided to try it. It stopped the cough in only a few days but I developed a throat condition which has been with me ever since. It is hard to describe except to say it is a constant feeling that there is something in my throat which I cannot loosen, (and a persistent desire to clear my throat).

"I have always felt there was some connection between the quick checking of the cough and the throat difficulty and after hearing your lecture the other day along this subject, I am convinced that the cough syrup was the cause of my present difficulties.

Very truly yours,

Mrs. B. T. W.
Pasadena, Calif."

This is but one example of what is typical in all cases of drugging.

I believe that our basic problem is to eradicate in the future those factors which

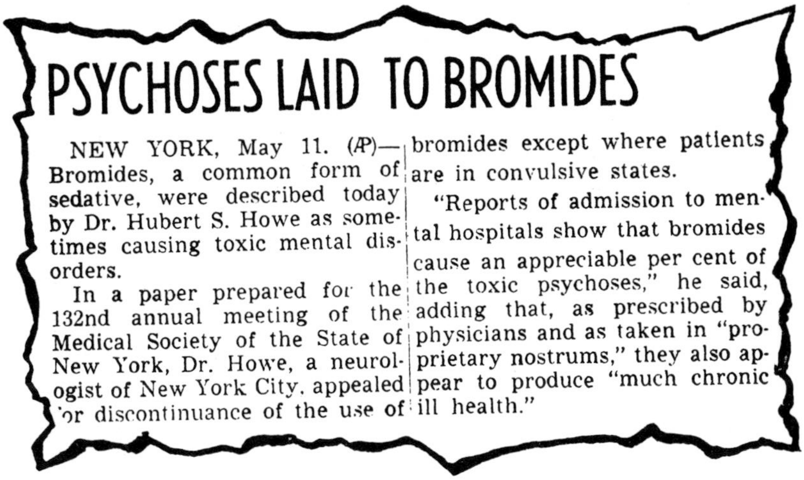

PSYCHOSES LAID TO BROMIDES

NEW YORK, May 11. (AP)—Bromides, a common form of sedative, were described today by Dr. Hubert S. Howe as sometimes causing toxic mental disorders.

In a paper prepared for the 132nd annual meeting of the Medical Society of the State of New York, Dr. Howe, a neurologist of New York City. appealed 'or discontinuance of the use of bromides except where patients are in convulsive states.

"Reports of admission to mental hospitals show that bromides cause an appreciable per cent of the toxic psychoses," he said, adding that, as prescribed by physicians and as taken in "proprietary nostrums," they also appear to produce "much chronic ill health."

FIG. 11.

eventually result in chronic disease. Patent medicines have been popularized through commercial administration. Back in the year 1921, over 108 million dollars were spent on patent medicines. Recently around twenty thousand tons of aspirin were sold in one year. This represents a lot of headaches, but it means much more than that. It means that many chronic diseases have been developed because of this particular suppressant drug!

The doctor must have insight into what underlies chronic disease. Without this understanding he cannot bring out the latent trouble, eliminate it once and for all, and make possible a cure. All past troubles will return in the reverse order in which they were acquired. Any other way of handling these conditions will only treat the effects and suppress the symptoms. Work to bring out symptoms that have been suppressed.

8

THE PRINCIPLES OF "CURE"

It is time to be definite in education,
It is time to be definite in the study of man.
It is time to be definite in talking, writing or
preaching about human questions—HIGH TIME.
To be definite is to understand the elements of
human nature.

—High Time To Be Definite

One of my past teachers in nature-cure work said, "All diseases are curable, but not every patient." It is difficult to know just exactly where to start in order to help a patient, but it seems to me that the first principle is the realization that what will prevent a disease will also cure it. The cure is found in the prevention.

It is evident that a philosophy is needed along with our practice. Theory amounts to very little if we cannot find a way to back it up by practical means. If theory and practice do not work hand in hand, then the theory must be changed. We know in the practice of this simple work that definite results have been accomplished, but many of the theories and philosophies which have been developed as to what could be accomplished, and how, were too personal or too far-fetched. I can state with confidence that those who have gained their philosophy of "cure" through the science of iridology believe it to be a reliable basis for their work of getting people well.

There are three principles of cure which we should particularly remember. First, the body must have a healthy blood stream, for without this the body cannot have a healthy cell structure. Since cell life is dependent upon the blood, this must be kept clean and toxin-free. Dr. Still, the founder of Osteopathy, said: "The rule of the artery is supreme." What flows in the arteries determines whether the body's needs can be met. Make sure that vital foods are going into the body so that cell life, through its inherent nature can absorb its requirements from the blood. Cell structures depend upon the materials that are floating around in the blood stream for their needs, and healthy blood carries all required elements. It is up to us to see to it that vital nutrients are taken into the body and are properly assimilated, so that the blood can carry the elements needed by all body structures.

The second principle is very important. It is that the blood must circulate rapidly enough to supply cell structures with all the necessary building elements. It must circulate fast enough to give the body the opportunity to build and repair as rapidly as is required.

The third principle is rest. Rest cures. The first thing a sick person feels naturally inclined to do is lie down. Gravity exerts its least detrimental effect when the body is lying in a prone position. Therefore, rest allows the body to recuperate and regenerate. Tiredness was given to us as a barometer and fatigue is the first symptom of all disease. When our body calls for fluid,

43

we have a thirst, a natural craving for a drink; and when we are hungry, we have an appetite, a natural craving for food. But when we become tired and do not recognize this as a signal that we should rest, we carry on with our work and abuse our bodies to the point of exhaustion. This factor is one of the greatest hinderances to recovery.

We all know the recuperative effects of a good night's rest when we are tired. If we would treat a diseased body as a tired body, we would give it a chance to recover. You cannot whip a tired horse and expect very great efficiency from him. One of these days he will lie down and not get up again. This is exactly what happens in many chronic diseases. Though we need not worry about the strong organs, we must take care of the weak ones. The weak organs in the body are like weak links in a chain, and we are only as strong as the weakest organ in our body. It is to our advantage to know which the weak organs are in order to assist them. If we know, we can use them as barometers; as a warning to slow us down when an organ expresses itself as being fatigued. Remember that enervation is the beginning of every disease, and that we should place importance upon the value of rest.

To repeat, purification of the blood is the first thing to consider in eradicating disease. There can be no disease if we have clean blood, a good circulation, and the right mental attitude concerning bodily needs. More and more we are not only convinced but forced, by the increasing number of deficiency diseases, to recognize the need for a balanced diet of *vital* foods in place of the numerous devitalized products in such wide use today. At various universities and experimental hospitals, diabetes has been produced in animals at will by feeding them too many starches and sugars. High blood pressure can be produced by giving too much coffee to animals, and even cancer can be caused in animals by the use of certain coal tar drugs. Our natural foods have been so denatured that none of the animal experiments made shows that the diet on which man exists today is adequate. The body is unable to build vital blood from such poor building material. Is it possible that anyone can seriously believe that coffee and doughnuts make a worthwhile breakfast or that spaghetti, dumplings, and the like made with white flour could give man a nourishing lunch in the terms of known body requirements?

Arthur Brisbane, in his column many years ago, said the American people fill their stomachs with "foodless food." This is truer today than ever before because of the commercialized processing of foods. Our blood is becoming more and more a carrier of synthetic and artificial materials. Is it any wonder then that the body is becoming more artificial also? Is it any wonder that all diseases seems to be on the increase—particularly those that have to do with nutrition and chemical balance, and those developed from a polluted blood stream, from foreign metallics, and from the use of drugs? Some of these diseases of course have been developed from the use of aspirin, cough syrup, etc., as well as devitalized foods. Sitting in a stuffy apartment, wearing heavy clothes, seeing how much work we can do after sunset, breaking down the body at every turn, are also ways to help develop disease. In order to regain or to maintain good health, it is necessary that perfect food be given the body —which the body can assimilate easily; and that one have pleasant surroundings, sunshine, and good water.

Man is allowing his own inventions to interfere with his rest and add to his fatigue. Late hours are encouraged by the radio, the electric light, the movies and other places to go after working hours. Thus many of us are enervated from these habits and are walking around with blood streams far from pure, circulation slower than it should be, and in an anemic, devitalized state of health.

There is only one way to effect a "cure," and that is the natural way. Eat natural foods, rest sufficiently, and stimulate active circulation. In studying how to eradicate disease, we must exercise care in the use of the word "cure" because many persons think they have cured a disease when they have merely suppressed it and sent it off to some spot in the body where it will likely become latent.

We are interested primarily in building health rather than in treating disease. When we treat and suppress a disease, we lay groundwork for development of a more chronic condition. I wish we could see that "doctoring" is not always the best thing for the body, and that by building a healthy body we build resistance. When built up to the peak of its needs, the body has everything required to maintain good health.

When a wrestler or a boxer goes into the ring he must be in the best possible physical condition in order to hold his own against his opponent. Life's opponent is disease. Let us train ourselves how to have good health so we resist disease. Consider how very few people take time to learn how to live constructively. It has been stated that about ninety per cent of us carry tuberculosis germs in the throat, but that does not mean we must have tuberculosis. On the other hand, the body may contract tuberculosis whenever it is run down; whenever the tubercular germ life has a favorable environment in which to thrive. So we see that *we* either build disease or build health. We can have a garden of roses or a garden of weeds. Where does the cure come from? It is not found in a system of treatment. It is found in the body. The body is self-curing, self-regenerating, and self-rejuvenating.

It is a shame that the doctor does not regard the body as a whole. There is a place for every art of healing, but the healing art should fit the patient. We can turn to any book of Medicine, Osteopathy, Chiropractic, or Homeopathy and find recommended remedies or treatment procedures for practically every disease. Although there must be something of value in all these systems, has the average individual sufficient knowledge to select the doctor he

needs at the time of his particular illness? Every doctor sees the patient's problem through the porthole of his own specialty and training.

We should not entertain the belief that disease is all-powerful over the body processes. If we use the right mental attitude and build the idea in the subconscious mind that health methods can overcome disease in the body, then disease must fail and health is given a chance to become supreme. With a positive attitude for health, what can disease do? Where will it go? It will automatically be eliminated through the body cleansing we have been talking about. It is time we learned truth and used the real laws of disease prevention.

There are many individuals who go through life trying to please everyone without realizing that the results may not be good from the standpoint of health. For example, don't you know persons who love to give children things that taste good? They may be killing them with "kindness." How many know that white sugar is the greatest "leech" that can be put into the body? It robs the body of calcium, and this loss may be the beginning of arthritis and other madadies.

The average person wants to do the right thing, but does not know what to do. Where is he going to go for his knowledge? Who is to be the protector of his health? Who should be looked up to for his care and health education?

Henry Ford once remarked that the day would come when man would take about three months out of the year to care for his health; to rest and recuperate. Man should take time out for this purpose and not attempt to accomplish so much that there is not time left for a proper health program.

One of the most impressive statements I have ever heard was made by one of the doctors at my graduation exercises. He said: "One of these days, my colleagues, you will be called in on many cases. You will find that eighty-five to ninety per cent of these cases will be acute. According to the law of 'cure,' you will find that these acute cases get well of their own accord." Then he added, "but for God's sake, do something about it so that you will get the credit." As I have progressed in my healing work, I have learned that the body is self-maintaining and "fearfully and wonderfully made." The Creator of the body has also given us the way to maintain it if we would only use the proper care. We should learn how to eat correctly, learn the right living habits, and learn how to think constructively. If we are worried, depressed, emotionally upset, and eat only devitalized foods, we are not living a life conducive to good health.

There is much to be said about the philosophy of cure. Many have the experience of going to a doctor and getting no results. Patients of mine tell me of the many doctors they visited before they came to me. Which doctor is the one to follow?

If we investigate the activities that go on in many doctors' offices, we find they are not following a good health program. The doctor is much too busy to teach the patient how to live correctly. He should be in a position to teach his patients the proper way to live, but if he works entirely from books and if he has never been sick, he could not know what it is like to get well. He cannot know what it is to actually feel the patient's feelings or understand the patient's needs.

In many instances patients have come to my office to improve their general health so that they could undergo an operation, but when their health is built up they do not need the operation. Once the body is in a superb state of health, it is disease-free.

A doctor I read about who had performed nearly 5,000 appendectomies, stated, in summing up his work in later years, that only two of all those operations were necessary. History records that many really

great doctors eventually condemn their own work.

Nature-cure is not the complete answer to all health problems, but I believe we should try these methods first. If they fail to restore a body to its natural state after it has been mutilated by operations or deteriorated through drugs, then other measures can be tried. Most of those patients who fail to gain completely normal functioning through nature-cure are those who have tried it after other treatments have failed. Then too, in many chronic cases the disease has become so well established that a return to normal health is impossible. There are cases, however, with the worst conditions who, through consistent efforts to cooperate with nature cure methods, have been enabled to avoid surgery and other drastic measures.

I once had a nurse with an extreme thyroid condition and the rapid heart rate of 120 to 130. She did not value my advice to use the natural-way treatment because I did not assure her of a "cure." After a friend told her about a "wonderful doctor," she called on him. He convinced her that an operation was the remedy. I had suggested, of course, that she stop her smoking, her "night life" activities, and a few other bad habits, but she did not wish to cooperate. All I could do was suggest; it was up to her to make the choice. She chose the operation, and died on the operating table.

It would be well to consider again the most important principle of all—one I strongly believe in: "All cure is from within out, from above down, and the symptoms disappear in the order reversed to the original occurrence." This law of Hering's is discussed and proven in the chapters on the healing crisis.

As a concluding thought, remember that while most patients are looking for a good doctor, the real doctor wants patients who are desirous of learning to live healthfully.

Part II

INSTRUCTION

in

METHODS of APPLICATION

9

TECHNIQUE IN IRIS READING

Wouldst thou enjoy a long life, a healthy body, and a vigorous mind, and be acquainted also with the wonderful works of God, labor in the first place to bring thy appetite to reason.
—Benjamin Franklin

As you progress in this science you will find the technique you prefer to use in analyzing patients. However, some suggestions are necessary to start you off on the right track. For example, when making an examination, it is best to sit directly in front of your patient. Make sure the patient's head is level; not tilted back, to the side, or to the front, or there will be distorted areas and you will not have good confirmation. With the iris in a position as straight up-and-down as possible, you will be able to make a more accurate comparison with your chart. Remember to read the iris as you do the hands on a clock, from one o'clock to twelve, but you must be facing the iris squarely.

Get into a comfortable position and have your patient comfortably seated. If you have a tall patient and you are a short doctor, use a chair that can be adjusted properly. There are times when you will need to spend only ten minutes with a patient and there are times when you will spend an hour. The work being of such a confining nature, I suggest that you take the patient's history over a period of two or three visits. On the first visit you will glean much general information in conversation that may be applied in the analysis and the treatments to follow.

You may suggest that the patient look at some part of your face in order to fix his gaze in one direction. It may be necessary to lift the eyelid to see more of the iris, but do not pull it away from the eyeball because this causes blinking. It is better to take hold of the lid and slide it up, against the eyeball, until you see that part of the iris in which you are most interested. At times when you want to study one specific area, you may ask the patient to look directly at your chin. If he has deepset eyes and the upper lid comes down over the iris, it is well that he look toward the lower part of your face so that the upper part of the iris is in clear view.

Look at the iris first without a magnifying glass or a light, to observe the patient's reaction to you; note the size of the pupil, the color of the iris, and the sclera and tissue-markings surrounding it. Now, in bringing the light to the eye, it is well to come up from the side, then forward, so that the light does not shine directly into the pupil and onto the retina. This prevents contraction and nerve tension which are not good for either patient or doctor. Diagnose with as much ease as possible. In my own office I use iridology all day long, and have been using it for so many years that if the work had to be done under tension it would very quickly wear me out, as well as the patients.

In looking at the iris with a glass, we study it as though approaching a forest. To begin with we see the whole forest, and then some individual tree catches our eye. It is that odd tree in the forest that is of particular interest for the moment. So the purpose of using the glass is to discover this oddity in the iris, this one marking or spot, this one part of the whole, and to study it for its unnatural coloring or marking, and to break it down for thorough analysis. Finding the largest, darkest, or whitest spot is finding the condition of the organ. And that which strikes you first should be of the most interest.

Consider the eye you have to analyze as having a normalcy that is probably an ideal you will have to conceive in your own mind. As we stated previously, there are very few people who have perfect health and you will see very few perfect eyes. However, we should all know what perfect health is and what a perfect eye should look like. The normal eye is not striking in any way but pathology in the body is represented by the abnormal spot in the iris.

It is convenient to have one of the iris charts directly behind the patient as you work so you can look first at the chart, and then fix your eye upon the iris of your subject. Get the chart fixed in your mind. Compare it to a wheel. You start at the hub and work outward. The stomach area is the first to bound the pupil, and the intestinal tract is the next. All of the organs seem to be placed as spokes from the center of this hub.

The first reflected condition I usually look for is that of the vital organs of the body. There may be trouble in the leg, but after all, the leg is subject to the blood stream, and the blood stream to the liver and digestive system; or the leg may even be subject to the condition of the heart. I therefore go to the vital organs first.

Try to get together with a few other doctors to learn more about symptoms and to compare notes. You will be surprised within a very short time, to note the extent to which the condition of the patient compares with the reflex signs you observe in the iris. Be careful, however. You may have several patients with white lines in the kidney area, and, while the white lines may mean pain in most cases, pain does not always have to accompany white lines. It may mean an extreme discharge in one case. In another case, the discharge may have to work itself out in a manner entirely different and under a great deal of constriction. There may be additional nerve rings along this white line that will distinguish this case from the ones you have examined with similar nerve rings.

So you cannot tell a patient he has a pain in the kidney merely because there is a white line in the kidney area of the iris. Reserve your remarks at first. Until you have gone over this work often enough, you cannot tell a patient what his condition is. Be careful to avoid suggestions which will send him home with a label of disease to worry about. Many people try to find out what is wrong with them, then after they find out they try to cure themselves without proper knowledge. I spent three years working with the eyes before I told patients much about themselves. We must always be very careful what we tell the patient. A little knowledge can be dangerous. In iridology you have one of the most powerful tools in the diagnostic field. Learn this science as completely as possible before telling your patient much of anything.

I do not believe in a program which forces a person to live correctly through fear. There is much being done in the healing arts today which coerces patients into doing what they should through fear. Fear is a disease in itself, a disease of the mind, and I do not wish to add another burden to the patient when he comes into my office. I would much prefer to help him feel he is on his way toward a brighter day and help him feel he has the opportunity of better living within his grasp.

Another helpful device is to try to get one or both of the patient's parents before you so you can check back on the inherent weakness of an organ by comparing its condition in the parent with that in the patient. You may even have the opportunity of examining the irises of the grandmother or grandfather, and you will see right before you the evidence of how inherent lesions are brought down through the generations. There is so much to be learned in this science that, to begin with, you may have to determine first by other means what is wrong with the patient and then confirm the trouble in the iris. It will be there.

It takes a great deal of training to look into an iris and concentrate on one area long enough to get a history out of it. To see a dark spot is not enough. Know the background behind that dark spot. How deep-seated is it? How did it get there? Is there a way of removing it? Have you had any previous experience in removing it? Is it there because of nerve tension or mental or nerve depletion? Is it there because of a chemical imbalance? Is it due to a reflex condition from another organ? Many times a toxic condition settles in one part of the body due to the faulty elimination of an organ in another part of the body. In making your analysis you will see the whole body at work reflexly in the iris.

Some students may be particularly interested in color as seen in the iris while others may be more interested in drug signs and drug discolorations, but these phases are only a small part of the science. What is going on in every organ of the body is actually taking place in the iris reflexly. You have a great thrill to look forward to as you study how tissue pathology is reflected in the iris. Follow this book in its sequential build-up to understand the subject correctly.

We will show by experiments how the iris reflects many of the conditions the body is subjected to. For instance, fear will cause the pupil to contract almost immediately, and a hot bath will relax an extreme nerve tension of the pupil. If you squeeze a finger there will be an immediate response in the pupil on the same side of the body as the finger. This is only to demonstrate how quickly the eye responds to conditions in any part of the body. You will, without a doubt, see the tissues of the iris change right before your eyes as pathological changes occur within body tissues. You will see drug signs actually leave the iris. At first you will see deposits and discoloraations in the iris, and then over a period of months healing fibres will appear that will surprise you. If you are administering certain drugs, drug signs will appear in the iris after a period of time.

Please remember not to become overly-enthusiastic in your work, and do not allow yourself to feel that in a short time you will know everything. You may ask yourself this question: "How soon will the iris show the conditions of the body?" And you will find yourself answering this question as you progress further. Your knowledge of the science will give you the answer. If you are asked about the condition of the teeth, you will look in this area of the iris for your answer, but if the question, "What tooth was pulled out?" is asked, you will have a very difficult time trying to find this information. While I believe it is possible, it is highly improbable that you will see this in the iris.

In the beginning, try to compare your findings with other tests. There is no reason in the world why you cannot expect all other tests to verify what you find in the iris. If you are diagnosing body conditions through reflexes in the feet, use that, and see how it compares to the iris diagnosis. Regardless of what you believe, see how your tests compare. I use a nerve meter to test inflammations of the body and when I compare these with iris findings, they invariably agree. Many times we find conditions of which the patient is not complaining at the moment but are on their way toward a crisis, either a healing crisis or a disease crisis.

It is always well to compare with the chiropractic analysis also, as a person found to have a symptom in any part of the bowel may have a major condition which will be brought back reflexly to the spine. On the other hand, we have spinal conditions causing disorder in various organs.

I already have recommended your knowing this work thoroughly before jumping to any conclusions with your patients. And do not use medical terminology to name conditions indicated by the iris analysis. Some day, through experience in comparative diagnosis, you will know just what to expect in an X-ray by having examined the iris and you will be able to tell just what to expect from laboratory reports. Until the time when you can say you really know your business in this science, do not make the mistake of discarding other forms of diagnosis for iris analysis alone.

Your first conceptions will probably change and you may need further qualification as you proceed with your instructions. I have developed some charts over a period of time that may be well for you to study. They are reproduced the same as I use them in my office so that you may compare and gain a better knowledge of this subject.

One of the important steps is getting the patient's history. What the patient tells you and what you find in the iris do not always agree; you cannot believe the patient at all times. Your own findings are the most important for this reason, and because the patient will have forgotten many conditions—especially those during his childhood. When giving their histories, patients consider many conditions unworthy of mention, but these may be the very conditions responsible for the chronic diseases which bring them to our office for correction. These conditions will have to recur in the retracing process. In handling cases, it is well to explain to a patient what is ahead of him in the healing crisis.

Before you get into this study too seriously, look over the finished chart, the one you are going to use with your patients. Become acquainted with all areas and mark-

ings, think of them as being on the face of a clock, and locate them in relation to the hands of a clock. When we say white, remember there are varying intensities of white. It is not necessary that you memorize everything, but it would help to keep a chart with you at all times. When you visit a patient outside your office, carry a pocket chart.

Every doctor has a certain amount of trouble in his own body that would bear investigation, and in many cases would bear improvement. If you would improve your own health and check the signs of improvement in the iris, this might be proof enough for you as to what could be accomplished with your patients. We fully realize the value of this science when we actually see old conditions leave, see how reflected conditions in the iris compare with the actions and reactions of the patient, and compare one iris with another.

In learning this science, I found it very helpful to study my own eyes. The best way to do this is to stand before a mirror and place a chart in front of you just below your eyes. As you look into your eyes in the mirror, you can look at the chart at the same time.

In this way the right eye of the chart is directly under your right eye. If you look at a chart when it is not reflected in a mirror, the chart and your eye are opposite and you may become confused.

Another method which helped in the process of learning this science was writing down my findings. As an example, when I found a kidney weakness in four or five consecutive patients, that did not mean they all had the weakness in the same degree. One patient may have had a small kidney lesion while another may have had a large one; and others may have had five or six kidney lesions. What different symptoms did each have compared to what I had expected? I usually tried to find the most important weaknesses and write them down closest to the outside edge of the paper. Those most indented or furtherest from the edge of the paper were the least important.

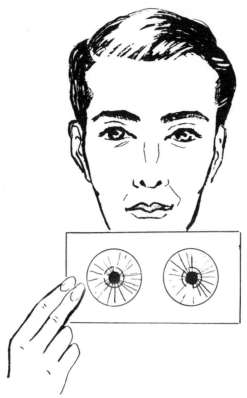

FIG. 12.   Reading the chart while standing in front of a mirror.

There are many other ways in which you can list conditions. Henry Lindlahr had them marked one, two, three, four and five: one, very serious; two, not quite so serious; and on to five, the least serious of all. Make a chart of your own of the different irises. Draw pictures of irises and keep them on record. You may use colored ones to begin with, or you may start in with plain white paper and use colored crayon. Refer to them later, as your own records are the records you will remember. I do not wish to set up a system for you because each person remembers a thing better if he does it for himself. At the beginning of my practice I drew the iris of every patient I examined, and I soon arrived at the place where merely putting it down on paper gave me an iris consciousness that helped me remember a person's iris conditions long after he had been in the office. Just as the doctor who studies bones remembers his patients by the bone condition he has, I remember my patients by the conditions seen in the iris.

When you are analyzing, it is well to start in with a definite spot. For instance, start at six o'clock and take in each area separately. I usually start with the gastro-intestinal field first but there are times when other systems seem more important,—the respiratory, the genito-urinary, the lymphatic, or the nervous,—because I have been trained to treat each one specifically and the most important first. When I know the functioning ability of each system, I know how I am going to handle it therapeutically, and what treatments to use. If I feel that the nervous system is in need of treatment immediately, I will start with that on the patient's first visit.

The physical care of the patient comes first. If there are any spiritual adjustments to make, I work on them last; it is best to know your patient before you delve into the spiritual side. You can talk about carrot juice to everyone, but you cannot easily talk about spiritual things. The subject is a sensitive one and so is the patient as a rule.

To commit yourself by saying that such and such an occurrence took place in the iris last week or in the last two months, or that you are expecting a change now, to-morrow, or the next day, is not a good policy. Leave out the time factor. Also, it is not necessary to tell the patient all that you find. To doctors who want to do the best for their patients, the important thing is not what information can be given the patient, but it is what he himself knows and what he is going to do for the patient that will mean the most in the long run. I never tell a patient any more than what I consider is wise for him to know. Above all things, no matter what is said or not said, it is not what the patient knows, it is what the doctor knows that is important.

Your object is to get information; to obtain a good history and a good background from which to work. The patient is expecting you to take care of him and help him out of his trouble, so you need information. The iris findings will help you come to conclusions. After you have read thousands of irises, you will come to more and more conclusions, and then I am sure you will be a great blessing to your patients.

Let us review a case history, taking an actual case I had in one of my early iridology classes. A young lady is seated before me, I am analyzing the iris, and dictating my findings. We record first what we find in the irises and then the patient's remarks are listed below.

Patient for demonstration: (student at L.A.C.C.)

Findings in the left eye:

1. Two pockets in descending colon.
2. Small pocket and considerable irritation in splenic flexure.
3. Stricture in sigmoid colon, causing reflex to kidney on left side and to left pelvis.
4. Toxic sigmoid colon.
5. Kidney lesion and left kidney weakness.
6. Nerve rings; very heavy nerve tension.
7. Sympathetic or autonomic nervous system is overworked.
8. Toxic thyroid.
9. Acute inflammation of left thyroid gland.

Findings in the right eye:

1. Extreme fatigue condition extending as far as the area of locomotion.
2. Inherent weakness and a heavy catarrhal lesion of upper lung, right side, with some acute inflammation at present.
3. Bronchial condition; heavy catarrh.
4. Liver over-congested.
5. Acidity and catarrh throughout whole body.
6. Slight lower back weakness.
7. Anemia in upper and lower extremities.
8. If patient becomes too toxic, she will have trouble with motion of the legs and lower back.
9. Sulphur deposit throughout intestinal tract, settled mostly in the sympathetic or autonomic nervous system.
10. Most of the toxic material is settling in the brain area. (There is a definite reason for that. There are two or three spokes going into the brain area which indicate the toxic material is settling in the brain and nervous system.
11. Duodenal disturbance at some time.
12. Healing signs show there has been a change in diet.
13. Pancreatic weakness.
14. Slight acute activity of the thyroid gland on right side.

15. Just opposite that, a chronic lesion in the small intestine, showing it is throwing toxic material into the thyroid. Patient is not digesting her food properly.

Subject's Statements:

Bronchial condition has been acute for about three months. Has been a vegetarian for the past two years. Pain in sigmoid colon feels like a walled-off section. Putrefaction goes on in colon, and food does not digest properly. Cerebral anemia at times. Circulatory disturbance. Anemia in upper and lower extremities and brain at the same time. Vertigo. Hands and feet cold, with profuse perspiration. Heart palpitation. Hypertension. Went to White Memorial Hospital and was told she had hypertension due to disfunction of the autonomic nervous system; also was told something about the skin.

Questions and Answers

Dr. Jensen: Do your hands sweat when you feel nervous?

Mrs. B.: Yes.

Dr. Jensen: The whole iris shows the acute inflammatory stage. Because of living habits and hard work, you are not getting the good out of your food. You are slowly starving to death. Aggravating factors are: weather, work, lack of rest. Around the torso the skin is more active. The body is trying to get rid of some of the drugs settled in the skin area. There is a small psora spot in the autonomic nervous system opposite the heart; the palpitation you feel is coming from irritation caused by this psora. There is nothing wrong with the heart. How about the left hip?

Mrs. B.: There is something wrong, but I don't know what it is.

Dr. Jensen: The condition goes down the left leg and into the foot. There is an inherent weakness in the left leg. There is an inherent weakness in the hip area where the toxic material has settled, as well as below the knee and in the foot. You are absorbing toxic material from the sigmoid colon.

Mrs. B.: Pain starts at the hip, travels down and settles at the knee. It is localized in both knees, but principally the left side is affected from the hip down.

Dr. Jensen: The sciatica or rheumatism or whatever the diagnosis reveals may be wrong in the left side will never leave until the sigmoid colon has been cleared.

There was more discussion but the above will suffice to get you started. It would be well to see a few similar analyses made and go on from there.

After you have made your examination and recorded what you have found in the iris of the eye, it is advisable to question the patient so as to compare his information with your analysis and findings. Remember that in many instances what the patient states and what you find do not compare too favorably. So conditions have to be unearthed that have long been forgotten, such as accidents, injuries, or childhood diseases. You will also find many conditions reflected in the iris that have not yet manifested their symptoms. In this way you are forecasting conditions yet to come. Sometimes it is difficult to tell there has been a crisis in the last few days or that a crisis apparently is due to begin in the next few days. Too, it is difficult oftentimes to see which side of the crisis line you are reading. on the other. His body was full of friction, wide-meshed, loose connective tissue.

Do not plan to check the iris at every appointment as the changes you are looking for may take two or three weeks. They are sometimes slow in appearing, but it is wonderful when you can begin to see them in the iris structure and can watch their development over a period of a month or so.

Remember the hills and valleys of the iris as you analyze, and note how the nerve rings are indented. Move your light around so you are able to see that the rings are deeper in some organs than in others. It is only in catching shadow that you can actually see how deep a nerve ring is. Keep your light moving and you will make dis-coveries that you would not have if you had kept your light in a fixed position. You analyze from shadow effects as well as from direct observation of the fibre and area itself.

Since you apply yourself to the science of iridology to learn as much as possible about it, keep an open mind. You will tend to say an eye is green or blue in color, but every green eye, every blue eye, and every brown eye is distinctive, just as is every nose or every ear. Do not try to tear iridol-ogy to pieces before you know more about it. There are many little details that dove-tail, and in order to see one fact clearly you must see another ten in relation to it. It is almost like saying you see a star when you see only one point of the star. So keep your mind open and think about the whole picture yet to come.

Although more theory will be presented as you progress, you should recognize from the start that theory and practice go hand in hand. You must develop a new type of thinking along with this work; develop comparative faculties and analytical abil-ities. Learn to pigeonhole certain thoughts in your mind so you can recall them at a later time.

You will have to be patient in order to letarn the science of iridology. A great deal of detailed study and patient application will be required. The iris is a comparatively small part of the body which must yet be broken down into even smaller parts. There are about ninety areas with which you will have to become acquainted in the break-down of the iris. It will not be easy, but bear in mind that nothing is impossible. Let us discover the truth together and as we go along we will attempt to prove our theories.

Equipment Required For Iridology

There are many exaggerated ideas re-garding the kind of equipment which should be used in iridology, but for the beginner, a good magnifying glass and a light with a

sharp focusing beam that comes to a point are the most essential. Whether or not they are the expensive kind makes no difference. In my travels in Europe I saw very high-priced and elegant equipment that I thought I would take back with me. Though the magnifying lenses were all right, the light-ing equipment was very poor, so it would have proven a poor investment. Bausch and Lomb have made some excellent equip-ment for enlarging the fibres of the iris and far looking into lesions. A magnifying glass with as little distortion as possible, as a four-power glass, is the best.

Many instruments that have been made for examining the eyes shine directly into the eye, which makes it very hard on the patient and makes it difficult to compare the fibres of one part of the iris with those of another. For reading shadows and seeing into deep lesions, it is best to have a mov-able light because it is necessary to shift

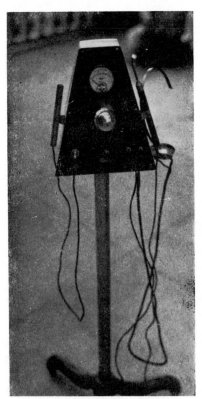

FIG. 13.   Nervometer for check-ing iridiagnosis findings.

from the top of the iris down to the bottom in order to distinguish the different layers.

The photographic eye equipment is very poor as yet. Most of my pictures have had to be individually developed according to the patient. Some of the reasons for this are that the degree of roundness of the iris is not uniform, the pupillary reaction may vary, a brown eye requires more light than a blue one, etc.

There are many pieces of equipment which can be used to prove your work in this science, and I believe the finest for this purpose is the nervometer which registers the acid-alkaline reactions of the body. There are other instruments which pick up nerve tensions in the body and can also indicate conditions as reflected in the iris.

The accompanying picture shows a machine being used in our office to test a lady whose chief difficulty was in the ascending

FIG. 14. A nervometer machine which we use to prove what we have found in the iris of the eye. When the pointer passes over an area where abnormal conditions exist, not only does the instrument register a change, but the doctor hears and the patient feels a slight shock.

colon. She had had this trouble there for about fifteen years and wanted to have it taken care of, but no one she had consulted seemed able to help her. She later devel-

oped cancer of the right breast which showed in the iris just opposite the iris spot indicating the colon pathology. The equipment here pictured showed that most of her trouble was in the ascending colon, and as we went over this part of the body she showed the usual reaction to this weakness by drawing away from the pointer when it was applied to this particular spot.

We also illustrate equipment made by one of the large optical companies. Through an inverted microscope you look directly

FIG. 15. Looking through an inverted microscope into the eye of the patient.

into the eye and see the areas blown up to a tremendous size. This equipment is not necessary for the beginner, however.

There are many iridologists who believe that only natural daylight should be used. But since weather conditions vary and we do not always have sunshine or even an unvaried light to carry on our work, it is well to train ourselves to do our work under the most adverse conditions.

Examination Methods and Office Charts

In our office, we have made numerous changes in the various charts used over the years so that they fit in with each patient's needs. These changes were necessary to keep a check on the progress of our patients while treating them and to more easily check back on them from year to year. I will give you a few ideas which may be used in making your own charts.

Of course, we realize that every person has his own ideas and generally prefers them, but we will reproduce a couple of charts which we have used in the past and develops a crisis because at that time he will tell you about troubles in the particular area about which you have recorded. In spite of the fact that the patient had no difficulty there for many, many years, those old troubles he had forgotten all about will be reactivated. The iris holds a complete history from years past.

Fig. 16.   A chart like this can be used to record the markings of the iris. Record in pencil, pen or colored crayon.

found satisfactory. These charts can be used by the beginning student and can be developed according to his own way of diagnosing. We will also take up one case history as it was given before a class, show how we made the examination, what we determined was wrong with the patient, and the patient's remarks.

The remarks were recorded on the chart. Notice the charts were designed so that a detailed record could be made and the healing crisis be predicted and recorded. In many cases the patients had not realized to what extent they had stored up accumulated waste and toxic material in the various organs.. It is well to list what you find in the iris for that time when the patient

EXAMINATION PROCEDURE

Preliminary analysis of patient, Mr. S. A.:

Chronic acid stomach. Nerve ring going through intestinal tract; nervous indigestion. Pocket half-way down descending colon; colon has healing lines as result of improved diet. Pocket caused heart trouble because it was full of gas but healing lines tell of improvement. Inherent weakness of left kidney; not seriously impaired but not capable of doing its work properly. Pocket opposite in intestinal tract in fainting and dizziness area. Inherent weakness of the neck area. Extreme amount of acidity and catarrh in the body; catarrh mostly in the brain area (darker there than in the rest of the iris). Spokes from transverse colon area; dropped transverse colon. Acute activity half-way up the ascending colon, causing acute activity of right lung and bronchial tubes. Chronic catarrh of gall bladder. Brain anemia and anemia of extremities.

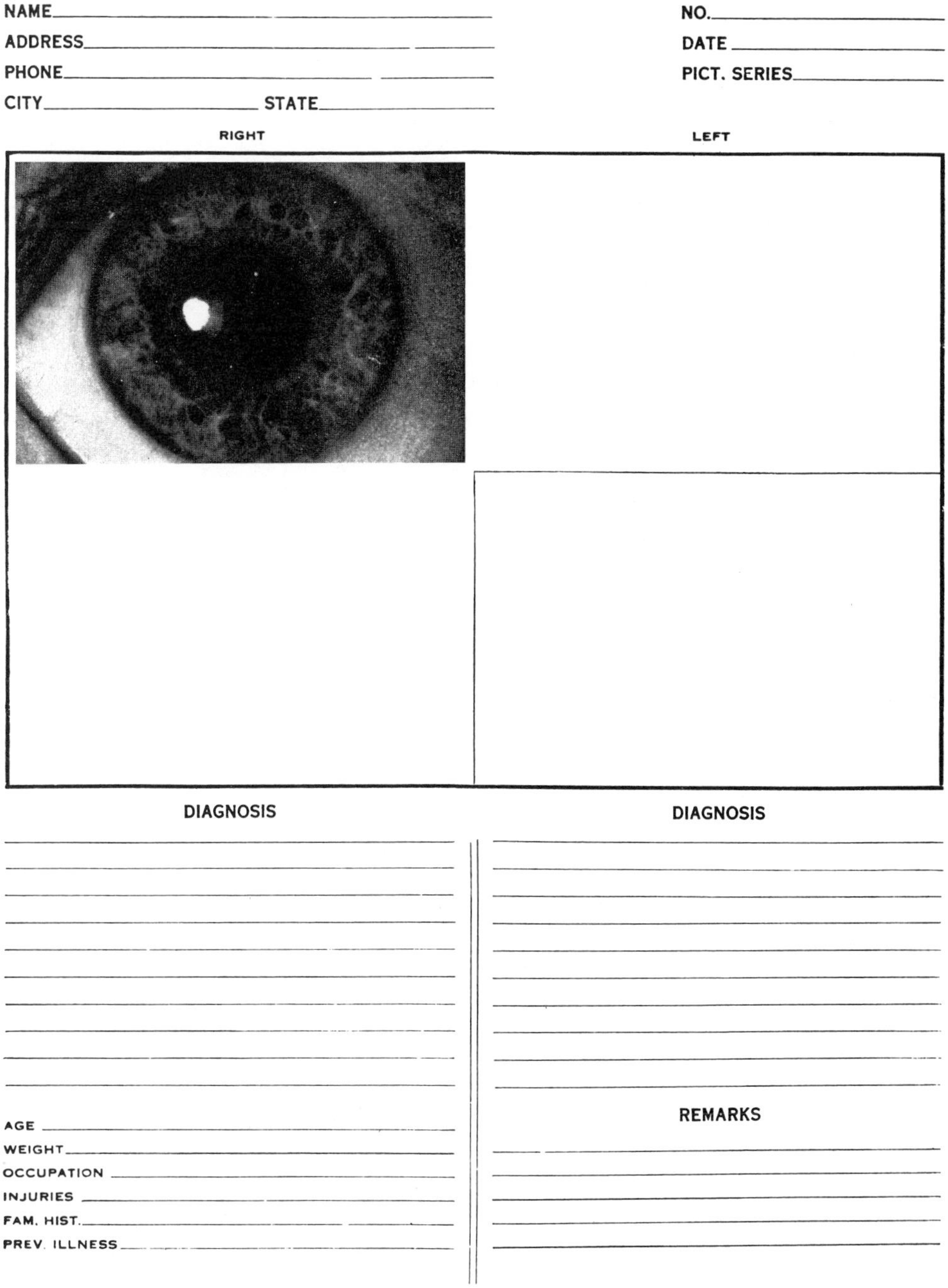

NAME_____   NO._____

ADDRESS_____   DATE _____

PHONE_____   PICT. SERIES_____

CITY_____ STATE_____

RIGHT   LEFT

DIAGNOSIS   DIAGNOSIS

AGE _____   REMARKS

WEIGHT_____

OCCUPATION _____

INJURIES _____

FAM. HIST._____

PREV. ILLNESS_____

FIG. 17.   One of the charts that have been used in Doctor Jensen's office.

Summary

Patient has difficulty in eating; cannot eat raw foods. Has difficulty with citrus fruits at times. (Have to be sparing with citrus fruits with chronic acid stomach). Has had quite a struggle to get well. Healing lines throughout intestinal tract. Inherent weaknesses which have been overcome 35 per cent to 40 per cent indicating they are deep. Calcium fixation poor; therefore, lacks tone, power, and energy. Circulation poor; feet cold at night. Bruises easily and does not heal readily. Has rectal trouble; dropped transverse colon. Has fainting and dizziness under excessive heat or pressure of job. Cannot put in hard day's work without feeling effects of it; can push hard, then all at once has to let go of everything. Most of trouble settled in neck. (In cases of inherent weakness of the neck, we know, as we go back to cervical lesions, that dizziness has its source there. We know where we will begin to work with mechanical manipulation). Has had sinus trouble. Active catarrhal condition of right lung; dry condition; did not know he had it. Has had gall bladder difficulty. Troubled with constipation; acute inflammation in bowel, with nerve ring going through it, indicating colitis.

Questions by Dr. Jensen, Answers by Patient

Q. How are the bowels?

A. In bad shape. Lots of gas.

Q. Did you ever have any heart trouble?

A. Yes, but it is better now.

Q. Any trouble with your neck?

A. Yes and headaches.

Q. Any sinus trouble?

A. Oh yes.

Q. Do you raise any catarrhal material now?

A. Yes, pieces of gray mucus. I have considerable pain on the right side of my head.

Q. Do your feet get cold?

A. Yes, my knees and feet.

Q. Do you ever experience dizziness?

A. Yes, pressure comes on left side of my neck. My head feels dizzy and sometimes I stagger like a drunk.

Q. Is there any condition I missed?

A. I have drainage from the nose and my ears get blocked up.

Q. How about the rectum?

A. It is all right now, but I have had lots of trouble. It cost me $13 a treatment, only to have the same thing over and over again.

Q. Any trouble with the rectum lately?

A. Some bleeding. A Dr. T. I am going to is doing a fine job.

Q. Do you eat raw foods?

A. I can eat soft raw fruit, but no apples or raw vegetables.

Patient's Comments a Week Or So Later

Re. Citrus Fruits:

"I took a glass of orange juice about six weeks ago, and it almost killed me. I was sick for two weeks. I used to have trouble with frequent urination, and didn't know where to place the blame. Dr. Jensen suggested cutting out lemons, oranges, grapefruit, tomatoes, and now I have no trouble."

In analyzing this patient, conditions were determined from the iris which were not determined otherwise. As soon as I took his hand and found it hard, I knew that calcium had settled in the joints; that he lacked sodium, and therefore had an acid stomach. He had no half-moons at the base of his fingernails, which indicated poor circulation. The wrinkles in his forehead were indicative of nerve tension. The sides of his body were not evenly matched, therefore glandular function was not even. He was subject to moods and extreme cycles. His mouth came up on one side and down on the other. His body was full of friction, the right side working against the left side continually. He was going to have trouble with nervous symptoms. Whatever his complaints, 50 per cent of them would come from the nervous system. He had more problems to handle than he should have, and most of them were health problems. (One's health is a natural state of affairs and should not require effort. As soon as there is a health problem, wrinkles begin to appear).

My advice to this man was to learn all he could about himself and to take corrective exercises. An X-ray examination of the bowel and a blood count were indicated. (Bring these to normal and other troubles will diminish). Chemically, the man lacked sodium, calcium, silicon, iodine and phosphorus.

We measure all the inflammation in the body by a gauge of from one to five, and consider three as average. If a person has one point of inflammation, or of toxicity, he can be in the sub-acute stage. He can be in the chronic stage when he gets to four. When five is reached he is in a very serious chronic stage and is on the way to complete degeneration. A three-plus acid stomach indicates a serious condition. If the condition has reached the place where it is close to the degenerative stage, is chronic and has been present for many years, it is four or even four-plus. If the acidity throughout the body is very heavy, judge over a period of time as to whether it is close to three or five. If just a slight inflammation needs checking, you can bring it down to two or perhaps one. You will soon

FIG. 18.   Taking an eye picture with one of Doctor Jensen's cameras.

He could not take citrus fruits (few persons with acid stomach can tolerate them). He had more trouble on the left side than on the right, so he would get along better on starches than on proteins. (The left side is the negative side in man and starches are negative. If left side is broken down, give negative foods to build it up—starches, stewed fruits, etc.).

This example is only of a preliminary examination, but it will help to build the foundation in this work.

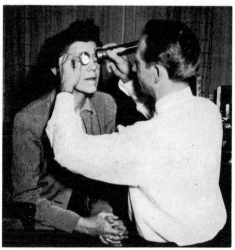

FIG. 19.   Examining the iris with light and magnifying glass.

be able to see how these charts work for you. A system can be developed for determining the degree and seriousness of the inflammation a person has, and it will help you to compare it with first one patient, then another. After you have examined a few thousand patients you will be able to compare degrees of inflammation.

If the time comes when there are sufficient funds for further experimentation in, this science, I believe it will be possible to take pictures of the patient's eye before and after treatment. As yet, photography has not offered an opportunity for the additional experimentation necessary to bring out a type of camera suitable for our needs. A great deal of money already has been spent in this science, and only a certain amount can be spent in experimental work by a doctor. The rest will have to be done by an engineer or one who would be interested in developing this work for the police department, the F.B.I., or any other groups who could use this science toward the good of humanity.

10

THE NORMAL AND THE ABNORMAL IRIS

Let no one presume to give advice to others that has not first given good advice to himself.

—Seneca

You may just as well look at the iris blindfolded if you do not have the proper knowledge of iridology. The skeptic usually looks at the iris of the eye blindly, anyway. It is folly to think for one moment that this science can be intelligently criticized without first having obtained the knowledge of what is in and behind the marking of every fibre in the iris of the eye.

In this chapter we will take up the structure of the iris and attempt to become so well acquainted with it that when we look at it we will know all its component parts. We must have something tangible to work with—something which we can compare with the studies and training we have already had. We will study a brief, concise, anatomical and structural outline. If you

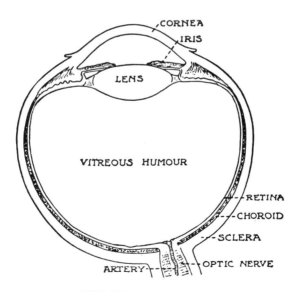

THE HUMAN CAMERA

Fig. 20. A diagram of the eye, showing the iris, which concentrates light rays, the lens which focuses them, and the retina which receives them as an image upon its surface.

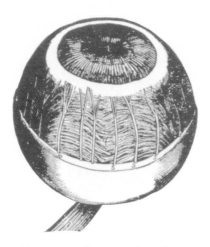

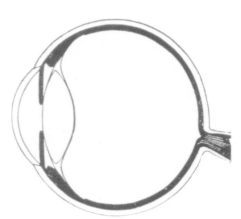

FIG. 21.   The iris, the ciliary
muscle, and choroid membrane.

FIG. 22.   Vertical section of the
pupil.

want to go into this phase more thoroughly, I suggest that you consult Gray's "Anatomy" or take up the training of ophthalmology.

The iris of the eye is the most highly specialized nerve organ with the most highly developed nerve tissue. In dealing with the iris you are dealing with a most sensitive body organ for it is a highly-tuned receiving station that receives messages from all parts of the body.

The iris gets its name from the various colors found there. It is a thin four-layered

structure, suspended between the cornea and the lens, and perforated slightly on the nasal side near the pupil. The four layers from front to back are:

1. Layer of flattened endothelial cells placed on a delicate hyaline membrane.

2. Vascular layer. Its vessels lie in a wide-meshed, loose connective tissue.

3. Muscular layer of circular fibres from the *sphincter pupilla*, which radiates outward toward the ciliary body.

1 Surface Endothelium	5 In Necroses
2 Normal Fibrillae	6 Pigment Layer
3 Fibrillae in subacute conditions	
4 In chronic conditions	

FIG. 23.   Shades illustrating the different stages of inflammation. The top layer is where you find acute lesions. The lower layers become darker and the inflammation you are reading is becoming more chronic.

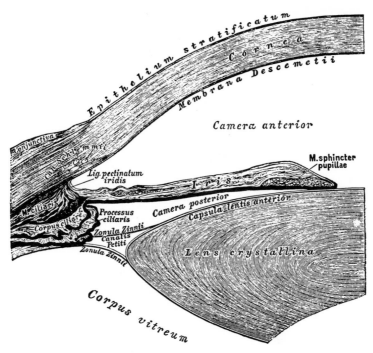

FIG. 24.   Anatomical cross-section of iris and surrounding tissues.

4. Deeply pigmented, purplish-black epithelium known as the *pars iridica retinae*.

Blood Supply to the Iris

Long and anterior ciliary arteries.
Vessels of the ciliary processes.
Circulus arteriosus major and minor.

Nerve Supply to the Iris

Long and short ciliary.
Sympathetics to *dilator pupillae*.
Parasympathetics to *spincter pupillae*.
Ophthalmologists prove that diseases like lues, diabetes mellitus, arteriosclerosis, brain tumor, and many others, can be determined from the retina. Simple neurology proves the reflex action in the iris. A pressure exerted upon the toes will cause the pupil to dilate on the same side of the body as the toes being pressed. The iris reflects pathology in the various systems and organs of the body.

The main point we want to emphasize in this study of iridology is that we are dealing with a structure which is an extension of the brain. We say we see something with our eyes, but actually the brain gets the picture first; the image is received by brain centers which reflect the picture to the iris. Through comparison and experience our interpretation is that we see a picture. Without being able to think of what we are looking at and without the brain to receive and interpret the image reflected on the retina, it would be impossible to interpret what we see. We know of a new healing technique whereby the reflex conditions to the heart or the kidneys can be controlled by changing the pictures which the eye receives.

The whole body is so linked with the nervous system that nothing can happen in any part but what every cell structure is affected by it. This is one of the reasons why chiropractic and osteopathy are so

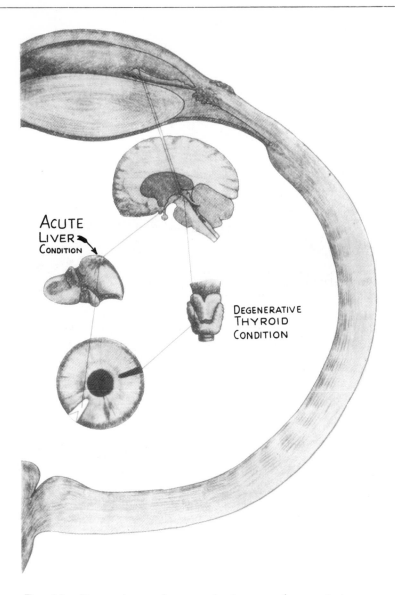

ACUTE
LIVER
CONDITION

DEGENERATIVE
THYROID
CONDITION

FIG. 25. Every tissue when not in its normal state is in a hypo- or hyperactive condition. These affect the rate of vibration going over the nerves. What starts in the tissues is reflected in a resultant picture in the iris of the eye.

effective. The seat of pain is not always where we begin our treatment. We can determine many reflex conditions of the body by examining remote organs. By obtaining a knowledge of the working activity of certain parts of the body, we can tell what is going on in more remote areas.

In our anatomical studies, we are able to break down and identify nearly all the body structures, yet in this atomic age we realize there is much to learn and accept. I believe there are many fibres within fibres that have not been discovered as yet. About twenty-five years ago in college, we had studied a particular nerve in the spine until we thought we knew everything that could be known about it. We thought it was probably like a wire, solid all the way through, but before I graduated we learned that an anatomical engineer in Sweden had broken down that particular nerve fibre and found there were over two thousand smaller fibres making up this one particular nerve.

While we do not know everything concerning the iris of the eye anatomically, evidence indicates that through certain actions and reactions in the body, changes take place in the iris fibres which reveal a direct relation, reflexly, with the various organs of the body.

white. These are the layers we are going to have to interpret in iridology.

The normal as well as the abnormal iris must be considered although you probably never will see a completely normal or healthy one. I have never seen one though I have worked with thousands of eyes. It is because of the inherent weaknesses of the human family that you are unlikely to see a normal eye—one without any indication of bodily weakness. Sections of the iris, however, will present what we consider to be a normal appearance where the body is functioning as nearly perfect as possible.

The pupil formation in many eyes is irregular and may be larger on one side of

FIG. 26.   This chart illustrates the four stages of inflammation recorded in the iris of the eye.

The iris of the eye can be compared to the actors on a stage, each one having a part to play. Seemingly, each fibre of the iris acts its part by registering a sign or coloration through the prompting of some body organ, apparently by remote control. As on the stage, so in the body do we not see the sound engineer, the prompter behind the curtain, yet we see represented through the actor (which in this case would be the iris), what is going on behind the scenes.

The accompanying chart illustrates the iris shadings, from the dark pigment layer underneath to the top layer, which is very

the body than on the other. Or you may find the pupil to be pinpoint in size. In still other persons the appearance of the pupil is very light, evidencing pressure symptoms from internal cataracts. These different appearances of the pupil all have a story to tell, but we will go into this only briefly here. This is another study though it may be used along with iridology.

Sometimes pupils reveal the habits of a person. Under alcoholic influence, pupils become quite dilated, while in opium poisoning they may be contracted to pinpoint size. In cases of stroke, the pupil fails to dilate or contract when light is flashed into the eye, so we see that pupils react according to bodily conditions. All orifices of the body relax and contract in proportion to nerve and muscle tone. In animal husbandry the muscle tone of a horse is judged by an examination of the *sphincter ani;*—his tail is switched aside and a quick glance at the rectal orifice reveals the tone of all the muscles of the animal. For centuries horse traders have used this method of determining the health and virility of the animal under consideration.

When a person has been working too hard and has drained his nervous system, his pupils will be quite dilated, as extreme fatigue produces a dilated pupil. Chemical imbalance can also cause altered conditions of the pupil; a lack of vitamin B lowers nerve tone and a lack of phosphorus results in nerve depletion. Fright, fear, and emotion, cause a variance in the size of the pupils.

One side of the body is always inherently different from the other. Sometimes the pupils are not even similar. The muscular structure on one side of the body is not the same as on the other, and when disease settles in the muscular system and there is a lack of potassium, you may find the pupil affected more on one side of the body than on the other. Where there is a lack of vitamin A you will find that light hurts a person's eyes—he cannot tolerate light or light reflections. He often strains the sphincter muscles of the pupil in order to keep out the light; thus these muscles are often strained and overworked.

As we look into the iris of the eye we are confronted with the layers we have illustrated. The top layer is white. It will be very white and taut if it is highly active, and in this acute, inflammatory stage you will find it to be considerably anterior to the other fibres of the iris.

Just as the pupil will register reaction from a toe, there is an acute reaction from every organ in the body, for they are constantly sending forth vibrations at a powerful, high rate of speed over the nerve pathways to the fibres of the iris. A white coloration represents an extremely active, highly nervous and sensitive condition of a tissue or organ. These white lines or colorations may be found in any area of the iris depending upon the organ or tissue affected. If the thyroid gland is affected you will find these white, acute signs in the thyroid area of the iris.

Inflammation or acute activity of any organ is first noticed in the iris as a white cloud, but if you will closely examine this you will find it involves many fibres. These fibres are raised toward you, anteriorly to normal placement. The reason these fibres appear so white and are quite plainly visible to the naked eye, is that they have been separated from the pigment layer below. It is interesting to see how they make up the white clouds and the white areas in the different landmarks which we will discuss shortly. You may like to examine these white clouds under high power magnification. Whenever you find a white cloud or white lines you know there is an acute inflammation in the corresponding area of the body, the right iris corresponding to the right side of the body.

The "normal" iris would not have any raised fibres such as those described in acute inflammatory signs. Its fibres would appear relaxed, with a normal amount of pigment showing through from underneath. Because of diseased conditions in the body, we can expect to be confronted, as already stated, with irises which deviate from normal. For instance, when the iris fibres separate and form a well or a hole, so to speak, this indicates an inherent weakness expressed by a separation or bending of the iris fibres so that its dark pigment layer shows through. A pine tree is not so strong as an oak tree because its inherent fibres and tissues are softer. The pine tree has less power and ability to withstand the ravages of storms than the hard wood of the oak. They can both be healthy, however. A

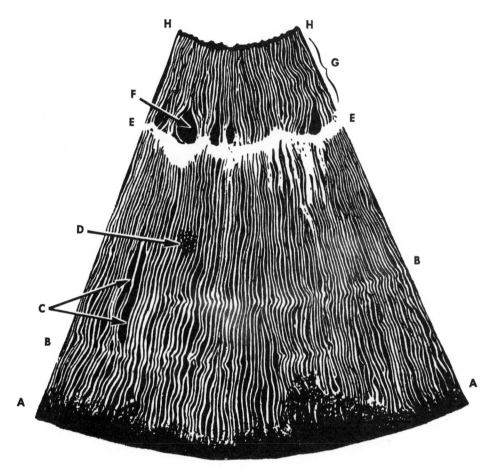

FIG. 27. A—Scurf rim   E—Autonomic nerve wreath
         B—Nerve rings   F—Toxic settlement in bowel
         C—Inherent weakness   G—Gastro-intestinal areas
         D—Drug spot   H—Pupillary margin

child born with a poor constitution naturally will not have muscles and fibres as strong as one born with a good inheritance. The fibres of this weak inherent tissue are more like the coarse weave of a gunnysack than like strong, closely-woven silk. It is not capable of great strength, normal recuperative power, nor normal vitality.

I make this comparison to show you the kind of tissue you have to deal with when you discover these inherent signs or "holes" in the iris. Whether you find them in the thyroid or adrenal gland area of the iris, or any other area, makes no difference. The

weakness of the organ will be indicated. We will discuss these markings in the various areas on the charts. This will give you something definite to follow. So, when you see black, well-like spaces in the iris areas, you know these signs do not indicate acute inflammation. Under treatment, these holes begin to fill in and disappear as the tissues of the body become healthy and strong.

I had the accompanying drawing exaggerated so that the fibres and markings can be easily studied. The circle cut out in the smaller end is the pupillary side and the bottom of the drawing is the periphery. Notice these iris fibres are not all straight and many times there are little spots where they are separated. These spots represent the inherent weaknesses we spoke of. Toxic material can settle here, and when the fibres themselves have become toxic-laden they become inactive, latent, and do not have the power to function normally. It is only the acute or white lines that are the active ones and they are not in evidence at the present time; they have gone into a recession. All we see now is the inactive pigment layer showing.

There are little lines in the iris which constitute what we call a cramp ring or nerve ring, and when these show up in the iris you will notice that the fibres actually appear to be cramped.

The white line you see separating the first two zones in the iris is the sympathetic or autonomic nervous system wreath. You will notice a small spot where the fibres seem to be broken. We will go into these conditions later on, but let us first get a picture of the fibres of the iris so we can see that we are looking either into a health mirror or a disease mirror, for the iris mirrors what is going on in the rest of the body.

Colors of the Iris

There is much to be said about the color of the eyes but we will confine ourselves to what is necessary to help make the subject of iridology clear. The various authors who have written about this science all have personal ideas on the subject of eye color, and opinions vary as to what coloration is normal. In our search for a normal eye we found both blue and brown eyes that we considered normal in color.

Color comes from the dark pigment layer we described in the anatomy discussion. The pigment is an inherent quality, part of an inherent structure, and is the most natural when a child is first born. After birth the iris becomes darker as the child is fed, either mother's milk or a formula. The original color is distorted as the child grows older. I have studied many children's eyes to learn these facts.

The Marine Corps recruiting service announced in their figures on enlistments in the second World War, that blue-eyed marines make the best rifle shots. Of a group of 1,252 men, 66 per cent had blue eyes. According to Lieutenant Colonel R. W. Peard, in charge of the recruiting office in Los Angeles, experiments have shown that a large percentage of men who were good rifle shots and who had attained proficiency with infantry weapons, have blue eyes. This is due to the fact that shifting light, caused by drifting clouds that obscure the target at that time, has little or no effect on the blue-eyed man. Men with dark eyes have difficulty in coping with this condition.

In this day of global communication and racial intermarriage, eye color is changing tremendously. There is no longer a person of one race because so many races have intermingled, and with the intermingling, the true color of the eye is being altered. The true blue and the true brown are lost. The eyes of the northern races are more or less of the true blue color and as we go south we come to the brown-eyed people. Possibly this dark pigment is there to filter out the intense reflection of sunlight. In albinos the iris is without pigment.

There are many places where iridology could be used to help society. It could be used in hospitals, for example, to avoid the mix-up of babies. The color and structure of a baby's eyes could be matched with those of parents, and the matter settled to the satisfaction of all concerned.

In diagnosing different irises, we find it much easier to see individual fibres in the blue eye. The brown eye seems to carry a filament along with the fibres so that it is difficult to make a separation in the fibre structure. The white in the brown eye will not be so white as it is in the blue eye. In the brown, the white will be a brownish white, but it will be so much lighter than the rest of the iris that you will be able to distinguish it.

A toxic condition has much to do with the color of the iris just as toxins in the body will make the complexion darker. It is an interesting experience to see eyes that have been classified as brown become lighter, and the blue fibres become more predominant through your treatments. The brownish cast will lighten up and go away, and many times can be likened to a fading sunset. Variations from the normal of these two colors, brown and blue, may be considered a toxic, systemic condition.

We have seen many darkened irises become lighter in color again through constant natural cleansing processes. Many eyes called brown, when seen under magnification, are actually blue in color. Under natural healing procedures, really blue eyes have come back to bluer eyes. Of course the change is developed in direct proportion to the amount of morbid matter that has been expelled from the body. We might consider the fact that there are in-between colors such as the gray and hazel eyes. Many iridologists consider these eye colors normal.

It is very difficult to come to a conclusion, especially from existing iridology books, as to what the proper fundamental eye coloring should be. After studying along this line, however, it seems that it is dependent entirely upon the color given off by the pigment layer of the iris, and this in turn is largely dependent upon whether the person's hair is brunette or blond. In general, the degree of blond and brown pigmentation of the hair determines the degree of blue or brown pigment in the iris. As we consider the different colorings we come to the conclusion that the child is born with the lightest eye possible, but that as toxins and disease conditions develop and both the exogenic and endogenic fibres manifest themselves, the iris changes in color. Many times the blue becomes brown and muddy looking and is often mistaken for brown.

Color which is acquired through living habits is there as toxic material or drug deposits, and indicates the body is encumbered with morbid or diseased material.

Here is a classification to go by: clear blue, whitish blue, whitish gray. The blue can turn into a grayish blue and then even into a darker blue. A clear brown can turn into amber or a dark brown. Between these there are the mixed colors and the intermediates. The last is the pink or the albino.

There has been much discussion as to whether the brown-eyed person is the more short-lived or long-lived than the blue-eyed. I personally do not think color enters into the question of longevity at all. Those who take care of themselves, whether browneyed or blue-eyed, can be long-lived. In my practice, however, I find those who have lived the longest life have blue eyes. Since this is only my personal experience, I do not say this condition exists throughout the world.

It also has been said that the blood chemistry of the brown-eyed is different from that of the blue-eyed individual. This is not a proven fact, and probably many of the RH factors we find today are recorded just as well in the person with brown eyes as in the person with blue eyes.

The difference between the two may be one of the factors we will use in determining what kind of blood we will have in the child in years to come. When Paolo Mantegazza, director of the National Museum of Anthropology in Florence, Italy, studied the Lapps, he was convinced there were many shades of coloring in the iris of the eye. In fact, he showed about fourteen shades in just one race of people. Here is a list of his findings: Chestnut brown, dark and light chestnut brown, grayish brown, turquoise blue, light turquoise blue, light azure, gray, light gray, light sky gray, azure gray, yellowish gray, greenish gray, and green.

The Vibratory Theory

Many practitioners like to question whether the iris reveals tissue conditions of the body. If you could have the opportunity of looking at the iris of a person immediately after he has been in an accident or has suffered from some great catastrophe, you would see the accident almost simultaneously registered in the iris, and it would make you wonder how these markings could possibly appear there so quickly. But they do, especially if the person involved in the accident is one who has not had anesthetics and other kinds of blockage which would interfere with the passage of vibrations between the injured part and the iris.

You may wonder how the color of iodine put on a cut on the knee shows up as the color of iodine in the iris in that organ reflex area. Does it travel through the body and become deposited in the iris, or has an image become mirrored there by means of vibratory transmissions? After you have used this science for some time, you will see that such drug signs have a definite place in diagnosing. Men in the tropics during the war who were given quinine for malaria over a period of time, will have green discoloration in the iris. Why, I do not know. The only explanation I have for this phenomenon is the one etsablished through the vibratory theory.

As an example, the chameleon can ably camouflage itself through color changes that blend with its environment. An interesting fact, however, is that only one-half the body of this animal will change color if the sight of one eye is kept from observing its environment. This demonstrates that each side of the body is connected quite definitely with the eye on that side. *This may clear up a point for those who wonder why the right eye corresponds to the right side of the body in iris reading.* Now we know the environment had no part in the physical change of color in that chameleon. It was produced by a vibratory change through the nervous system. Is there any reason why there should not be mirrored or recorded in the iris of the eye the end-result of every nerve impulse in the body? Is there any reason why the vibration of an acute or sub-acute lesion or of any drug settlement cannot travel through the nervous system and be recorded in the iris pic-

ture with the same vibratory rate it had at its origin?

Television is probably one of the best comparisons we could make of these markings appearing in the iris reflexly from remote organs. What we actually see when we watch a baseball or football game on the television screen, is probably taking place many miles from where we are viewing it. But this picture is actually going through the air, silently, via a vibratory channel. What you see in the iris involves the same principle. The picture reflected in the iris comes from some part of the body by remote control. When we see these markings from disease, we may consider that the iris is a screen and that a stage show is going on in one of the body organs or tissues. The iris "screen" will register trouble in the body whether it be caused by drug poisoning, by settlements of acid or toxic waste which the body has been unable to eliminate through catabolic processes, or by nerve depletion from continual worry, excitement and uneliminated body wastes. Where the body must continually struggle against foreign substances, it becomes enervated and disease is bound to result. This activity is always shown in the iris. If a person is continually worried about something, it is going to irritate and affect his nervous system, and the resulting nerve degeneration will also show in the iris of the eye.

Vibration can be changed from one thing to another, and we are seeing many wonderful demonstrations of this today. Through controlling vibrations of music, for example, we can see color come forth, apparently by remote control, right out of the ether.

In stepping up a vibration or stepping it down, we know we can alter its manifestation. When vibratory waves travel over copper or other kind of wire, they must travel at a different vibratory rate—a different speed—than if they were passing through air or water. The law that allows this vibratory rate to change—to become faster and then slowed down again—in relation to the substance in which it is carried, belongs to the various laws of the universe. Man is just discovering some of these things, but they have always been here. "There is nothing new under the sun." Certainly man did not create the means whereby these phenomena occur.

When we deal with the vibration of different diseases and the discoloration of the iris from drug deposits and bad living habits, we are dealing with electrons and ions. Much of our healing today is done by re-establishing normal vibratory rates in the body—through electrical energy, radionic treatment, and the vibration of our voice through color, as well as through laboratory methods, electrical equipment such as short wave and diathermy, food and physiotherapy. The old saying, "the eyes are the windows of the soul," takes on new meaning in this age of vibratory knowledge. Electronics is coming into its own in the healing art and is being used to detect and to treat different diseases through vibratory methods.

We gain some insight into the implications of the vibratory theory when we consider some of the vibratory correspondences between certain chemical elements and certain human tissues. For example, according to electronic measurement, the vibration of sulphur is in harmony with that of our skin. Mercury corresponds similarly to syphilis and quinine to malaria. This is why they are used as specific remedies for these diseases.

In the study of homeopathy there is apparently no explanation from a physical or a tangible standpoint as to why homeopathic remedies should break up certain fixations in the body. The only explanation they can give for their wonderful results is the vibratory theory. The theory on which they are working is almost identical with that of the radionic therapist of today, who is attempting to restore normal vibratory rates to the body of a patient to break up the disease vibrations carried in his body.

The homeopath takes the various drugs

and foods from which he makes his remedies, and develops through trituration or dilution a remedy that no longer contains any crude drugs. It is only the vibratory effect that determines his high concentration or dilution. No laboratory can test any of the original drug used in his 200 or 300 or 2,000 dilution, yet we find it has a definite effect upon the body and can only be explained through the vibratory theory. We have used many of the homeopathic remedies to start a reaction in the body. We find the person who is settled in some chronic disease sometimes needs a little trigger response or electrical activity to start him on the process of returning to health by way of retracing the various diseases through which he has gone; by the healing crisis.

One of the most outstanding things in the homeopathic field is how certain vibratory actions in the body can be neutralized by the use of homeopathic preparations, and different foods from those which the patient has been accustomed to eating. Note that most of the homeopathic remedies used to accomplish a cure by the reversal process are neutralized immediately if one uses the drugs camphor or caffein. The vibratory effect of coffee seems to neutralize all the good effects that result from any of the homeopathic remedies, or from all the fine work done to keep the body in good health. You also neutralize the good to be derived from proper food when you drink coffee with it. I would advise the person who is trying to get well to give up coffee or he will not get well. It is amazing to see how the good effects of different kinds of treatment are neutralized almost immediately through the use of coffee.

The psoric diseases and many taints that have become fixed in the organs do not usually move until there is some high-powered electrical influence to change the vibratory rate or unseat it. As soon as this takes place, a reaction is set up and we are on our way toward bringing on the healing crisis or eliminative process that is necessary for a cure. It is wonderful to see how a homeopathic remedy can break up certain symptoms developed during the course of disease, how the symptom is overcome, and how a better health condition is established. Before very long a new symptom arises, which is part of the healing crisis the body is going through in the elimination of toxins. It is necessary to know that these diseases are being eradicated through the breaking down of the chronic condition, accomplished through the use of nature's higher and finer forces. It can be done through foods— concentrated food and teas. Many times, merely employing sun, air, and water for the different reactions is all that is necessary. With the proper program, the static condition of the patient is broken up and we see a change in tissue structure.

To show how various diseases and symptoms operate in the body through inherited taints and conditions, a psoric person, for example, may develop a headache which grows worse as the day progresses, until sundown. This condition may recur day in and day out. How foolish to treat that headache every day at six o'clock when it is at its worst! Certainly that is not treating disease properly. Rather, get rid of the psoric taint which is the cause of the trouble. Whenever we resort to suppressive measures in trying to get a patient well, we only develop a greater problem to take care of in the future.

Diet has a definite vibratory effect on the body. In some specified cases it is best to use the mono-diet so that there will not be a mixture of high and low vibratory foods. This theory is probably the basis for separating starches and proteins in the diet. The underground vegetables have an entirely different vibratory action than those grown above the ground. Starches will slow down the heart activity while proteins will increase it, which indicates that these two types of food have entirely different vibratory actions. So as not to mutually neutralize their vibratory actions, it is best not to take them together at one meal. Over a period of time we have observed better results when high-protein foods are eaten at one meal and predominantly starchy foods at another.

Fruits have a higher vibratory action than vegetables. They stir up the acids in the body and bring on an acute form of elimination, while vegetables seem to carry off toxic material and are very soothing, especially to the nervous system. The person who is constantly taking citrus fruit juices may feel that his teeth are "on edge," but this condition can be overcome by using vegetable juices. Separate the fruits and the vegetables. When using these juices separately, a different effect in the body is obtained. Hahnemann, the founder of homeopathy, says it is the dynamic energy derived from the remedy and the food that does the work in the body. The vibratory effects of foods will be discussed in greater detail in a later chapter on the differences between the right and left sides of the body.

Disease comes into existence through abnormal vibrations. Every disease has its own symptoms, its own calling, its own craving, its own appetite. These conditions are expressed in the form of vibratory rates. In working with vibratory action, we increase the vital energy of the body by using health-building methods. The activity for health will overcome the activity of disease. If the factors which are breaking down the vital health of the body are being nurtured, you can readily see without any trouble how chronic disease can be developed. To break down chronic disease, starve the disease; it must not have a chance to exist. Build vital energy and healthy vibratory activities into the body and eventually health will be the result.

We become aware of disease through the nervous system, which is highly attuned to whatever is going on in the body. Due to the intimate communication between the brain and every cell of the body, vibratory inharmony in either body or mind is bound to be mutually interactive. In Hahnemann's opinion, drug vibrations affect the mind and the will most of all.

The body is built of everything that the universe is built of—earth, air, color, light, etc. We can go far in our imagination when we consider the similiarities in the nature of light radiations and nerve impulses. To express it pointedly, light radiations and nerve impulses are made of the same stuff.

The aeroplane was discovered only some thirty or forty years ago, yet we find everything that goes into the making of an aeroplane has been here for thousands of years. Likewise everything in the vibratory field has been here all the time, but it is only now that man is discovering its possibilities and applications. I believe we are going to find iridology explained more fully by the vibratory theory in the future. The image in the iris, the shadings in the iris (the light of the acute, the dark of the chronic), the color in the iris, the tension of iris fibres —all are conveyed there by vibratory impulses.

11

STUDY OF DENSITY

The course of nature is the art of God.

—*Edward Young*

In the iris, the closeness of the fibres themselves and the fineness of the structure determine density. When a tissue is represented in the iris by fibres compactly constructed, the density is considered to be good, but when separation of fibres and holes appear, the density is poor. The density may have a value of only two points, or it may become worse—three or four, or even five. Five denotes the lowest degree of density in the body. The average person has a density of two and a half to three.

The anterior portion of the strong iris has more fibres, closer together, than the inherently weak one. Close-knit structure in the iris denotes a body with inherently strong well-developed tissues—comparable to the oak. A desk made of oak can stand more abuse than a desk of pine, but a pine desk may last just as long as one made of oak if it is handled with the proper care. An oak desk, however, can withstand a lot of abuse, be kicked around, and still be polished and brought back to its former beauty, while it may not be possible to restore the original appearance of an abused pine desk. Some persons seem to be in good health, but when tested to see how much they can stand, how far they can run, how many hours they can stay on a job, how much nerve irritation and nerve depletion their bodies can tolerate, we find they will give way easily if they do not have tissue and power comparable to the oak.

The density in the iris may be considered as corresponding to the constitution of the individual. Both can be likened to the substance of a person. He who has a lot of substance built in between the rafters of his house, and enough cement between the sand and the rocks, has a fine structure which will withstand bad weather. A person with a loss of substance in his body has little chance of overcoming sickness. You can give the prognosis in many cases by knowing a person's constitution.

Unless he abuses his body, the person with exceptionally good density has the opportunity of living a long life; he has the capabilities of overcoming disease. On the other hand, the ability to overcome sickness and keep well is very poor in one with a low degree of density; extra effort is needed to carry him through. Density can be regarded as the measure of the body's vitality. It shows muscle tone, the power of body resistance or recuperative ability, and the regenerative quality of the structure of the muscles and the different tissues. It shows elasticity, quickness of response and action and reaction of various body structures.

When there is defective tissue density, the fibres in the iris are unevenly developed and arranged. Some seem to be sunken and some obliterated, leaving a large hole; others are crooked and intermingled with swollen fibres; others are warped. In some

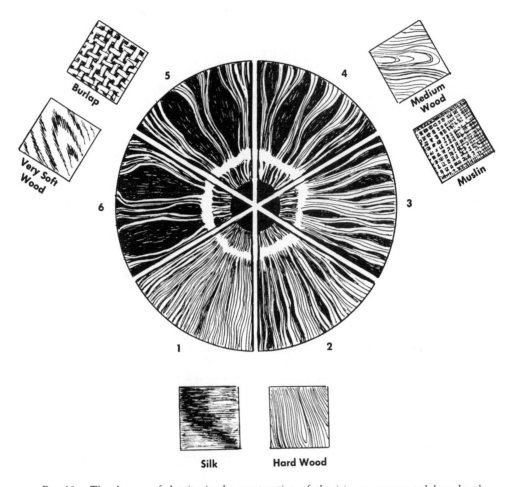

Fig. 28. The degrees of density in the construction of the iris are represented here by the comparative density of markings in hard wood, medium wood, and soft wood, and in silk, muslin, and burlap. An iris with fibres such as those in section 1 of the diagram shows that its owner has strong recuperative power and plenty of energy for regeneration. Sections 5 and 6 indicate the other extreme of low resistance and poor inherent ability to overcome difficulties.

areas the fibres are massed into little bundles, the darker pigmented layers from underneath becoming more visible and showing up as the black spots we see in the iris. Actual holes are found there and it is these holes which represent very poor structure. Serious wounds and fractures many times show up in this black layer. This was the kind of spot that von Peczely saw in the iris of the owl with the broken leg, to which we previously referred.

Along with density we must consider heredity. Throughout the ages our ancestors have followed living habits that have deteriorated some organs,—the weaker ones. According to Hahnemann's theory there are only three diseases or three "miasmas," as he called them, brought down through the years: psora, psychosis and syphilis. In the past, when these diseases settled in the body they caused certain destructive influences. In France, back in the fifteenth century, over two thousand houses were necessary for the care of venereal diseases alone, and the lack of sanitation resulted in many itches and skin conditions that were suppressed with lead ointment and washes with various waters. These suppressed diseases

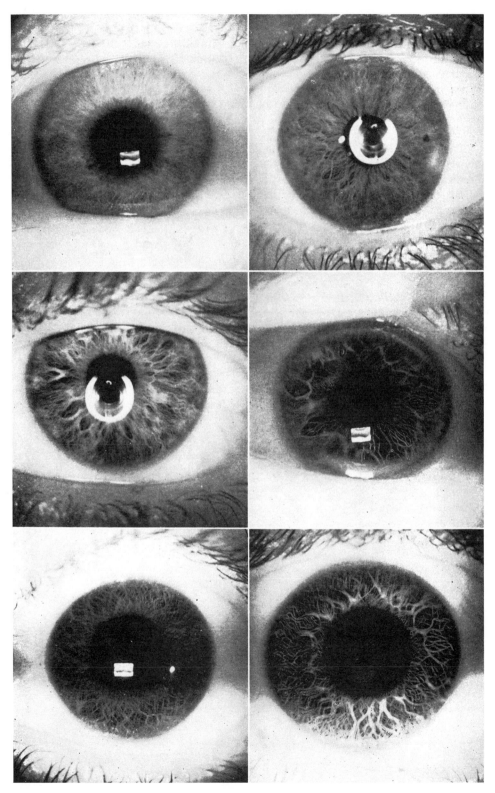

FIG. 29.   The above iris photographs show densities ranging from 1 to 6.

were passed on to coming generations as inherent weaknesses. Inter-marriage of one race with another also has resulted in the passing on of numerous conditions to the people of today. Past weaknesses and suppressed diseases are partly responsible for the lowered density and fibre structure you see in the iris of the eye.

Where the fibres are swollen, the cause may be from some taint, such as syphilis or gonorrhea. Taints are reflected in the iris not only from our grandparents, but even from our great great great grandparents. We are subject to the inherent tendencies and inherent structure handed down through our ancestors to the present generation.

Colorings in the iris from various drugs used by past generations are transmitted to the present generation. The signs become more prominent as we grow to adulthood and the pigment layer in the iris of the eye becomes more definite. Many children, even in vegetarian families and those who live in the country on the best possible food,

still have the taints of their grandparents well established in the fibres of the iris. We are guided by these taint signs of the different disease manifestations and symptoms. To see these taints broken up and the body cleansed is a revelation to those who handle patients with the nature cure system.

It is a common occurrence to find these congenital signs in the iris, and we are able to distinguish them very easily through iridology. No other form of analysis can show inherent weakness so clearly. Darkened colors and defective density show hereditary organic defects that are present in the iris at birth. The condition of the parents is transferred to their child and shows up in the iris at the time of birth in acute eliminative signs and nerve rings.

As far as tissue strength is concerned, when we are born we have the finest body we will ever have. The color of the iris darkens with degeneration in health. The density and hereditary defects together are therefore indicative of our hereditary conditions and acquired tendencies in relation to health or disease.

12

STUDY OF LANDMARKS

Come forth into the light of things. Let nature be your teacher.

—Wordsworth

Before we take up the study of landmarks you must realize that every landmark in the iris of the eye has its story. It may be a story of normalcy, a story of over or underactivity, a story of battle or peace, of action and reaction, a chemical story, or a nerve story. You may also find a reflex story, not only from the organs to the iris, but among organs. You also have to read the story of reflex actions among the areas in the iris.

You may say diabetes is found in the pancreas yet many times there is a kidney lesion that is just as important to consider in a case of diabetes as the pancreas itself. We must look at the whole picture reflected in the iris and consider the hyperactivity or the hypoactivity going on. Our job, then, is to bring the hypo- up to normal and we must find some way of inhibiting the hyper-, probably by helping other parts of the body to do their job and thereby bring about normal activity. Many organs over-act in compensation for other organs not doing their duty, thereby being forced to carry an extra burden. Some organs cannot do their part because they are inherently weak, or possibly do not have the proper chemicals with which to function. There is also the possibility that they are toxin-laden.

We have a very big picture represented in the iris of the eye. Organ areas will be compared as we proceed, and eventually you will be able to put them all together.

As you look at the different lesions or markings, bear in mind that each of them has its own story. The amount of pathology in the organ can be determined by the degree of discoloration and the size of the lesion in the particular area with which you are dealing. The amount of repair work to be done can be judged by the stage of inflammation and how the rest of the body will respond to help that particular organ get well. We have much to consider as far as an organ's recovery is concerned. If we find a nerve ring in the iris, we question what is responsible for the tension. Is it tension in the iris itself or is it tension derived from some bodily or organic irritation? Or could it be an external environmental problem? A stomach condition is one problem to take care of, but if there is a nerve cramp ring, then we have another question to answer. If we find that the organ we are working on has poor density and is in a very heavy toxic condition, and that the intestinal tract is quite toxic, you can readily see the many complications preventing the body from becoming well. Like the chain and its weakest link, it can be no stronger than its weakest organ. From the iris analysis standpoint we are most interested in discovering which are the weak organs we have to take care of and which are those that have the greatest amount of encumbrance to overcome. The strong organs can take care of themselves.

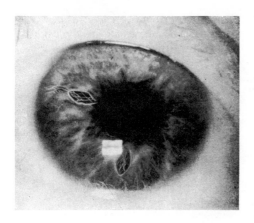

FIG. 30. In the above photograph of a left iris you see two inherent closed lesions. One is within the bronchus area leading into the thyroid area; the other is in the kidney area. In my iris chart these two organ areas have been made definite landmarks.

Let us understand one point thoroughly. In reading the fibres of the iris, we are reading the reactions of tissues within the body. As we read the iris we cannot tell what is flowing through an organ, we cannot tell the fluid condition that has settled in the body, nor can we tell the severity of a bacterial invasion. We can, however, approximate a chronic state if we know the conditions that have developed in other organs over a period of time, though we cannot tell what acute problems will develop at a particular moment. There may be pressure symptoms that cannot tell you the exact condition of an organ at the very moment the symptoms are experienced. We must look at the all-around picture to give a good analysis. Do not jump to a conclusion because of one irritated or inflamed fibre in the iris. Consider the cause behind the cause. The location of the acute sign indicating pain may be in a different area from that which is the cause behind the pain. What are the reflex activities there? For instance, it is difficult to determine tuberculosis from the iris, but you can see whether the tissue soil is bad enough for tuberculosis to be present.

We repeat that it is best to use all the other diagnosing facilities as well as to detect abnormalities in the iris. And it is a good experience for those taking up this science to use as many of the other diagnosing methods as possible to compare with their iris findings. The time will come when you will rely upon what you have discovered in the iris to tell you what the other tests corroborate.

One of iridology's greatest assets is that it ascertains the problem immediately. We can then send the patient to a laboratory to get a completed picture of the problem with very few tests, rather than run test after test in an effort to find out what is wrong. As an example, we have found many cases with gall bladder disturbance recorded in the iris that was not revealed by the patient's symptoms even though X-ray examination showed definite gall bladder pathology. After including other tests with iridology you will soon come to the place where the treatment indicated may be the same, no matter what the tests bring out. You will find in some cases of colitis, ulcers of the stomach, and inflammation of the bowel, that you can use practically the same diet in each case, remembering, of course, that changes may have to be made according to the temperament of the patient. Other considerations also are his working conditions, the density of the iris, his power to react, and whether he is able to handle heavy coarse foods or should be given light foods. Many factors will have to be considered, but you will get to the place where, after studying these lesions and the conditions of the body supporting the lesion picture, you will be able to form definite conclusions as to how the patient should be treated.

These lesions can be walled in or they can be open. An open lesion is open at one end, but it is possible for it to be open at both ends. In an open lesion, the toxic material, or the flora or basic tissue fluids flowing back and forth within that particular organ, can be moved along and an exchange easily made. A closed lesion indicates encapsulated fluids and difficulty in moving secretions along quickly. This accounts for sickness in cycles or one manifestation of disease after another or a continual return of the problem. A tumor can be encapsulated and is a good illustration as many times tumors take on toxic material. But because of the poor blood supply within the tumor itself, there is so little activity that the only exchange we can bring about is through osmosis or a direct exchange of fluids through the tissue by improving the quality of the external fluids around this tumor. The pus in an open lesion can be discharged freely. A closed lesion is difficult to bring to a head. It sometimes takes the form of an abscess and we find it difficult to arrive at the crisis point or a finished elimination. Active treatments must be resorted to in order to bring about a change in these closed lesions. Water treatments are the most active. Use cold water for contraction purposes to change the blood stream and to move cleaner blood into the lesions.

When a baby is first born his eyes are lightest in color. As he goes through life he acquires toxins through poor living habits and these result in a settlement of different fluids within the body which cause changes in the color of the eyes. Very few of us live in the right environment, eat the proper foods, breathe clean air, or live harmoniously—one with another—as we should. Though we acquire these dark areas as we grow older, we can reverse conditions and make the color of the eye much lighter by living correctly. Our living habits do not make up the shape of these lesions, however. We inherit their shape and acquire the toxic material that goes into them.

The iris of an animal is a wonderful study since it is the clearest of all. The animal adheres to its own species and mostly lives in normal and natural surroundings, and consequently has very little abnormality in the iris. It would be interesting for you to go to a veterinarian and study the cats and dogs brought in with different types of accidents. You would find the areas and lesions in the iris correspondingly the same as in the human eye. If a dog breaks his leg it shows in the leg area of the iris.

In the lesions and other landmarks we must consider the degree of tension, whether the organs represented are hyperactive or hypoactive. If the patient is under a great deal of tension—is a braggart, and expresses a lot of egotism—the fibres are tense in the blood pressure center or the ego pressure center. If the ego is under an extreme amount of pressure, the blood pressure is bound to be high. On the other hand, any organ that has been overactive or has been stimulated for a period of time, will come to an underactive period; will become hypoactive.

Many thyroid cases which have been hyperactive over a period of time, finally recede to develop into a hypoactive condition. Maybe a person has had a basal metabolism test and the test shows a normal reading. The iris analysis may give a picture that is entirely different from the usual basal metabolism test given by the doctor. An inherently weak thyroid gland with extreme tension and overactivity, possibly to the breaking point, of course cannot compare with a normal thyroid gland in its output of hormones or in regulating nerve tension within the body. Though a basal metabolism test may indicate normal thyroid activity, the iris may present a picture which shows the basal metabolism test to be wrong. Many times I have seen the thyroid underactive on one side of the body and overactive on the other. This condition would result in a normal basal metabolism test. Thus you can readily see that we cannot rely entirely upon tests as we use them today. You will see, after you study and use this system of analysis, how you can help the patient and why the average doctor is often unable to determine just what is wrong.

Another example is that a laboratory test of the patient's blood may show a normal count, yet the iris of that patient will reveal that anemia exists in different parts of the body. Why? Because the suprarenal gland, or the circulatory tone of the arteries, is impaired to such an extent that the blood does not circulate fast enough. A body can be anemic with the best blood stream in the world if the blood does not circulate fast enough. Anemic tissue is unable to repair and rebuild well. It is almost like living on an island with a demand for a certain amount of food, and, while there may be plenty of ships bringing food, they come in only half as fast as they should so the people on the island will surely die. This is what happens to the organs of the body if the amount of blood, though of good quality, is only half of that necessary for life.

There is one other point I wish to bring out regarding lesions. Where an organ has been destroyed and no anesthetic has interfered with the reflection in the iris, this destruction will show up absolutely black in the iris. You cannot see signs in the iris representing operations because anesthetic cuts off all the nerve feeling and telepathic recording of what is going on in the body.

Comparing, adding one landmark to another, and adding the chronic condition existing and the inherent background, should give you a complete picture of the patient.

13

IRIS CHART DEVELOPMENT

The Constitution of this Republic should make special provision for MEDICAL SCIENCE. To restrict the art of healing to one class will constitute the bastile of Medical Science. All such laws are un-American and despotic.

—Benjamin Rush, Physician, Signer of the Declaration of Independence

Iris Charts Brought Up To Date

Let us look into the development of the charts. From what proven source did the chart develop? Has there been enough proof for the different areas we find in the chart? Is it possible that all the organ areas are placed properly in the chart? These questions are difficult to answer, but when you begin to practice this science and use the charts you will then have a basis on which to work.

One of the proofs came to me one afternoon years ago while I was running with my cousin's dog in a field. The dog had three or four fits. Upon looking into the dog's left eye I saw a black line through the epileptic area corresponding to that in the iris chart. This was just a small incident, and if it was coincidental, it was timely, for it strengthened my faith in this science and helped me to break down some of the skepticism in my own mind. If there had been only a very small spot the size of a pin point, there is the possibility I would have missed it and might have gone on to the conclusion that there was nothing for me in this science.

I had further proof one time with a patient who had a mangled knee which was treated with a drug pack. I saw this man a few days after the drug pack was used, and I could detect the drug sign in the iris. Not having examined him before the accident, I could not say whether the drug spot was in his iris previously, but I do know it was in the knee area of the iris when I examined it after the accident. This gave me further incentive to go on and find out whether there were other signs that could be seen in the iris of the eye.

Sometimes these areas are not in exactly the same positions on all the charts, but when you are treating the body as a whole and watching the whole iris work in relation to the complete body, you will find revelations that one organ alone cannot reveal. The accomplishment of good work for the patient should be the ultimate goal of all healers, and one of the best methods for accomplishing this goal is the use of iridology.

In the year 1886 the first chart of Dr. Ignatz von Peczely was published. Since then many charts from time to time have been developed and published. An exceptional chart was published by an up-to-date Swedish iridologist. Others were published in Germany that are wonderful, although incomplete. These charts will have to be

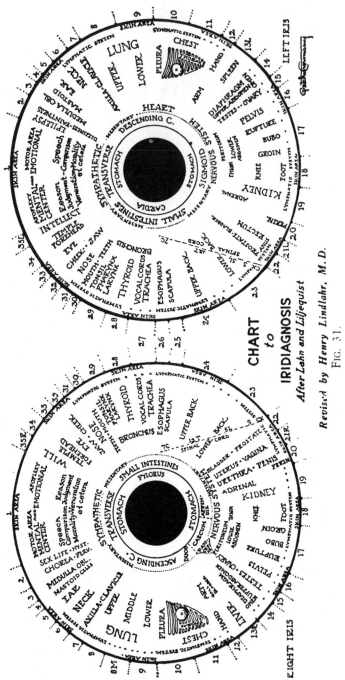

CHART
to
IRIDIAGNOSIS
After Lahn and Liljequist

Revised by Henry Lindlahr, M. D.
FIG. 31.

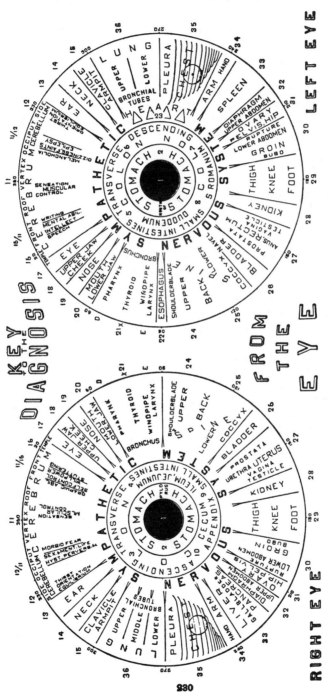

FIG. 32.   This chart was used by Dr. Henry Edward Lane.

referred to in their text books. In this country charts finally have been developed and published which designate the specific position in the iris of each organ represented there. Although there have been certain discrepancies in some of the areas in the past charts, at least 75 per cent agree.

As you progress in the study of iridology you will make certain decisions for yourself which will lead to disagreement with some authorities and the inclination to folow one in preference to another. In chart comparisons you will find in some instances that new areas have been added and that others have been changed considerably. From such comparisons certain conclusions are outstanding. Let us look at all charts with an open mind. We do not wish to criticize or break down anyone else's ideas, but while endeavoring to teach this science, we must keep within the scope of this book. You will find that we follow a definite teaching and our chart may be the only one which can be used for certain of our purposes.

Of all the progress accomplished in this work, the most important is that of establishing the lines separating the different areas. Note the Lindlahr and Lane charts, for example. It is very difficult to look at the areas and actually see where they start and where they end because the areas have not been well filled in. However, there have been a few areas in the brain that iridologists like Havard and Kritzer endeavored to fill in. In looking at any chart, most of you will remember areas only when they have been well outlined. Remember to look at areas on the charts as you would on a clock. It is easy to designate the area between one and two as on a clock for this definitely locates the area. Kidney troubles appear in the area of the iris designated as the kidney area on the chart. When we say that the area between three and four is the pleural area and that at the midpoint between three and four is the location of the breast area, you can see in a moment exactly where the breast area is.

Theile's chart has advantages over other charts in showing where the organs are located, but it is difficult to tell exactly where areas begin or end. Dr. Petritsch's chart seems to be one of the first developed using the idea of the line to designate definite areas. Dr. Marko J. Petinak made a wonderful chart and evidently spent a great deal of time on his work. A chart we found in an old magazine shows us an entirely different chart again—the separations not being where they should be, however. Dr. J. Haskel Kritzer has contributed one of the most up-to-date charts, but further development and a few changes are indicated.

We go back again to look at von Peczely's firs chart of the iris to see how difficult it was in the very beginning to know exactly where organ areas should be placed. Seeing the development of the charts from the past will help you appreciate the value of the charts we have today. It is impossible for one man, even though he study a whole lifetime, to know all there is to know about iridology. It is impossible for anyone to claim his chart is the last word, and that applies to my own chart as well. There are many new areas yet to be found. Also, there are probably many areas to be changed, but there is general agreement regarding about 75 per cent of the areas.

The iris can reflect many toxic conditions for you. Sometimes the finer conditions cannot be detected, but they must be present if the gross conditions are shown. When you consider the great number of tissues represented in such a small area as the iris, it is understandable that if you wish to locate an infinitesimal area such as that representing an infected tooth or a certain joint on a certain finger that has been sprained or broken, it will necessarily be difficult since you will be looking for an area within an area. It is as difficult to teach this science as it is to learn it, but my attempt to teach is because I know what practical value this science has for the good of humanity. It seems that those who have this knowledge do not have the faculty to teach or impart their knowledge to others. For this reason I have taken it upon myself to present points in my own chart in such a way that many new features are presented which no other charts have shown in the past. For example, I have a definite area marked off for the brain. If you will locate the dark, heavy black line that outlines the brain, this will give you a definite picture in your mind as to where the brain area begins and where it ends.

My chart tells you where the digestive system starts, where the colon begins, and where the borderlines of the small intestines are. In my chart the small intestinal area

Although at this stage we must admit that in some cases we cannot prove our diagnosis from the iris, there are many documented cases proving this work. One doctor asked me if I had ever measured the distance between the acute line and the sub-acute line, and if I had never measured it then how did I know one white line was raised above the other? I asked him how far away his plate on the table at which he was sitting was from him and he said, "Four feet." I asked him if he had measured it and of course he said, "No." This was my answer to him as far as iris measurement was concerned. There are certain things you know without touching, dissecting, or

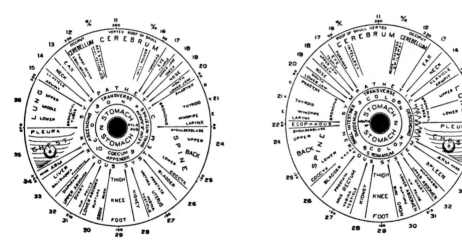

FIG. 33.   My friend Dr. J. F. Petritsch used this chart for many years.

is separated so that it can be spotted at a glance. The flexures are in a position where you can definitely determine them directly in the iris. The chart thus shows you exactly where the large colon begins and where the flexures are. From X-ray pictures observed over the years, I have noted that the flexures of the colon have a definite reflex activity in certain organs, and I have placed these flexures in definite positions in the iris chart so that you can tell where and when the flexures are producing reflex disturbances. From this chart you also can determine more exactly the genitourinary system.

breaking down as a laboratory technician might do.

We all are accustomed to the positions or areas one, two, three, etc., on the face of a clock, so rather than give you new locations to remember, we put the designated iris areas into your subconscious mind in the same positions as clock numbers so that you can put all of your attention on the exact area itself.

Many key points have been set up in the chart with extensions of black lines and black areas. For example, the kidney area

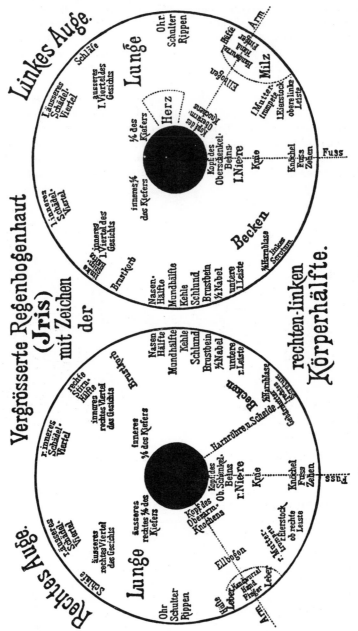

FIG. 34.   The first chart developed by Dr. Ignatz von Peczely.

is just inside six o'clock. The thyroid gland has been extended to show it is exactly between nine and ten o'clock. It should be easy for you to remember these extensions and to use them as key organs so that you can place the other organs around them in their proper relative positions. You have key points to start with; what remains is the filling in of all other organs.

Extreme fevers, especially typhoid or scarlet fever, attack the Peyer's patches in the small intestines and invariably a great change is made in the life of the person who has the fever. These severe illnesses shock the body and seldom are victims the same as they were before their illness. The fever

If you can get them pictured in your mind, the other organs will fall into their places automatically. Those areas which deal with the brain have been changed in the charts during their development over a period of years.

When we speak of the lung, the pleura or the spleen, we feel there is something tangible with which to work, but with symptoms such as high blood pressure or apoplexy we are dealing with effects. Referring to an apoplectic center is still more intangible. Since apoplexy or high blood pressure is an effect, we do not reach the cause or the center from which the condition arises by calling it the high blood pres-

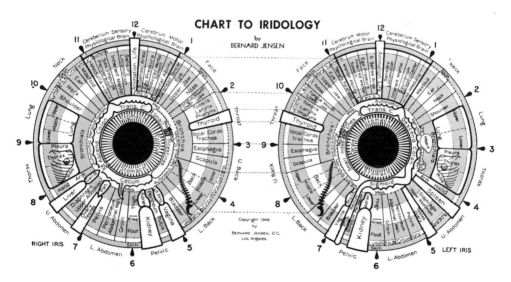

FIG. 35. This chart was developed with the idea of so clearly circumscribing each organ area, as we know it to date, that we can more easily determine where each organ area begins and ends.

has damaged the small intestines and specifically the Peyer's patches. The Peyer's patches, we have discovered, are opposite the thyroid gland in the iris.

I have blocked out in black the areas of the lungs and the pleura, the spleen, the sex organs, the kidneys, the thyroid, and the animation and life centers. The intestines and the stomach have definite positions. All these areas are most important.

sure or the apoplectic center. That center from which it arises should be called the "ego pressure" center. According to our psychiatric studies, those who have the ego centers strained because of occupational pressure, over-exertion, or the extreme activities of city life today, usually develop high blood pressure. It is impossible from study of the iris to determine how high the blood pressure is or how close a patient is to having a stroke. One person may have very

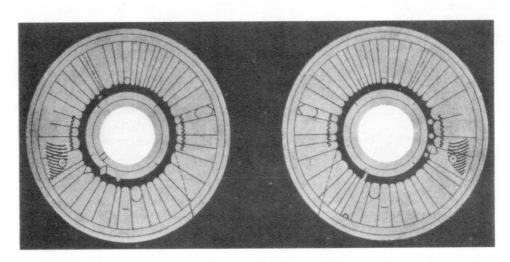

Fig. 36.   These drawings show definite separation of the intestinal area from peripheral organ areas, and placement for such landmarks as the areas of the adrenal
glands, pancreas, gall bladder, heart, etc.

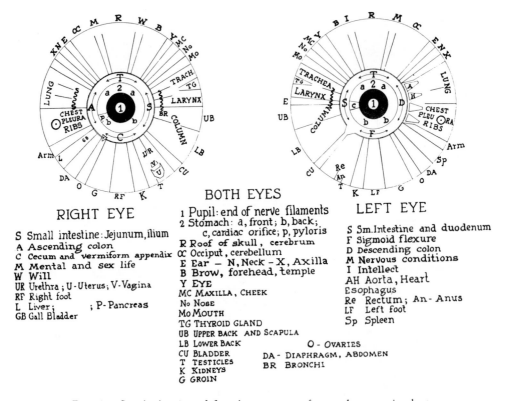

RIGHT EYE

BOTH EYES

LEFT EYE

1 Pupil: end of nerve filaments
2 Stomach: a, front; b, back;
    c, cardiac orifice; p, pyloris

S Small intestine: Jejunum, Ilium
A Ascending colon
C Cecum and vermiform appendix
M Mental and sex life
W Will
UR Urethra ; U-Uterus; V-Vagina
RF Right foot
L Liver ;   ; P- Pancreas
GB Gall Bladder

R Roof of skull , cerebrum
OC Occiput , cerebellum
E Ear — N, Neck – X, Axilla
B Brow, forehead, temple
Y EYE
MC Maxilla , Cheek
No Nose
Mo Mouth
TG Thyroid gland
UB Upper back and Scapula
LB Lower Back
CU Bladder
T Testicles
K Kidneys
G Groin

S Sm. Intestine and duodenum
F Sigmoid flexure
D Descending colon
M Nervous conditions
I Intellect
AH Aorta, Heart
Esophagus
Re Rectum; An- Anus
LF Left foot
Sp Spleen

O - Ovaries
DA- Diaphragm, Abdomen
BR Bronchi

Fig. 37.   Simple drawing of first degree stages of area placement in chart.

RIGHT LEFT

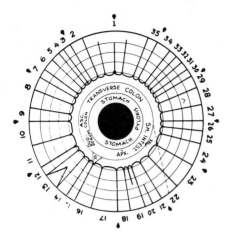
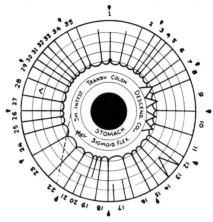

RIGHT

1	BRAIN REGION, EMOTIONS
2	SEX LIFE
3	PAROTID, MEDULLA
4	MASTOID
5	EAR
6	NECK
7	AXILLA, CLAVICLE
8	LUNG, UPPER AND MIDDLE
9	LOWER LUNG
10 }	PLEURA
11 }	CHEST
12	ARM AND HAND
13	LIVER, GALL BLADDER
14	DIAPHRAGM, UPPER ABDOMEN
15	TESTES OR OVARIES
16	PELVIS
17	LOWER ABDOMEN, GROIN
18	THIGH, KNEE, FOOT
19	KIDNEY, ADRENAL
20	URETHRA, PENIS, PERINEUM
21	UTERUS, VAGINA
22	PROSTATE, BLADDER
23	LOWER BACK } SPINE
24	UPPER BACK }
25	SCAPULA
26	ESOPHAGUS
27	VOCAL CORDS, TRACHEA }
28	THYROID } BRONCHI
29	TONSIL, PHARYNX, LARYNX }
30	MOUTH, TEETH
31	NOSE
32	CHEEKS, JAW
33	EYE
34	TEMPLE, FOREHEAD
35	WILL

LEFT

1	BRAIN, EMOTIONS
2	EPILEPSY, DIZZINESS, FAINTNESS
3	MEDULLA, PAROTID
4	MASTOID
5	EAR
6	NECK
7	AXILLA, CLAVICLE
8 AND 9	LUNG
9 AND 10	HEART
10	PLEURA
10 AND 11	CHEST
12	ARM AND HAND
13	SPLEEN
14	DIAPHRAGM, UPPER ABDOMEN
15	TESTES, OVARIES
16	PELVIS
17	LOWER ABDOMEN, GROIN
18	THIGH, KNEE, FOOT
19	KIDNEY, ADRENAL
20	URETHRA, PENIS, PERINEUM
21	RECTUM, ANUS
22	PROSTATE, BLADDER
23	LOWER BACK } SPINE
24	UPPER BACK }
25	SCAPULA
26	ESOPHAGUS
27	VOCAL CORDS, TRACHEA }
28	THYROID } BRONCHI
29	TONSIL, PHARYNX, LARYNX }
30	MOUTH, TEETH
31	NOSE
32	CHEEKS AND JAW
33	EYE
34	TEMPLE, FOREHEAD
35	INTELLECT

FIG. 38. Second stage in chart development.

high blood pressure and may not be at a danger point while another person may have only slightly high blood pressure and be in a much more dangerous condition. I believe, however, that you can learn more about the patient's conditions from his iris than from other diagnostic means. For example, by using the blood pressure instrument you cannot determine whether an inherent weakness is a factor in the high blood pressure, but from the iris you can.

At the top of the spine is the first dorsal, as illustrated in the iris chart. The cervicals of the spine are shown in the medulla area. The extension of the spinal cord goes through the medulla area.

Throughout this book we will determine and prove from X-rays the existence of diverticulitis as diagnosed from the iris of the eye.

Developing A Chart

It is well before getting into the study of the individual areas of the iris to look at the general field and see how a chart is made. Let us take the simplest iris chart with very few lines and very few organ areas as they were designated when first discovered, and add the areas to complete the chart as we know it today. At the same time picture in your mind the various systems of the body that are used in iris analysis. For instance, picture the respiratory system on the chart. Get a good mental picture of every indication that can be checked in the iris. Consider not merely the lungs, the pleura and the bronchial tubes, but the nerve source found in the medulla, the glandular system, the endocrine system and the gastro-intestinal tract.

The first fact to file in your mind is the separation of the gastro-intestinal tract from all the organs by what is called the autonomic nerve wreath, formerly called the sympathetic wreath. In my chart I purposely include a picture, in the colon area, of the colon as it actually is. This enables you to see the relative positions of the small and large intestines, the exact locations of the

flexures, and the locations of organs in relation to any part of the colon in which you are interested. The nervous system can be demonstrated by the brain areas and the nerve rings; the urinary system and the bony structure can be demonstrated in their specific areas. Let us take in all the areas that can be affected and look at the whole field. Get a clear picture in your mind of the location of most of these organs. Then we will take each individual area and tell where it is located, what it means, and how it is built into the chart. The autonomic nerve wreath may be considered as a hub with all the organs emanating from it.

In going over your chart you will find much that fits in with new scientific developments and the new healing arts, especially in the sciences that deal with the nerves. You will find that conditions in the pancreatic area, for example, correspond very closely with conditions opposite in the brain area. Many mental cases are treated with insulin shock, and iridology will show how the pancreas is damaged in these cases and where your care should be directed.

We know from our pathological and neurological studies that there is a definite relation between certain nerve plexuses in the body and the epileptic centers. Illustrated (Fig. 39) is a photograph taken some years ago showing the black lines in the epileptic center. Compare it to the epileptic center of our chart (Fig. 35). This will demonstrate the need for a landmark, and you will find the epileptic center near one o'clock in the left iris; it is on the twelve side of one o'clock.

After locating the epileptic center in the left iris, notice what is exactly opposite in the right iris. You will find the sex life and the mentality area exactly opposite the epileptic center in the hemisphere of the brain in the other iris. We know the sex life can affect epilepsy in many cases; we know masturbation can be the source of some epileptic troubles. You will find the male and female sex organs located in the iris directly opposite the sex life center in the brain area. In studying opposites in the iris you may find the clue to the real cause of manifestations in other centers or other organs of the body.

Although in cases of anemia you cannot tell from the iris the degree to which it exists, it is helpful to know that some organ is not receiving enough blood to carry on the healing processes. Such conditions as gallstones, kidney stones, and pregnancy, cannot be told from the eye, but do not judge the value of the science by these facts alone. I make no claim that this diagnosis is a simple method or that you can tell everything from the eye. Iridology is not a simple science to understand and with all the knowledge you can acquire on the

subject, you will still not know it all. What science can claim more? We have verified examinations of other doctors and laboratories innumerable times, showing the relation of the iris to the body and to the disease.

Zone Areas

One of the chart developments to date is the superimposing of the zone chart upon the regular diagnostic chart. This has been done so that where they fit exactly can be seen immediately.

There are seven zones:

1. Stomach area.
2. Intestinal area (small and large).
3. Adrenal glands, heart area and aorta, solar plexus, kidneys, pancreas.

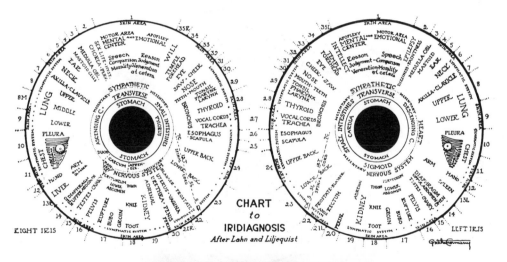

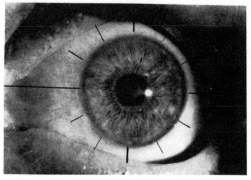

Fig. 39.

4. Bronchial tubes, pituitary gland, pineal gland.
5. Brain and reproductive organs.
6. Spleen, thyroid, liver.
7. Skin area, lymphatic and circulatory systems, sweat glands, motor and sensory nerves. (We will illustrate the zones in a separate chart).

The animation and life center has been so named because we find that life and activity and direction of the body energies are dependent upon the brain. The topmost part of the brain feels the effects of gravity, fatigue, and enervation first. This brain center is at twelve o'clock on the chart. It acts as a barometer and is dependent upon the amount of blood circulating through the center. The *arcus senilis,* which is a term for the arc of old age or anemia or the sign of enervation, has its greatest width at the topmost part of the circle, which tells us the greatest amount of anemia is found at twelve o'clock. First to be affected when there is not enough blood is the animation and life center. This affects both physical and mental animation and unless the center is well nourished the body lacks the power and ability it needs to carry on. It is truly one of the best barometers placed in the body, for our daily lives are dependent upon the function of this area. Fatigue, enervation and lack of animation, are the beginning of all diseases. I consider this center to be one of the most valuable areas used in iridology.

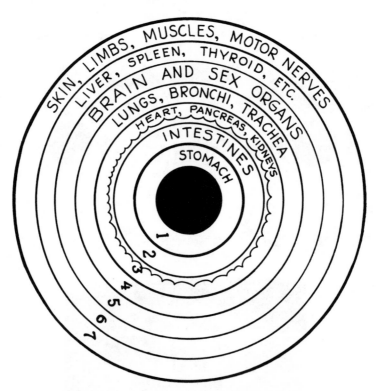

FIG. 40. This illustrates the seven areas in which various organs are placed as definitely as possible (in accordance with present knowledge), outside of the inner ring. No. 2 is the landmark of the autonomic nerve wreath.

1. Stomach
2. Intestines
3. Heart, Pancreas, Kidneys
4. Lower Respiratory Organs
5. Brain and Sex Organs
6. Liver, Spleen, Thyroid, etc.
7. Skin, Limbs, Muscles and Motor Nerves

We will consider the mental centers as we develop the chart. They may be likened to the reaction of an organ in that they can be stimulated or they may starve for lack of expression. I believe the day will come when many areas of the brain will be changed still more in the chart. We will have a further breakdown to indicate such faculties as awareness, love, understanding, and discrimination, because all of these particular areas have valves of expression. Each mental expression can affect the physical body and vice versa. Melancholia, depression, and worry, are demonstrable in our brain areas. We must remember we have diseases in the mental centers which have to be cared for and handled correctly as well as in the physical centers.

I believe that more history lies recorded within the iris than we are presently aware of, and anyone who wishes to call himself an iridologist has much to learn in order to qualify in this field. There will be times when you will miss some sign and when you will feel like giving up iridology, but do you give up the use of X-ray because it did not reveal the cancer before it developed into the perforation stage? Learn to use iridology along with other forms of diagnosis that will help the patient not only to get well but to stay well, and in time you will be so well-trained you will be able to tell the patient what is wrong merely by scrutinizing the iris.

14

GENERAL FIELD AREAS

*And therefore as a stranger give it welcome. There are more things
in heaven and earth, Horatio, than are dreamt of in your philosophy.*
—Shakespeare

We will now discuss the individual field areas and the organ areas contained within them.

The Nutritive Gastro-intestinal System

In working out the problem of getting a general picture of the gastro-intestinal system, let us first look at the over-all picture and then take it individually and minutely. The first step is to find in the iris of the eye the autonomic nerve wreath. It is a line that is usually very white going completely around within the iris. It is located about one-third of the distance from the pupil to the outer edge of the iris, with some variations as we will learn later. This line separates the area of the gastro-intestinal tract from the other organs and is one of the most important landmarks for you to become acquainted with. This wreath, representing the autonomic nervous system, will be described in more detail in the following section on the nervous system.

We have started with the nutritive gastro-intestinal system because we would like to start from the pupil and work outward. Proceeding from the pupil to this wreath-like circle, the autonomic nerve wreath, you will always find an area which is darker than the area outside the wreath toward the periphery of the iris. This system, is the most heavily laden with

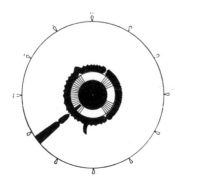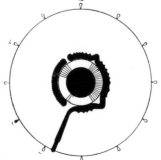

Fig. 41.   The Nutritive Gastro-intestinal System.

99

toxic, drug, or systemic settlements. The intestinal system, as a rule, carries the greatest amount of toxic material and is therefore the darkest part of the iris. In many cases, in looking over the whole iris, you will find dark areas in certain organs but very seldom will you find them darker than the intestinal tract area itself, showing that the intestinal tract is usually the beginning of toxic settlements found in the organs throughout the body. This area usually occupies about one-third of the iris. Comparing the colon area in the iris to the small intestinal area, the colon area is usually larger.

While I believe many doctors pay too much attention to the intestinal tract insofar as treatments are concerned—colonics, for instance,—I do believe it is the most important area in the iris to take into consideration. Let us look over the area first and then discuss the different parts from a physiological treatment side later.

About half-way between the pupil and the autonomic wreath is the stomach area. This area lies directly around the pupil. While I have said it usually is about half-way between the pupil and the autonomic nerve wreath, many times it will extend beyond this wreath. Sometimes you will not be able to see it at all. Experience will show what this means.

The area for the duodenum is directly opposite the gall bladder. You will find, whenever you are handling a duodenal disturbance, that the area can extend all the way from the black pupil to the gall bladder area. While the whole stomach area may be white, if there is an ulcer in the stomach, the ulcerated portion will appear even whiter, showing that more acute inflammation is in this particular area of the stomach. There is no definite shape for the duodenal ulcer. It may appear as a circle or as a straight line, or it may be of various sizes and shapes. An ulcer represents an acute inflammation of the tissue so you will find the reflex areas in the duodenal area of the iris to be very

white and the lines raised anteriorly from the other fibres.

Sometimes it is difficult to see these extremely white lines in acute inflammation because they become almost transparent when they have been raised some distance away from the pigment layer. Of course, if there is a perforation of the duodenum you will find the dark pigment showing through, which indicates a chronic destruction of tissue taking place. As the pathology increases in this area, you will find that it drops down into the deeper layers and becomes darker and darker. The duodenum seems to be well placed because it is at the point where drainage of the gall bladder and pancreatic fluids come together. It is an important area to look over because it can be the source of a good many symptoms such as vomiting and spasticity, and also can be involved in mental disturbances.

The navel is located at the end of the area representing the large intestine or at the beginning of that representing the transverse colon. The pylorus and the cardiac end of the stomach are found bordering the pupil medially.

Remembering that the right eye corresponds to the right side of the body, let us start with the right iris as we deal with the colon. We find the center of the transverse colon begins where the black line comes down from one o'clock in the right iris. The transverse colon carries on to the left until we come to eleven o'clock in the right iris. This is the hepatic flexure. The ascending colon extends along the side until we get to the pancreatic area, near which is the cecum. The cecum area begins between the bladder and the vaginal areas at five o'clock in the right iris.

We pay particular attention to this area of the cecum in the iris when we are trying to differentiate between inflammation of the cecum and of the appendix. In a case of inflamed appendix we notice the area extends into the abdominal wall area, and sometimes inflammation is carried completely through the abdominal wall area. In many an appendix difficulty, however, the source of trouble can still be in the cecum. Many cases of cecal inflammation have been mis-diagnosed as appendicitis. These two centers are very closely related, but we can still tell from the iris whether the inflammation actually is in the appendix or is elsewhere.

You will find that the area of the small intestine fills the space medially between the autonomic nerve wreath and the pupil, extending from the center of the transverse colon to the cecum. Between two and three o'clock in the small intestine (opposite the thyroid gland area), I have discovered the area for Peyer's Patches, where extreme fevers arise and settle. Disturbance in this area can cause destructive conditions and interfere with the proper nutritive balance in the body by preventing proper absorption from food. It is my belief that the greatest control of digestion and chemical absorption is in this part of the small intestine. Invariably, when we find chronic lesions in this particular area, we find that though a patient may be eating good foods, he still is not getting all the good from his food.

It takes a certain amount of time to break down a chronic lesion anywhere in the body, and it will take a crisis of some kind to return to a state of acute inflammation in this area. In such a crisis a fever almost always develops because there was a fever to begin with when this process first settled in Peyer's Patches. After the crisis or the reversal process, the patient will feel much better; he will be able to absorb his food better, and he will have less gas and intestinal disturbance. Until the time of change in this particular area, many patients will lose considerable weight and probably will keep this low weight until the crisis has been accomplished. With a condition in Peyer's Patches, you usually will find a sympathetic effect in the thyroid gland.

In speaking of drugs here, it is difficult to know exactly where to start. Many times you will find discoloration in the intestinal tract area, usually due to sulphur. In the past sulphur has been used much too freely, as for example in the combination of sulphur and molasses for a spring cleanser, sulphur waters, sulphured fruits, sulphur drugs, etc. This sulphur has its effect upon the intestinal wall and you can easily detect a yellowish color in this iris area. Many of the drugs used in treating diseases affect the mucosa of the bowel and small intestine, and some of them have a greater effect on one part of the intestinal tract than on another. It is difficult, however, to see in the iris when these drugs have settled in the stomach and intestinal wall areas. Digitalis usually causes spasms in the stomach wall. Bismuth, when used over a period of time, dries up the stomach wall and also causes irritation.

Most drugs not only fail to work with natural principles, but create definite reactions which damage certain tissues and further burden the organism. Usually more chronic conditions result from the use of drugs, and areas of the iris darken, denoting disturbance in the intestinal tract. The sodium benzoate and other salts that are used as preservatives can be a source of irritation to the intestinal tract. In my opinion, bicarbonate of soda can cause injury to the mucosa of the stomach, and probably is responsible for more gastric ulcers than anything else. Sodium chloride used in salt deficiency cases, and alum and copper sulphate used in cooking processes, also can cause irritation. I believe a good deal of disturbance is caused by food absorbing metallic substances in preparation and in cooking. Cooking in aluminum ware, I am convinced, will cause a definite action on the sensitive mucous lining of the stomach and intestinal tract. In fact, I agree with those who regard this metal as a causative factor in many of our chronic diseases, including cancer. No doubt there are as many who defend the use of aluminum cooking ware, however, as those who oppose it. For example, certain writers who apparently take pleasure in humiliating those who encourage the use of "health" foods and cooking utensils which cannot contaminate foods, go so far as to declare that aluminum cooking ware is "safe." One such person writes:

"Some of the fad followers have thrown away all of their aluminum cooking utensils because they have been told aluminum is poisonous and also causes cancer. This is a needless waste of money and material.

."Dr. Russell M. Wilder of the Mayo clinic writes: 'We have no information in the Mayo clinic that aluminum ware is in any way responsible for cancer or any disorders either of the stomach or other organs. This question is one that has arisen repeatedly, apparently chiefly as a result of the efforts of salesmen of the various other utensil companies to discredit the use of aluminum utensils.

'The information which follows is from the bulletin sent to us by the secretary of the American Medical Association, council on foods and nutrition:

'While some persons make the claim that aluminum causes cancer, and therefore should never be used as a utensil for cooking, we can assure you that there is no basis for such belief.

'Further information bearing on this subject is the quite significant fact that many physicians at the present time are giving hydrated alumina as an antiacid in the treatment of ulcer of the stomach and duodenum. This treatment has been popular for many years and so far as I know has never aroused any suspicion of provoking cancer in the stomach. The amount of aluminum given by this means exceeds by many hundred times what would be obtained from the cooking of foods in aluminum utensils'."**

I am glad this writer brought forth such convincing evidence in order to illustrate her point, for this gives us state-ments directly from well-known doctors themselves as to the extent of their drugging. Be sure to note their admission to administering dosages of hydrated alumina which exceed "by many hundred times what would be obtained from the cooking of foods in aluminum utensils." Such quotations should be very interesting at that time in the future when testing methods have been perfected and we can determine whether the emanations from aluminum cooking ware are harmful or not. There will also be evidence in the iris.

The United States Government prohibits meat packers from using aluminum which will in any way come into contact with meats. I wonder, why?

I recall seeing at one time a pamphlet issued by some prominent hospital association stating that the human body needs aluminum in its chemical makeup and therefore we should consider as beneficial any aluminum entering our foods from aluminum cooking utensils. Other individuals, trying to defend the use of aluminum, point to its prevalence in the soil throughout the earth. Some persons do not know yet that our mineral requirements should not be supplied directly from the crude metals in the earth, but from foods grown in the earth.

These irritations all add up to chronic tendencies and show up in the intestinal area of the iris as dark gray or various drug colors. Any foreign substance that does not belong in the human body will become part of the blood stream as the body tries to eliminate it. Foreign matter which thus becomes part of the blood and tissues will finally cause a darkened area to appear in the iris.

One such substance is the iron frequently used as a blood builder. It is very constipating, and persons who take a great deal of it into their systems accumulate a heavy, chronic, dark rust-colored settlement throughout the intestinal tract area. This dark area denotes constipation. I am speak-

---

**Elna Miller, "There Are No Health Foods," THE UTAH FARMER, Vol. 71, No. 11. p. 35, June 7, 1951.

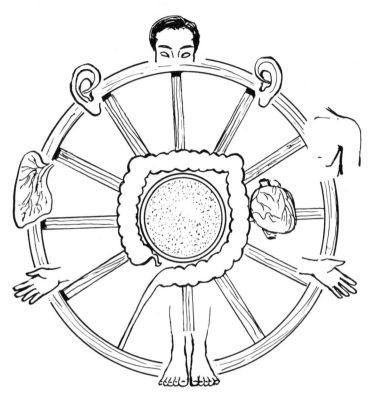

FIG. 42.   The intestinal tract is the hub.

ing of the iron in an inorganic state, not the iron in foods naturally.

Note that the organs represented within the autonomic wreath—the transverse colon, the ascending colon, the cecum and the small intestine—form a hub; all the other organs have connection with the intestinal tract. As you practice iridology, one of the most remarkable things will be revealed to you: *every organ is dependent for nutriment upon the intestinal tract.* In the iris it is part of the hub previously mentioned in connection with the autonomic nerve wreath—the hub upon which the organs rely that the wheel of life may continue.

In the chapter on Reflex Areas, we will take up a specific study that may be very interesting to the practitioner, showing the relationship between conditions in the organs and definite areas in the intestinal tract. It has been my observation, for instance, that trouble in the hepatic flexure may cause a disturbance in the right ear, or be basically responsible for a mastoid problem. This you can prove, for by correcting the trouble in the hepatic flexure through cleansing processes and dietary control, the mastoid will clear. Also, in the chapter on Reflex Areas, you will be shown how you can use other methods of diagnosing and proving your iris findings.

The Radii Solaris—In the intestinal area of the iris is the beginning of the *radii solaris.* These *radii,* which look like spokes in a wheel, branch out from the intestinal area to or through any organ area. They are quite indented, usually dark, and may be even black. Where the iris fibres are quite separated, the dark underlying pigment layer shows through. This represents a settlement of toxic material, and wher-

ever the *radii solaris* penetrate they indicate
that this heavy, dark toxic material is settling. If the *radii solaris* have penetrated
extensively into the brain area, this indicates that toxic material from the transverse
colon is settling in the brain tissues. It is
as though they were troughs carrying toxic
settlements to organs in which we find these
signs.

When a patient presents psychological
problems, it is well to consider that if the
brain is heavily laden with toxic material,
it will be difficult for him to comprehend
a plan of reeducation. Though his blood
may be circulating well, if it is filled with
toxic material, the thinking centers will
act slowly. It will be difficult to concentrate, to meditate, and the memory will
be faulty because the memory area is not
clean. Clean blood is one of the first cor-
rections we must strive for.

It is impossible to separate the physical
and the mental, except verbally, and it
is wonderful to have signs to show you
where to begin your work. The deeper
the *radii solaris,* the greater the amounts
of toxic settlement. Some persons have had
these signs in the iris for years and years,
and the longer this absorption continues,
the darker, wider, heavier, and deeper the
radii solaris become.

Autonomic Nerve Wreath—The autonomic nerve wreath should form an even,
round line in the iris, but usually it is
jagged, and we find that the colon follows
these pointed areas into any organ in which
these points extend. If a jagged point extends into the mastoid area and it is very
black and dark within the jagged point,
—probably darker than the rest of the intestinal tract,—this is where you will find
the greatest amount of toxic material and
probably the seat of the trouble of the
organ that is manifesting the pain. When
there is distention or widening of the
wreath, usually there has been suppression
of disease in the organ represented in the
area opposite this portion of the wreath.
It is interesting to see dark areas change
under proper care, so watch them closely.

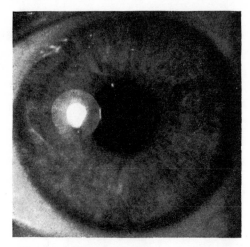

FIG. 43. The autonomic nerve wreath
can be detected easily by noting the
line of separation which it makes between the peripheral organ areas and
the darker colored gastro-intestinal area
around the pupil.

The *radii solaris* can come directly from
the nerve wreath. This is not so dangerous
in its disease implication as when they
come out from the pupil. The *radii solaris*
extending from the pupil usually carry a
high amount of toxic material from the
gastro-intestinal tract. They may be inherent or acquired. The wider and deeper
they are, the more toxicity is found in the
organs involved. The degree of health depends upon the degree to which the body
is toxin-free.

Another thing to consider regarding the
autonomic nerve wreath is that while it
is supposed to be round, you will usually
find in the upper part of the iris an indentation and swing toward the pupil. This
shows that the transverse colon is prolapsed.
All the X-rays I have taken of the transverse colon show a direct relation between
the position of the nerve wreath—how it
draws toward the pupil—and the position
of the transverse colon. And the degree
of prolapsus is comparable to the extent
of this dip in the autonomic nerve wreath.
This prolapsus causes extreme pressure
symptoms and there will be a narrowing

FIG. 44.

FIG. 45.   These are photographs of a preserved tapeworm, well over twenty feet long, removed from a lady's bowel. Symptoms about which this patient had been complaining for years, disappeared after the elimination of this parasite.

of the cecum area or of the sigmoid colon area, showing that the transverse colon is causing an extreme amount of pressure on the lower organs. Many times you can measure the lack of tone in the abdominal organs by the amount of space between the nerve wreath and the pupil opposite the sigmoid colon and the cecum. Pressure symptoms have to be taken into consideration. When the transverse colon has dropped, you will find that all organs are affected. While toxemia may be responsible for many of the disturbances in the body, pressure from the transverse colon upon the lower organs can cause many obscure symptoms.

If there are pains in some organs which examination shows are not in a toxic condition, the origin of the difficulty may be in the nervous system. In this case, the autonomic nerve wreath will appear very white.

When the intestinal tract shows up very dark, one thing you may feel certain of is that the patient has been a heavy user of laxatives. You may also assume with certainty that there are great numbers of bacillus coli, a gas-producing bacillus, within the intestinal tract and a lack of the friendly bacterium, acidophilus bacillus. In palpatation of the bowel the most gas is found in those parts designated by black pockets in the iris, and you will find the patient complaining of gas. Gas will be produced when these intestinal settlements are broken up by healing processes.

When the bowel area shows many black dots and blackened portions throughout, this can be a sign of worms. Many times I have suspected their presence in organs reflecting dark spots in the iris. With the inherent tone of the bowel so weak that it could not eliminate properly, it became a stagnant cesspool in which worms could develop. This black coloration represents an acid-alkaline imbalance of the flora, or a toxic condition, and is conducive to the development of worms, bacillus coli, etc. It is not uncommon to find worms in the intestinal tract. It depends upon the amount and the type of toxic material in the bowel. This toxic material can be changed by diet. Many persons eat too much starch and not enough protein, or vice versa, or starches and proteins of low biological value, or do not include enough vegetables and fruits—so that the result is imbalance. Therefore, various intestinal floras will be produced and different types of worms may develop. Black iris spots may represent diverticuli in the colon, which are ideal breeding places for worms.

You have an opportunity to see these conditions change if you make stool tests. These tests over a period of years will show that the average person invariably runs as high as 80 to 85 per cent in bacillus coli and only about 10 to 15 per cent in acidophilus bacillus. As this condition is corrected the intestinal signs in the iris lighten and new healing lines appear, showing that new tissue is replacing the old; then the stool tests will show entirely different contents. The bacillus coli will begin to diminish and the acidophilus baccilus will increase. We have had laboratory fecal tests run by the hundreds, and have found in nearly every case that the bowel harbored about 85 per cent bacillus coli and only 15 per cent acidophilus. These percentages should be reversed. We found that the condition changed from the heavy bacillus coli to the acidophilus balance when the healing lines appeared in the bowel area or the dark spots in the iris changed to white. By the time white healing lines had permeated the dark spots completely, we had acidulated the bowel properly and there was the right acid-alkaline balance.

There have been times when examination of the bowel did not confirm the condition indicated in the iris, but through persistent re-examination, X-rays, etc., the iris findings were proved to be correct.

A case in point is that of Dr. D. from Idaho who was complaining of heart trouble. I took pictures of the bowel because I suspected that as the location of the main difficulty. The first picture taken after a barium enema did not show much of a problem. So while the colon was ballooned from the barium meal, immediately after emptying, we took a second picture. This picture revealed the spot and the source of the trouble. The bowel condition was causing reflex symptoms in the heart. (Refer to chapter on Reflex Areas).

I advise checking both the iris and the body itself, especially the bowel area. Get two X-ray pictures each time,—the first with the barium meal in the bowel and the second immediately after it has been ballooned and emptied. In the second picture you will find conditions which a bowel filled with barium meal sometimes does not reveal.

The best suggestion for those who would like to prove for themselves what is going on in the colon (as I did after years spent taking X-rays to try to verify what I found in the iris of the eye), is to take at least two X-ray pictures. There have been times when only after the fifth X-ray picture could we determine the existence of a duodenal ulcer indicated by the iris. One picture may give evidence of abnormalities not apparent in another due to the fact that the muscular structures were under different conditions of strain and pressure. In the chapter on Reflex Areas, we will demonstrate this point with X-ray pictures showing where the problem is, and how at times, though the laboratory report shows no pathology, the patient is complaining about gas troubles and pains in this particular part of the colon, which are verified by the findings in the iris.

This amounts to analyzing bowel conditions in the iris and then proving them by X-ray. Only the X-ray can show the shape of the bowel, but it cannot reveal the various tissue conditions which may exist. This is one thing you must remember in reading the iris of the eye. It can reveal the tissue structure of the particular organ you are dealing with, while X-ray cannot reveal inherent structure unless

there is an abnormal shape or a ballooned condition. And we are inclined to believe that these misshapen areas of the bowel are due to inherently weak muscle structure. After you have an X-ray picture of such an area, you have only an indication of the condition—not a definite determination. Neither X-ray nor laboratory analysis can tell the constitutional condition of any spot in the bowel area, but iris analysis will reveal it. Thus we see that many of these conditions can be foretold in the iris of the eye while an X-ray can only determine these conditions after they are drastically expressed in forms such as cancer and tuberculosis.

X-ray pictures the bowel only at a particular moment. It may be emotional stress or an extreme irritation resulting from stricture that is causing colitis. Bowel trouble may appear only under certain mental conditions. In some cases bowel disturbance occurs at certain times only. This may come when the patient is extremely tired or has exceeded the limit of his nerve energy. If an extreme pain developed in a certain part of the bowel resulting in contraction and an X-ray was taken at that very moment, then only would it reveal the condtion causing the extreme contraction.

Combine other forms of examination with your iris diagnosis since it is impossible to determine the condition of the patient twenty-four hours a day. We are constantly in a process of change, making changes according to our mental attitudes, our eating habits, and our outlook on life. The kind of change we effect will depend a good deal upon working conditions, weather, the way we slept the night before, the amount of coffee we had for breakfast, or the different ill-chosen foods that we ate from day to day.

The accompanying diagramatic illustration is to show that the brain area in the iris of the eye is affected reflexly by toxins from the transverse colon.

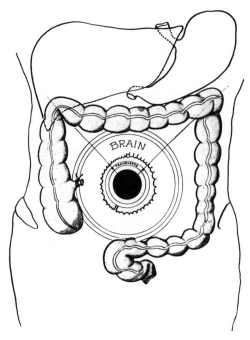

BRAIN

TRANSVERSE

FIG. 46. Due to the very close relationship between the colon and the rest of the organs, we should consider the extent to which the colon is responsible for the condition of any organ. Reflex conditions in the brain are from the transverse portion of the colon.

The fact that concussion of the second lumbar will contract the intestines while concussion of the eleventh dorsal will dilate them, shows the relationship between the spine and the intestinal tract. In treating spinal conditions, let us look for the seat of the difficulty in the intestine. The iris will help to reveal it.

In checking the black spots within the bowel area we are not confined in our iris analysis to that which is in the bowel. A black spot in this iris area represents a physiological inactivity of the bowel *wall* itself; toxic material is retained there. It can be a *diverticulum* or a pocket which is sluggish in passing along toxic material —a foul place where gas is produced and the *bacillus coli* multiplies. If the bowel was tested under these circumstances, the ratio between the *acidophilus* and the *bacillus coli* bacteria would be very abnormal.

Because of the relationship between inflammation in the nervous system and the condition of the bowel wall, we must watch the autonomic nerve wreath. For instance, a spastic condition reflexly centered in the intestinal tract may have been instituted by some mental or environmental circumstance. Colitis in many cases is caused by a nerve-wracking environment or a nervous tendency of the patient, and is reflexly brought to that part of the nervous system which controls the intestinal tract. You find these condtions in the iris by following the nerve wreath.

Such conditions bring on much tension in the bowels and much inflammation in the bowel wall. When there is lack of nerve tone or nerve force, we have the opposite condition of sluggishness. Thus we see conditions of both overactivity or underactivity of the nervous system. Watch the nervous system in relation to bowel conditions to be better able to handle these problems.

Whenever the autonomic nerve wreath comes to a large point and there is an extremely dark area within the point, this indicates poor muscular activity at that particular part of the colon. It may be inherently weak, and the reason for the dark coloration is that the waste material does not pass along in this particular part of the bowel as fast as it should. The greatest amount of toxic absorption can take place in this part of the bowel and cause reflex troubles, as will be explained in the chapter on Reflex Areas.

Adhesions in the bowel are indicated by white signs that usually are a little different in color tone, almost like that of scar-tissue, and sometimes have a slightly yellow cast. Where an adhesion is attached to some part of the bowel, the wreath goes in to meet the area representing this little band that seems to hold the bowel wall down. We illustrate this in one of the colored iris plates.

The appearance of a stricture is just opposite that of a ballooned bowel. Note that the stricture causes the autonomic nerve wreath to be pulled directly toward the pupil, while the ballooning causes it to press toward the periphery. It does not have to touch the pupil, but usually there is a small narrow area where the wreath comes very abruptly toward the stomach area or toward the pupil.

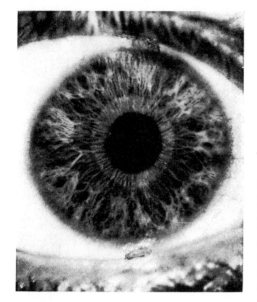

FIG. 477. This photograph shows the white ring seen in the stomach area when there is an abnormal condition. Under normal conditions there is no stomach ring. In this case the ring represents sub-acute inflammation.

The stomach is represented by a white ring around the pupil. This ring will be shaded according to the degree of inflammation. (The front of the stomach is in the lower part of the stomach area of the iris while the back of the stomach is found in its upper part. This is the same in both irises). It is possible to have a nerve ring go through the stomach area, which indicates a nervous stomach. While we are not diagnosing in accordance with that method which must name a disease, we can readily see that a nerve ring going through the stomach area will compare to what may be diagnosed as gastritis or nervous indigestion.

The stomach is the first organ to suffer from abuse. It is an organ not only requiring a great deal of sodium in its tissues, but is considered to be a storage depot for sodium. When the body lacks sodium, therefore, the stomach is the first organ to react. I do not know of any one chemical element more needed in the body than soidum. A little farther on we will see, in the chapter called The Sodium Story, how important it is that we have good chemical balance in the body. The stomach ring is one of the first malformations or lesion signs detected in the iris, as the stomach is one of the first organs to be involved in chemical depletion.

The blood is only as clean as the intestinal tract because it absorbs both nutritive and toxic materials from there. Those pockets we spoke of whose iris area occupied a point or jag in the autonomic nerve wreath may be foci of infection. Any part of the body can throw out toxic materials, such as a decaying tooth; we know a tooth can be a source of infection. But the darkest area in the iris and the greatest source of infection is usually the colon. The darkness of color reflected in the colon areas of the iris will be in direct proportion to the degree of putrefaction and fermentation in the colon.

It is easy to see why we consider cleansing of the intestinal tract as primary in importance. Of course, putrefaction and fermentation may increase and more gases be produced temporarily during the cleansing process, especially as the healing crisis approaches. When the crisis is imminent and the elimination of this toxic material begins, there will be less gas formation. During the crisis, when white lines in the iris signal that acutely active new tissues are replacing the old, there will be a great deal of activity and bowel disturbance. These we would expect, but they may surprise and alarm your patient unless these reactions are explained to him.

Be particularly observant of the food allowed the patient at the time of crisis as these foods are the means of building the healing signs we wish to establish in the iris. Laxatives and purgatives are not producers of the new healing lines, but rather consume energy and result in a more chronic condition. Build up the tissues themselves through correct diet, and develop tone so that the body can perform its own eliminative functions without any help from laxatives. This all takes time and work on the part of both the patient and the doctor. You have to educate your patient as to what you are doing. Time, patience and perseverance will prove that this work brings good results. You will be a blessing to your patient ten years from now as well as today, something you cannot accomplish by administering drugs to overcome a symptom or by the use of a laxative or purgative to carry out waste material for temporary relief. The real changes come about through a natural healing program. In other chapters we discuss diet and right-living habits.

It has been said, and can be found stated in some medical books, that it makes no difference how often the bowels move— that there is no toxic material absorbed from the intestinal tract. It is even stated that if there is no bowel movement during a period of from three to six days there can still be no toxic effect or absorption of waste material from the colon. But we differ in our views considerably. After we have changed the living habits of the patient and have seen the intestinal area in the iris lighten and clear up, we notice that the bowels improve; the tone of the bowel becomes stronger. The nervous system has been tempered properly and natural bowel movements are the result. The amount of time required to overcome this condition in the bowel depends upon the patient's inherent structures and his cooperation in changing habits which are debilitating.

The dark iris areas reflected from the bowel indicate weakness of inherent struc-

ture and, of course, of functional ability. Weak organs are easily susceptible to absorption of toxic material from the colon. The organ that has an inherently weak structure will take on the toxic material that flows through it. If there is toxic material settled in the colon area directly opposite an inherently weak organ, as reflected in the iris, you will have to take care of this particular place in the colon because this area can be the source of infection for that organ. Since the various organs absorb toxic material from the colon, we find it more important to take care of this than the organ structure itself. Then too, the colon wall itself may be inherently weak and require attention just the same as any other organ.

Individual spots in the colon may affect certain organs. The urine, for example, in passing through the kidneys can be affected directly by absorption from those spots in the bowel. The amount of indican in a urine test verifies this fact. In order to eliminate this condition we start with the bowel.

There are many things to consider in treating the colon and in making changes so that you can watch the signs of new tissue fill in the old dark holes in the iris which represented chronic conditions. We can assist the bowel through colonics, but this is a crude and partial method. The most constructive process is the rebuilding of the bowel wall itself. What you see in the iris of the eye is not a representation of what is *in* the bowel, but of the *structure* of the bowel. You are reading the condition of the bowel *wall,* and in doing so you are able to evaluate the chemical balance therein. When you know what chemical elements are required to build better bowel tissue, you can supply these elements and the bowel wall will improve. All new filament changes, all new fibre changes, reflected in the iris, are not a matter of a bowel that has been made clean by colonics or purgatives, but rather the condition of the bowel *wall* at the moment of your analysis. You cannot tell from the iris what a person has just eaten or what is in the bowel at any particular time. It is only through a building process, in which you re-educate your patient and he adheres to a good health program, that healing lines in the iris can be developed.

If the bowel is very toxic, the colon area in the left iris usually shows more toxicity than in the right. The reason for this is that as waste material passes through the large colon, it becomes dryer, considerable fluid having been absorbed. If bowel movements are not regular there is a backing-up process and a greater amount of concentrated toxic material is found on the left side of the body, in the sigmoid and in the descending colon. This backing-up is responsible for a good many of the troubles that are developed on the left side of the body—such as angina pectoris, heart palpitation, heart incompetence, aortic insufficiency, diaphragmatic pressures, ovarian and bladder disturbances.

We spoke about the pressure symptoms that can be developed from a dropped transverse colon. In this condition, the stomach also drops, resulting in what is known as a "fishhook" stomach. There may be rectal pressure, uterine pressure, and even a floating kidney condition may be due to this cause. Along with pressure symptoms, toxic conditions and stagnation can develop. A lack of the proper blood supply to any organ can cause degeneration. Either an extremely dark or an inflammatory sign may signify that these organs are trying to bring about an eliminative process and normalize themselves, but are unable to do so,—either because the pressure will not allow perfect blood circulation, or because the absorption of toxic material is so heavy the organ cannot throw it off fast enough to rebuild.

Black colon areas indicate pockets filled with toxic settlement. They show up in X-ray pictures as diverticuli and are sources of infection which cause an extreme amount of disturbance in the body. We discuss this further in the chapter on Reflex Areas.

When the outer border of the intestinal tract area in the iris appears to be wide and irregular, this indicates that the intestinal tract is flabby, inactive, and in a prolapsed condition. It may be atonic, with constipation often the result. There are patients with these signs in the iris who will tell you they have two, three, and even four bowel movements a day. Many a patient may have as many as six, and may insist that he has a clean bowel, but this is not so if the iris reveals chronic toxic settlement in the bowel wall. Frequent movements do not mean that one is not constipated. I believe you will find that when changes have been made through right-living methods, which are recorded in the iris, your patient's fecal material will be entirely different. The odor will be less foul than before and he will not be passing foul-smelling gases.

Our best nature cure men have stressed the point that toxemia is found in all disease. To verify this statement and to get a good understanding of what toxic condition means in disease, it might be well to read Doctor George Weger's book "The Genesis and Control of Disease." In his opinion, enervation and toxemia are the beginning of all disease. Doctor J. H. Tilden also emphasized this fact, and John Harvey Kellogg was an advocate of taking care of the bowel and the intestinal flora as first fundamentals. No one can deny the good these men accomplished. As healing signs develop in the intestinal tract area, you will see healing signs appearing also in all other black areas in the iris. You can verify results by patiently using this science, and it will be deeply satisfying to see it working out before your eyes.

The Nervous System

The nervous system controls every organ of the body. Every fibre in the iris is in direct communication with the nerve structures of the body. The main nerve structure located in the iris of the eye is the autonomic nerve wreath. On old-type charts this was erroneously called the sympathetic wreath. It is named according to its neurological function when called the autonomic nervous system wreath. The nervous system takes in the whole brain area, as outlined on my chart, where it is placed within dark black lines.

The autonomic nervous system wreath, usually quite jagged, is about one-third of the distance out from the pupil towards the periphery of the iris. As previously mentioned, it is the line which separates the intestinal tract area from the organ areas which surround it. This nerve wreath in the iris is in direct contact with every organ area.

We must understand that the autonomic or vegetative nervous system is self-governing and not under the control of the will. In its function it exerts a regulatory control and maintenance over circulation, respiration, digestion and elimination. In other words, it adapts the individual to his environment. The autonomic nervous system consists of two divisions—sympathetic and parasympathetic.

The sympathetic division of the autonomic nervous system includes all of the thoracic and the first three or four lumbar nerves, and often is called the thoracolumbar system. An example of its function is its fright mechanism. When a person is frightened the pupils dilate, the blood supply to the abdominal organs is restricted, the blood supply to the muscles is increased, glycogen in the muscles is released, and liver glycogen is made available. This person will either stand his ground and fight for self-preservation, or will run. The parasympathetic division includes the cranial and sacral nerves. In the organs having both sympathetic and parasympathetic nerve fibres, one is antagonistic to the other. An example of overstimulation of the parasympathetic nerves is a spastic colon in a nervous individual. The iris area representing the autonomic nervous system includes both the parasympathetic and the sympathetic divisions.

When you progress to the place where you analyze in detail the individual iris fibres and follow them to their source, you will see that the autonomic nerve wreath seems to be made up of a network of plexuses or communicating centers leading from each of the organ areas to this wreath. These plexuses seem to be connected and to have communication one with another. All of them seem to be in harmony, and they seem to be in sympathy with the organs, functioning as a hub for them. Every organ is related to this nerve wreath. It registers all the sensations of the organs and reflexly carries them from one organ to another. Study the wreath well. As stated, it forms a line of demarcation between all organ areas and that of the in-

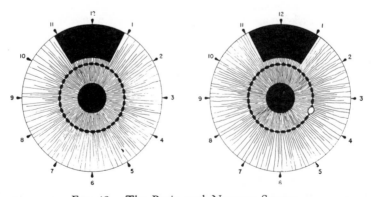

FIG. 48.   The Brain and Nervous System.

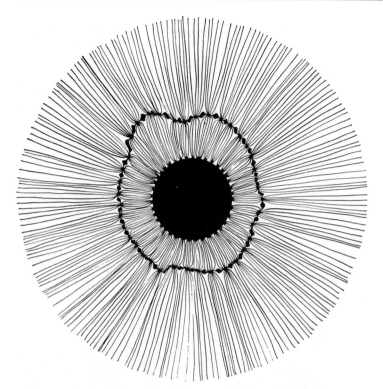

Fig. 49. This drawing shows how the fibres coming from the pupil to the autonomic nerve wreath form centers of communication with the fibres coming in from the periphery, through the various organ areas. This demonstrates the contact that every organ area has with the wreath.

testinal tract, and you will note there are fibres leading from the intestinal tract to this wreath as well as from the wreath to the organs.

When the antonomic nerve wreath is regular in shape and well placed, this indicates a normal functioning of the organs of the body. Distortions are found only in disease conditions. When the wreath is irregular and extends into points, more jagged in some places than others, this denotes poor activity of the organ or organs to which the jagged points are directed. The individual whose nerve wreath is distorted in all directions will have definte oversensitivity, nervousness, and lack of tone. Definite hypertrophy or atrophy will develop in any organ to which the wreath points. When it is pointed to the area of

the rectum, that patient may have tenesmus, with possible pruritus. When it is pointed to the bronchial areas, there may be nervous asthma or difficult breathing. When it points to the bladder area, there can be bladder disturbance; when to the nose, loss of smell and dryness of the mucous lining; when to the tongue, lack of taste; when to the eyes, twitching of the lids; etc. In cases of intestinal prolapsus, the wreath in the upper part of the iris will extend toward the pupil. Compare both the right and left irises in order to determine on which side of the body the greater amount exists.

Note that the wreath is made up of the plexus points where the nerve fibres coming from the periphery meet those coming from the pupil. When there is greater

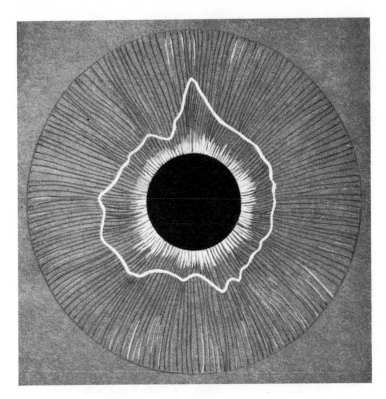

FIG. 50.   Irregularity of autonomic nerve wreath indicating
tensions produced by various activities of the two divisions
of the nervous system.

tension or activity on the nerve fibres between the wreath and the periphery, the
greatest amount of irritation exists within
that organ where these fibres go through.
The reason for that is that the toxic material has become so chronic around the
nerve plexus within the bowel area that in
that chronic state it has lost its tone and
its power to equal the tone of those fibres
between the wreath and the periphery.

Organ areas between the wreath and the
periphery eventually will be broken down
by the toxic condition in the bowel area
opposite them.

The wreath can be raised or inflamed in
any one spot, or the entire wreath can be
raised and inflamed and be in the same
state of acute inflammation as the fibres
of any organ area in the iris. The raised,

FIG. 51.   Varying levels of the autonomic nerve wreath.
The height of this wreath varies according to the acute,
sub-acute, and chronic inflammations.

high points of the wreath can be detected easily by placing the light very near the patient's face but not in front of it.

The nerve wreath contains a story if you watch for it. Follow it around the iris in its entirety, and where you see the greatest number of irregularities, look for the pathology—either in the bowel area or such as colitis, duodenitis, etc. The wreath is the response organ to any adverse influences from the outside which may be disturbing any organ, or from the inside,—as toxemia, which may originate in the bowel. Doctors who deal with nerve reflexes should watch the wreath for it is there that the reflexes to the spine and other parts of the body are in evidence.

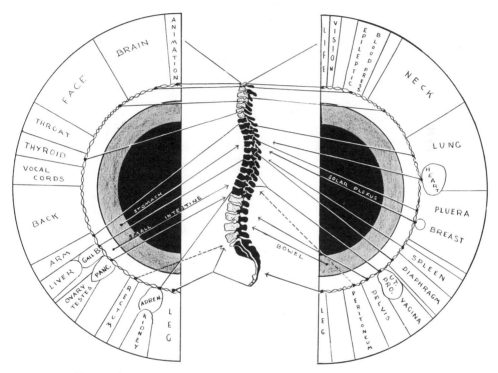

FIG. 52.   The spine and spinal nerves have a direct relation to the autonomic nerve wreath.

in the corresponding organ, or in both. A good deal of the activity in any one part of the wreath may be reflected from the organ opposite it, or it may be caused by a toxic condition of the bowel which shows just medial to the wreath. We can also have irritation to the fibres from our external environment (financial problems, love affairs, etc.) which may disturb some organ and result in many of the somatic conditions which end up in the stomach and intestinal tract. For instance, any circumstance which disturbs the thyroid gland can produce reflex conditions in the bowel

This is verified by the views of Doctor Bennett and Doctor De Jarnette on reflex therapy.

Irritation in any part of the body causes a reflex action in the nervous system, which is recorded in the autonomic nerve wreath. Either balancing or blocking reflex activities of the nervous system in some parts of the body, will produce reaction in others. For example, many cases of rectal tension can be relieved by blocking; and nerve reflex conditions due to pressure in any part of the body, especially in the feet, can be

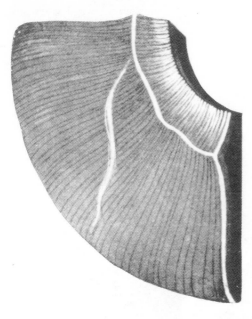

FIG. 53. Spinal inflammations show up in the back area of the iris chart.

relieved by blocking. In trying to balance the nervous system, one side of the body with the other, we often have to deal with complications such as toxemia and pressure symptoms, and these must be corrected before the reflex activity can be balanced.

The nerves leading from the spinal column also have their area in the iris. The first dorsal begins at the point where the back and the nervous system come together. The sacral area is at the lowest part of the back area. The cervical nerves are represented in the medulla division of the brain area. Inherent weaknesses in any part of the back show underfuctioning of that particular spinal area and those spinal nerves. Curvatures may be inherent and the condition may be made weaker through improper chemical balance. A lack of calcium will make any weak part of the back weaker and a curvature can easily develop. I believe many spinal irritations can be detected from the back area in the iris. One of the most important things we will

see is how a toxic condition can set up reflex nerve conditions in the body quicker than anything else. Another revelation is that after the removal of this toxic material, the nervous system usually will balance itself.

I believe the autonomic nervous wreath represents the intricate telegraphic network of the entire nervous system, but it is difficult to say how it is put together in its minute form. The day may come when we will discover thousands of intercommunicating lines connecting up many more plexuses in the body than we see today. Among the principal ones known today are the solar plexus and the rectal plexus. While these are centers of the greatest amount of nerve activity, there are numerous smaller plexuses throughout the body with which these are in communication—all being represented in the wreath.

In the chapter on Reflex Areas we will discuss further the relationship between the wreath and the intestinal tract and other organs, and the possible reflex relationship between certain parts of the bowel and certain organs. Wonders can be accomplished with greater knowledge and better understanding, particularly of the autonomic nerve wreath.

The Circulatory and Heart Systems

The heart area is found at exactly three o'clock in zone three, usually on the line representing the autonomic nerve wreath. Although in some cases it will be located a little to one side, in others it will appear to be enclosed or encased within the nerve wreath.

After you have pictured where this heart area is, you may often find the nerve wreath pierced by one of the *radii solaris*. This denotes an inherent weakness, which does not always mean a disease condition. It may mean a weakened nerve supply to the heart or a toxic condition draining into it. Whenever the heart is involved, you will invariably find the wreath also involved. This is how to differentiate between heart trouble and bronchial disturbances since the heart is in the bronchial zone also. Watch for toxic intestinal settlements that can cause reflex condtions to the heart.

The area representing the aorta is situated just above the heart area within the autonomic nervous wreath, seeming to split the wreath when pathology exists. This is also true of the solar plexus area, which is located slightly below that of the heart.

Since there are no two lesions alike, very seldom will you find the heart condition of one person comparing exactly to that of another. After you have learned to recognize each organ tissue represented in the iris, you will be able to tell under what conditions the heart is functioning. You will also be able to tell the inherent structure, the toxic conditions, the strength of the nerves, and the reflex actions from other organs. After studying the iris of the eye you develop a different conception of the activity of organs from what you learned in the past.

It is difficult to realize that the skin has so much to do with the circulatory system and that there are so many reflex activities between the skin and the various organs of the body. The iris skin field is on the periphery and the skin circulation area is in the last zone, the seventh zone. The skin field will show the amount of toxic material contained in the body. Where the skin does not eliminate properly, extra toxic material burdens the circulatory system and heart. It also burdens the kidneys, especially in cases of nerve depletion where excessive phosphates requiring elimination have been produced. I regard the skin as the third kidney. It is one of the most important organs of elimination and gives us a good picture of the tone of the body.

The sixth zone, which is just inside the outer zone, contains the areas representing the veins, the arteries, and the lymphatic system. The area for the arteries and veins usually has the same color as the skin field, showing their close relation. When the veins and arteries carry toxic or pathological blood, this zone is represented in a very dark color. We will take this up further under Scurf Rim in Chapter 15. The lymph system is not represented in the iris under normal conditions; therefore you cannot find it when the body is in good health. When the body becomes overladen with toxic wastes, however, the lymphatic system tries to eliminate the excess acids, catarrh, etc. And this condition of congestion will be evident in the iris.

In this sixth zone we have represented what we call the "lymphatic rosary". When you find a complete rosary it will be a series of little white spots connected with one another as represented in one of the colored iris plates. After you have seen one you never will forget it. This does not necessarily mean there is lymph congestion in all the organs represented; it may be in just one organ. Many times the lymph congestion is confined to the thyroid or lung areas. The lymphatic system area seems to follow the inner margin of the scurf rim. We cannot say it is exactly in the sixth zone at all times because, if the scurf rim widens, the lymphatic area seems to be pushed closer to the pupil. Many times the lymphatic rosary or lymphatic nodules are closer to the pupil at three and nine o'clock than at six or twelve o'clock, showing that the greatest congestion is in the lungs rather than in the extremities.

The Respiratory System

The respiratory system includes the lung areas. The two lobes of the left lung are represented between two and three o'clock in the left iris, and the three right lobes are indicated by separating lines between nine and ten o'clock in the right iris.

The pleura, thorax, and ribs are represented within heavy black lines between three and four o'clock in the left iris and between eight and nine in the right. The nipple and mammary gland are represented in the middle of each of these areas. The bronchial tube areas are represented in zone three. Immediately adjoining these and towards the periphery in each iris, are the lung and the pleural areas, between two and four o'clock in the left iris, and between eight and ten in the right.

A good deal of control of the respiratory center comes from the medulla and much of its involuntary activity comes from the brain. In looking for a healing in the respiratory area we must consider both the nervous system and respiratory system. A person can have a low response in the respiratory system due to lack of nerve supply as well as lack of tone and activity in the chest muscles.

The bronchi are represented on the medial side of each iris—between eight and ten o'clock in the left iris and between two and four in the right. This area should be examined along with the reflex conditions in cases of shortness of breath, as many times this difficulty may not be from lung abnormalities but may be a reflex condition from the diaphragm, whose area is between seven and eight o'clock in the right iris and four and five in the left.

In most cases we can readily point to the cause of trouble and know exactly where to start treatment by noting where inflammation appears in the various areas. The heart is very closely related to shortness of breath, as are all zone three organs— the bronchi, adrenals, and solar plexus. The thyroid gland area which projects into the bronchus area on the medial side of each iris, also can be responsible for this condition. It is well to see the close relationships among heart, lungs, bronchi, diaphragm, solar plexus, and medulla, when giving your patient an analysis.

The Genito-urinary System

The genito-urinary system is represented by one of our most important landmarks. The iris area, marked "kidney," lies near six o'clock in both irises. The bladder area is represented just after seven o'clock in the left iris and just before five o'clock in the right. Many of the reflex conditions found in the kidney and bladder may come from intestinal disturbances, which are represented on the inside of the nerve wreath opposite these organs. There are times when the general acid condition of the whole body has to be handled by the kidneys and bladder, and when inflammation and irritation result from a pathological condition or disturbed chemical balance in other organs.

FIG. 54. The Respiratory System.

The Reproductive and Glandular Systems

In the reproductive system, the uterus and the prostate gland are conceded to be in approximately the same area. On my chart they are represented in the third zone by the dark outline of the uterus and the dark outline of the prostate gland. The vaginal area is represented by a canal-like formation surrounded by extremely dark lines. This area is used as one of the landmarks, and is found opposite five o'clock in the right iris and opposite seven o'clock in the left. The ovary and testes are surrounded in a definite dark landmark opposite seven o'clock in the right iris and five in the left.

The mental response area of the sex organs in the cerebellum is between eleven and twelve in the right iris. Note that it

eral. Our ideals will be intensified whenever an acute white inflammatory stage exists in this mental center. When a dark area representing a chronic condition develops, there is always a weakening of will power. The area opposite in the left iris, includes the equilibrium and epileptic center. You will find here many closely related conditions. There is a direct relation between the epileptic and the sex centers in most cases, and there are other related organs in the sexual system which will be taken up later. All glands have an inter-related effect and every organ plays a definite part in the reproductive system.

The glandular system can be divided into various parts, which we only mention here. The liver of course, is a gland, as is the pancreas. In zone three the pancreas is listed as one of the main digestive glands. It appears opposite the ovary and

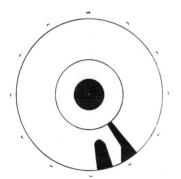 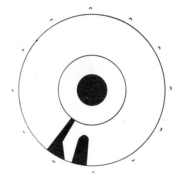

FIG. 55.   The Genito-urinary System.

is directly opposite the uterus, prostate, and vaginal areas. Here are found recordings regarding the sex life, the sex impulse, perversion, and mental sex questions. A sign of acute inflammation in these sex centers indicates perversion, masturbation, undue passion, or over-stimulation of the sexual organs. It may indicate an upset sexual life or fear of impotence. A chronic dark line is a definite sign that inhibition of sexual impulses, and coldness and frigidity, are developing. Such a person will feel repulsion toward the opposite sex and indifference regarding sexual matters in gen-

testes landmark at seven o'clock in the right iris.

The adrenal gland is also in this zone and is found directly over the kidney area. The pituitary gland and pineal gland are found here next to the autonomic nerve wreath. The thyroid gland has been definitely marked and is one of the main landmarks. As you will use this landmark often, it is advisable to memorize it.

There is an effect, especially in women, that should be particularly noted when there is disturbance in any of the glands. For instance, the thyroid gland and ovaries in the woman play an important part in menstrual disorders and weight building. The mammary glands may enlarge, and from the iris you can determine whether this is due to a local condition or is reflex from the thyroid, the ovary, or both. The area representing the mammary gland is at the midpoint of the pleural area, as marked in the chart, between three and four o'clock in the left iris and between eight and nine in the right iris.

The pituitary and pineal gland areas have not been included in past charts, but are placed in my chart where, based on my glandular studies, I believe them to be. The pineal gland is placed in the mental

The Liver, Spleen, and Gall Bladder Areas

Both the liver and spleen areas are good landmarks, and the black lines which circumscribe them extend beyond the periphery of the iris in my chart. The liver, being on the right side of the body, is reflected in the right iris. The liver area is just before eight o'clock in this iris. Since the spleen is on the left side of the body only, it is represented in the left iris, just after four o'clock. It is advisable to fix in your mind the exact location of these two organ areas.

Adjoining the liver area and next to the autonomic nerve wreath is the gall bladder area. This is in the third zone, usually

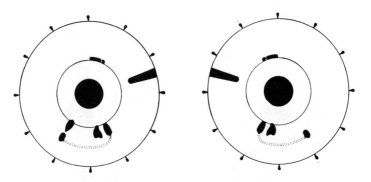

Fig. 56.   Glandular System.

ability area due to the fact that this gland has much to do with mental ability. The pituitary gland area is near twelve o'clock, bordering the autonomic nerve wreath in zone 3. In some abnormalities the pituitary gland does not take the exact shape as I have it on the chart. It can be elongated, and many times the autonomic nerve wreath extends part-way into the brain areas, showing the disturbance to be more in the pituitary gland than in the brain tissue itself. This can be verified later when we take up the activities of the pituitary gland and see these activities reflexly expressed in different parts of the body.

within a circular area or as part of the autonomic nerve wreath. It will be represented to you in many different ways. Inherent weakness in this organ is represented by a spreading of the fibres. When you see a spoke (of *the radii solaris*) passing through both the gall bladder and liver areas, this indicates that a gall bladder condition accompanies the liver condition. Most gall bladder conditions, however, are represented by a closed lesion marking, which resembles a small football. Inside this "football" you will see the pathological condition that exists. In many cases this lesion may be an extension of part of the autonomic wreath, making it appear that the gall bladder area is within the wreath itself.

You cannot determine the presence of gallstones from the iris of the eye. What you read in the iris fibres is related, not to what is *in* the gall bladder, but directly to the *tissues* of the gall bladder. You cannot tell what is in the gall bladder from the iris any more than you could determine that two or three swallowed apple seeds were lodged in the transverse colon. This also holds true with kidney stones and bladder stones. There is no nerve response from such stones to the brain. The response in the iris is from the tissue that surrounds the stones. Whenever there are stones, the iris will indicate a chronic latent condition within the tissues.

and gall bladder belong with the gastrointestinal system, but we isolate them to emphasize their importance and to show where they are located in the iris of the eye.

Pains under the right shoulder and arm usually are reflected from the gall bladder and liver. The proximity of the gall bladder and liver areas to the arm area in the iris demonstrates how closely they are related in their reflex symptoms.

The Bony Structure

The bony areas are well marked in the iris chart. However, the following will give you a detailed picture.

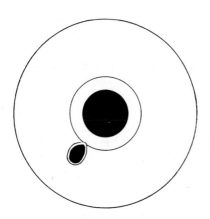

FIG. 57. In the iris of the eye there is no clear marking to signify the presence of stones in any organ. But a chronic condition such as is indicated in the above drawing represents a very sluggish toxic settlement where stones are likely to develop.

FIG. 58. Since in the iris we read the condition of the wall structure only, we cannot by this means determine the existence of stones. Whenever there is chronic toxic settlement, however, in gall bladder, urinary bladder, or kidney, we should suspect the presence of stones.

The liver and the spleen are very closely related in many of their activities, especially those connected with the blood cells, the blood count, and the blood stream in general; also in congestive states, due to the inter-related blood supply. The liver

To begin with, the most important area in the bony system is probably the leg area. The thigh, knee and foot are represented at exactly six o'clock in both irises, while the arm and hand are represented at four o'clock in the left iris and eight o'clock in the right iris. The hand and foot areas are found in or close to the skin area. The centers for the arm and leg areas are in zone four. The rib cage is in the thoracic area between three and four in the left iris and eight and nine in the right. The shoulder girdle is at two o'clock in the left iris and ten o'clock in the right. The scapula is found about half-way between eight and nine in the left iris, and half-way between three and four in the right. The bony section of the spine is found in the back areas between seven and eight-thirty in the left iris and between four-thirty and five in the right iris, with first thoracic segments starting at the wreath. The seven cervicals of the neck are represented in the medulla area, which is at one o'clock in the left iris and at eleven o'clock in the right iris. The area for the top of the head is at twelve o'clock; that for the back of the head is towards one o'clock in the left iris and towards eleven o'clock in the right iris. The face area, with front of face towards the periphery, extends between nine and twelve o'clock in the left iris and between twelve and three in the right. The pelvis is just beyond five o'clock in the left iris and just before seven in the right.

The Muscular Structure

The muscular structure is represented in every organ area of the iris. Everywhere in the body there are muscular fibres attached to organs. I believe the muscular system represents a reserve upon which we can call for emergency repairing and rebuilding in any part of the body. It is the one body system that can degenerate and still be restored more quickly than any other structure. The condition of the muscular structure is well represented in iris shading, especially in the scurf rim. Since it is located close to and underneath the skin areas, it is found in the periphery of the iris, and is represented in every organ area.

The Brain Area

We have deliberately left discussion of the brain areas until last because of their complex structure and activities. It is very difficult to lay out the individual brain centers in such a way that we can label them and place them properly in the iris chart. They are the most important areas in the whole iris structure, however. A great deal more study is needed on brain areas, and probably in the future someone will be able to localize them more accurately. My chart shows some deviation from older charts in this respect.

Much of the automatic functioning of any organ has its origin in the brain areas. We do not move a finger or walk without the use of the brain. We cannot breathe and our heart cannot beat without the brain. The brain area must be kept in good health in order to have good function in the kidneys, the bladder, or in any

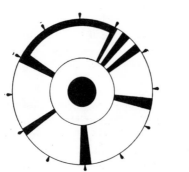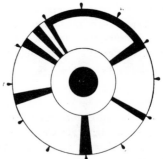

FIG. 59.   The Bony Structure.

other organ. We have to visualize the activities of the entire body rather than those of just one organ.

In cases of apoplexy, high blood pressure is an important contributing factor. "Ego pressure" would probably be a more descriptive name than apoplexy. Many times there is something much deeper than just the blood pressure itself; factors we cannot tangibly get hold of. We do know that a person's age greatly influences the blood pressure. Most cases classified under the high blood pressure categories develop to the point of a stroke which affects the right side of the body. This will show up in the left hemisphere of the brain as represented in the left iris. The majority of high blood pressure cases develop because of a toxic condition, and, coupled with ego pressure, strokes are more probable under these conditions than under conditions of lesser strain. Where the greater amount of toxic material is found on the left side of the body, the paralysis resulting from a stroke would be bound to affect the right side of the body more than the left side.

The area for the sensory part of the brain is just after twelve o'clock in the left iris and just before twelve in the right. This is the part of the brain controlling a good many of our automatic physiological activities. In the sensory area are recorded our inherited, latent capabilities; our natural ability, from a constitutional standpoint; what can physiologically take place in the brain. Our intellect, from an inherent standpoint, is represented more in this part of the brain than in another.

The psychological part of the brain, which is represented between eleven and twelve o'clock in the left iris, and twelve and one in the right, deals with what we have acquired through our living habits and what the present environment is doing to affect our lives. An unhappy environment has a great deal to do with this part of the brain. What we study, how we think, what our reactions are—all leave

their marks on this area. Sometimes our greatest physical reactions come from this area of the brain. Our bodily sensations come from here, and the reaction to these sensations is referred back into the body again. This is where "psycho" conditions arise which cause our somatic reflexes. Our egoistic control is responsible to a great extent for the relaxation or tension in the body, and a lack of control may lead to many blood pressure, bowel, and other disorders.

One of the main areas in the brain is the animation center. This is represented at twelve o'clock and is one of the key centers to remember. I believe this is one of the most important we have to deal with in consideration of the amount of nerve force we can expect in the action and reaction of the various organs. One of the greatest laws of life is gravity and it works on this animation center more than any other in the body. This center is the great barometer of life telling us when we have the power to accomplish the thing that has to be done. This is the life center in a person which determines what he is capable of doing physically, mentally or spiritually. Exhaustion and tiredness is demonstrated more in this center than in any other.

The medulla is also a very important center from which many of our automatic activities originate. For example, difficulty in swallowing may be in the medulla rather than in the individual area of the larynx or pharynx. There are many other automatic centers which may have their origin of trouble in the medulla rather than in the particular organ registering the symptoms. Automatic breathing problems and many heart disturbances may also be centered in the medulla. Even the pancreas may have a good deal of disturbance starting in the medulla.

The accelerating center, the cardioinhibitory center, and the coughing center, which is above the respiratory center and center of deglutition which controls the function of swallowing, are all found in the medulla. Vomiting is controlled by this center and sneezing sometimes originates in the respiratory center of the medulla. Automatic salivation is sometimes over-stimulated by the medulla; sometimes the automatic sweat centers have their origin in the medulla.

We mention these symptoms to call attention to how far-reaching may be the effects of inflammation in the medulla. But with all the symptoms which may arise from this one inflamed center, it is still difficult to tell the patient the exact trouble about which he may be complaining. You may not always be able to determine the symptoms of the patient, but you can detect the inflammation and where it is. At other times you can foretell symptoms which have not manifested themselves physically at the time of the diagnosis. For instance, in the locomotion center of the brain there may be signs that symptoms will develop in the lower back and legs which have not yet appeared in these parts. Many conditions can be detected, as in the locomotion center, for example, long before there are symptoms showing up in the body.

The equilibrium center is close to the epileptic center and is found behind the left ear. If you are checking with a nerve meter, you will usually find a reaction set up when testing this particular part of the patient.

There is much to be said about the brain areas and further developments could be added to the present-day chart. This will have to be left undone for the present, however, as it takes years to understand this science, as given to us by the past masters, and a great deal more study and research will be necessary to develop new areas in the chart.

Forecast of New Areas

Much can be said on the subject of the development of new areas in the iris chart.

It will take newer ideas and probably a different system of analysis to bring out all the areas, especially the brain area. The brain faculties are found in the mental ability center as indicated on the chart. There is no reason why they cannot be placed under a different heading, as they no doubt will be in the near future.

The brain activities are being studied more than ever before. However, we are interested in the patient's symptoms as a whole—the causes behind the symptoms— rather than just one organ. We are not interested in the expression or treatment of one symptom only. In counseling the patient we must look at the whole iris and we must recognize every phase of his make-up, if we would put him back on his proper health footing again.

At the present time it is good to use other forms of analysis with iridology to help you come to more definite conclusions. We believe the science of physiognomy, or the study of the facial features, probably will demonstrate more than other forms of analysis what is in the brain and what is going on from a physiological standpoint. These observations could then be incorporated into iridology to make the analysis of your patient more complete.

In years to come iridology will be used in aptitude tests as the iris shows the latent capacity to continue or fail. The iris shows the inherent background that can hold a chemical reserve or can cause the body to play out quickly. Why give a man a job, even though he has the mental faculties to succeed, if he has not the physical structure with which to follow through?

We know that a person can be born with too serious a nature and as he grows older he may acquire an appreciation of details that can be detrimental to his health. We know now that we can determine will power by feeling the muscular structure of the arm. If it is flabby the will power is in direct proportion. We know a strong

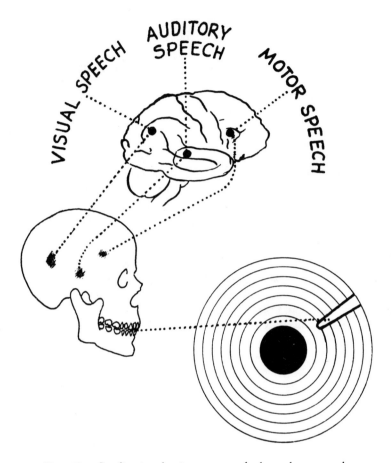

FIG. 60.   Studies in physiognomy and phrenology may be
of great assistance in the future establishment of individual
brain centers.

responsive body and an alert, coordinating brain go together. This we recognize by determining the structure or density in the brain and organ areas.

In the future, we will have graphs made showing the pathways that the various organs follow and their relationship in certain degenerative processes. Diabetes, in many cases, will be found to have its origin in certain brain centers. Perhaps a rectal condition will be found to be the cause of reflex troubles in the epileptic centers. Much work is yet to be done on the iridology chart, along with the increasing knowledge of man.

There is no doubt a place on the chart for the inferior vena cava leading from the heart areas. But it is difficult to place it in the iris of the eye and I have yet to hear anyone give a suitable explanation as to where it should be located.

I had a patient at one time whose thymus gland had developed quite a cancerous growth on it. An operation revealed this condition to exist directly next to the aorta. I observed that it was next to the heart area in the iris. I felt very sure the thymus gland would be located in time on the iris chart, between two and three o'clock, nearer two o'clock in the left iris, adjoining the aorta. This location was difficult to. determine because we had not had the experience of seeing many thymus gland conditions. Through the study of this patient's iris, the right placement for the thymus area became apparent, and continued study showed me that iris inflammation in this type of case was greatest within this area. As I saw this condition change and progress in the iris of the eye, I felt certain that I had found the correct placement for the thymus area. The patient developed many of the aortic symptoms, but these I believe were caused mainly by pressure. Nevertheless, we found that the pressure symptoms which were working on the aorta had to come from the organ next to it.

In analyzing a condition we should be particularly interested in the inflammation, what stage it is in, and should plan correction of the condition accordingly. Whether that inflammation is in the brain, the big toe, the kidney, or the thyroid gland, should make no difference. Of this we are sure: When inflammation has been detected in the body, through proper care *it can be eliminated.* So, whether these organ areas in the iris are exactly in the right place or not, this will be your opportunity to start making changes.

You will find many of these areas may vary in their position as you go along, but again, remember, you are not studying to demonstrate what you know to the patient; you are trying to find out something that will help you help the patient. Iridology gives you an opportunity to check on yourself constantly, until you have arrived at the proper analysis of the patient that will help him. Remember, we are interested in getting the patient entirely well—mechanically, chemically, physically, and mentally.

Part III

INTERPRETATION of
IRIS MANIFESTATIONS

15

MARKINGS OR LESIONS
IN THE ORGAN AREAS

Dr. Alexis Carrel has said, that although modern hygiene has made human existence far safer, longer, and more pleasant, diseases have not been mastered. They have simply changed in nature. The organism seems to have become more susceptible to degenerative diseases, but we must still die and we die in a much larger proportion from degenerative diseases. The years of life which we have gained by the suppression of diphtheria, smallpox, typhoid fever, and so forth, are paid for by the long sufferings and lingering deaths caused by chronic infections and especially by cancer, diabetes and heart disease. Medical care under all its forms costs about three billion five hundred dollars yearly.

Along with the knowledge of the location of organ areas as they appear in the iris of the eye, you will find a certain amount of practice necessary to become acquainted with the many lesions that can settle in the iris areas. Until now, we have studied the appearance of a "normal" iris mainly, showing certain abnormal conditions which are marked in the iris by specific diseases. From now on we will concentrate on the abnormal body conditions as reflected in the iris from disease, inflammation, chemical poisoning, and from injury.

We realize there will be some personal ideas injected, regardless of our attempt to minimize them, but in bringing these out, we want you to know it is done only to impress certain observations upon your mind, to help you remember.

There are very few "normal" people in this world; we are all psychiatric cases in one way or another. No two persons think or talk exactly alike, or have systems that function exactly alike. In all parts of the United States whole communities can be found with different mannerisms, different modes of expression, and with entirely different dietary habits. The health of a community is affected by the condition of its soil, air, drinking water, and even certain habits of dress can eventually result in disease. The resultant weaknesses are often passed on from one generation to another. An inherent weakness can be passed on to the child of a parent who has a bad liver or a pancreas that does not function perfectly. We know from statistics that whole families have died from arterial disturbances, heart disease, lung conditions, or kidney trouble.

We will discuss these inherent weaknesses in more detail as we proceed and we will show you how they leave their mark in the iris of the eye.

129

A—TYPES OF INFLAMMATION

In the chapter on the anatomy of the eye we discussed the various iris markings in acute, subacute, and chronic inflammation. Let us recall the fact that in acute inflammation a white coloring is manifested; in the subacute a darker white is shown; the chronic appears darker, shading to dark gray. When the color appears almost black, an extreme chronic state is indicated and degeneration of tissue has set in.

Destruction of tissue has usually taken place when there are no fibres whatsoever to represent the organ under consideration.

In determining the difference between tissue destroyed by an accident and tissue destroyed through an excessive amount of toxic material, you will find the fibres broken in accident cases, which allows the underlying pigment to show through. There will often be a line going across the fibres, almost as though the mark was made in the iris at the exact moment of injury. For example, if the leg has been broken, there would be a cross-fibre following the peripheral line through the leg area in the iris. It need not follow across exactly; it could go in a diagonal line. (This condition is discussed further under "Injuries and Operations.")

FOUR SIGNS IN THE IRIS

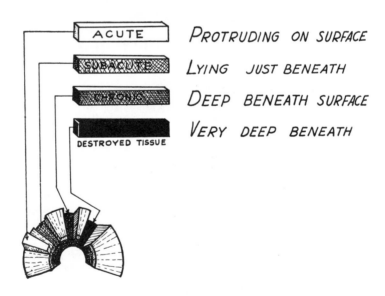

ACUTE — *Protruding on surface*

SUBACUTE — *Lying just beneath*

CHRONIC — *Deep beneath surface*

DESTROYED TISSUE — *Very deep beneath*

Fig. 61. This chart illustrates the four pigment layers of the iris of the eye. Notice the lines drawn around the location of the pupil to indicate these layers. The deep black represents the pigment layer at the lowest level, and is the sign of degeneration. The white layer, representing the acute active eliminative sign, is raised closest to the iridiagnostician. Between these two are the sub-acute and chronic layers.

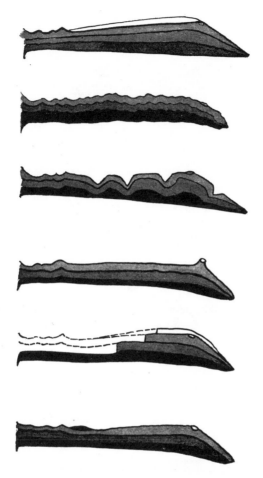

FIG. 62. Drawings to illustrate cross-sections of the iris. The acute, sub-acute and degenerative stages are demonstrated. These also show the nerve rings from the side view.

The whitish color in the iris showing acute inflammation is one way you will know of pain in the body. There will be no pain with the chronic condition, but whenever you find the chronic lesion, mark it down on your chart because, as treatment progresses and the healing crisis sets in, most all the old symptoms and pains of the former acute condition will return.

Some organs have very poor nerve reaction and pain will hardly register. In the chronic stage there is very little blood supply to the diseased organ and there is an underactive condition of the nervous system, while in the acute stage the blood supply is increased and nerve activity with swelling is the usual natural result. The acute sign represents hyperactivity of the organ while the chronic sign represents hypoactivity.

Many people become conditioned to a chronic state of dis-ease and seem to be resigned and even satisfied with it. They feel no pain so they go on in the same chronic condition for years. But before healing can take place, they must be warned

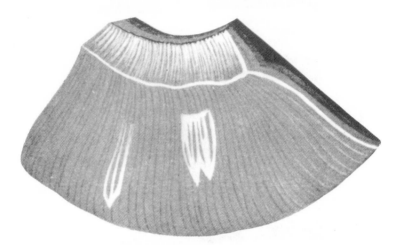

FIG. 63.   The above drawing illustrates the appearance in the
iris of an acute inflammation in the painful, inflamed, running
stage.

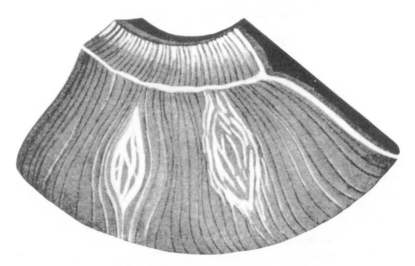

FIG. 64.   An acute closed lesion that illustrates a heavy catarrhal
settlement in whatever organ it may represent. Catarrh settled in
any organ with this particular lesion in its iris area will not easily
drain out, many times developing into cysts or other forms of
accumulated waste.

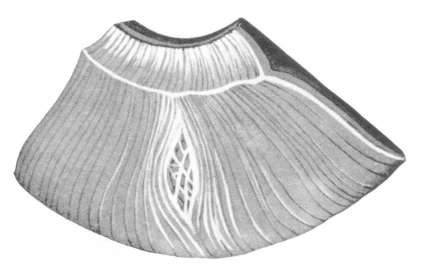

FIG. 65.   When an organ area contains a sub-acute closed lesion such as the one illustrated above, it indicates that the drainage of catarrhal settlement has been incomplete, and that morbid waste is beginning to accumulate.

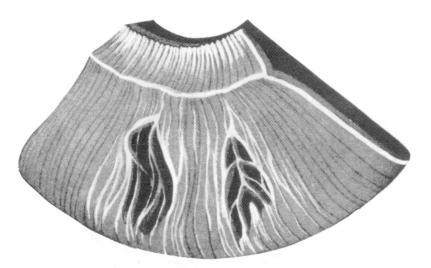

FIG. 66.   This chronic open lesion indicates that the body has been depositing toxic waste in the organ represented by the area in which this is located for a long time, producing a chronic inflammation of the tissues.

that the old pains and symptoms may return for a short time during the healing crisis. It is very important to so instruct a patient with a chronic condition before beginning treatment.

Some conditions of disease are actually eliminative processes trying to rid the body of toxins, but when the patient does not understand this and he experiences pain, discomfiture, or swelling of any part of the body, he goes to a doctor for an operation. The operation may apparently cure the patient, relieving him of the pain he had, yet many times, the cause of the patient's trouble has not been removed and will remain there unless the proper therapeutic measures are applied.

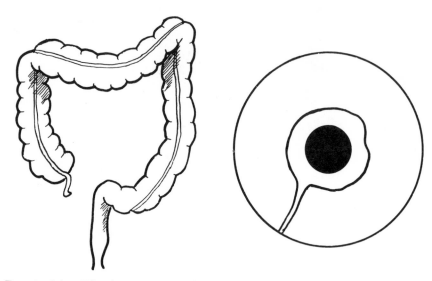

Fig. 67 (a). The drawing to the left represents the normal colon, and the drawing to the right indicates the outline of the normal colon in the iris.

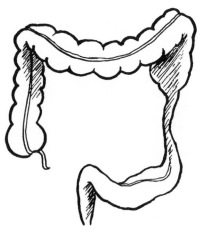

Fig. 67 (b). Colitis.

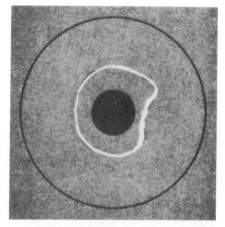

Fig. 67 (c). Acute inflammation, descending colon.

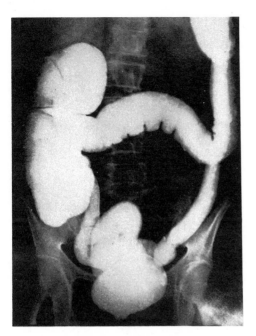

FIG. 67 (d). Colitis verified by the lack of haustrations throughout the colon.

When an organ is to be removed by an operation, you will find the iris registering the condition of that organ only up to the time when the anesthetic is administered. The anesthetic cuts off the nerve reading in the iris. For this reason, in examining a patient, it is well to question him about any operations he may have had in the past.

If you will refer to other chapters herein which discuss inflammation, you will find that all inflammation of vital organs is definitely registered in the iris of the eye.

B—INHERENT LESIONS AND WEAKNESSES

We have talked about inherent lesions and weaknesses before but it is very necessary to stress the idea that we are all products of our parents. When a child is born of parents who have pancreatic weakness from living on too many starches and sugars, you could not expect that child to have a strong, healthy pancreas. Nature gives us the finest body possible from the material with which she has to work, but

if that material is more like pine wood than oak—is soft, flabby, with no tone and with poor nerve reactions—how can we expect a strong healthy body? We inherit conditions from our parents from the time we are conceived right on through the time we are fed from our mother's breasts. You cannot change inherent weaknesses, which register in the iris of the eye, any more than you can change a pine tree to an oak. With good care, however, a body with inherent weaknesses can last a long time.

Inherent lesions do not have to be filled with toxic material; they do not have to be dark; they do not have to be diseased. People with inherent lesions can reflect as good a health condition as those with the best constitutions. Iridology is the only

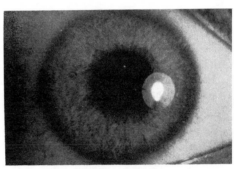

FIG. 68. This iris represents a good constitution, good vitality, good recuperative power.

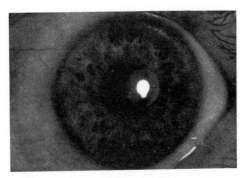

FIG. 69. This iris indicates fair density. Recuperative and regenerative powers are in direct proportion to the above.

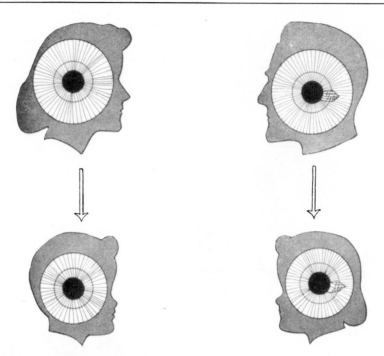

FIG. 70 (a). A child usually favors one parent more than the other. When the inherent characteristics of the child favor those of a parent who has no organic weaknesses, the child will have no inherent weaknesses. If the other parent has an inherent weakness in the bronchial tubes, for example, the child whose tissue structures are patterned after his, will inherit the bronchial weakness.

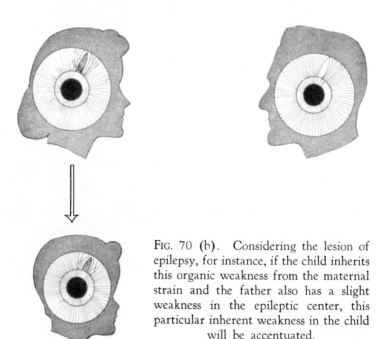

FIG. 70 (b). Considering the lesion of epilepsy, for instance, if the child inherits this organic weakness from the maternal strain and the father also has a slight weakness in the epileptic center, this particular inherent weakness in the child will be accentuated.

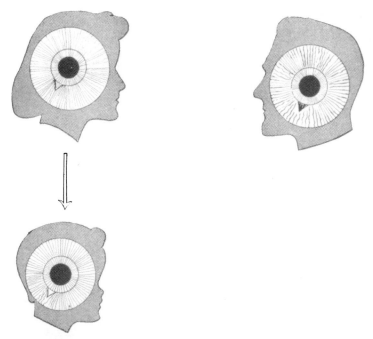

Fig. 70 (c). In diabetes, if the child favors a mother who has an inherent weakness in the pancreas, the child will inherit a weak pancreas. If both mother and father have an over-worked pancreas due to excessive use of starches and sugars, the child can inherit a weakness in the pancreas which can readily develop into diabetes. This often occurs though neither parent has the disease. In such children, diabetes is more difficult to overcome than in the adult who acquires it.

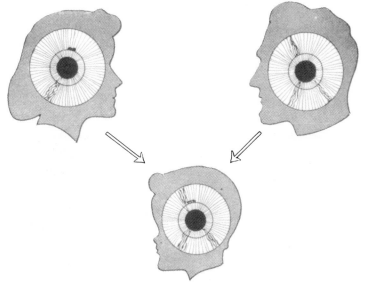

Fig. 70 (d). If the child does not favor one parent more than the other, it will take on both parents' weaknesses and strong tissue tendencies.

form of analysis I know of that can determine inherent weaknesses in the body, show where they are, and indicate the inherent capacity of the person to overcome his present trouble. If a patient suffering from rheumatic fever has a poor constitution, he is going to need entirely different care during his lifetime to overcome this fever and prevent a recurrence of the trouble than a patient who has a good constitution. The person who has a weakness in the pancreas, for example, should be given more specific advice with his diet to help prevent the weak organ from breaking down. This holds true in any organic weakness of the body.

C—ACIDITY AND CATARRH

There are many kinds of acids developed in the body, depending upon the type of tissue that is overworked and abused. For instance, if all the carbon dioxide is not filtered out by the lungs it can back up into the body producing an excess amount of carbonic acid in the body tissues. Also, acid can accumulate from abused kidneys and phosphate crystals can gather in the urine if the nervous system is overworked. It is said that there are about thirty-two kinds of acids that can develop in the body. Every tissue develops acids as the end-product of work. Any fibre that has become white in any area of the iris is the result of overwork of the reflected organ.

If hyperacidity of the stomach accompanies hyperemia, the stomach area in the iris will appear entirely different in color than when the stomach is lacking in hydrochloric acid. A hyperacidic lesion of the stomach should appear in the iris as very white, showing the excess activity of the stomach wall and the overactivity of the hydrochloric-secreting membrane. But invariably the organ is so stimulated to over-secretion that it finally develops into the hypoactive or underactive stage.

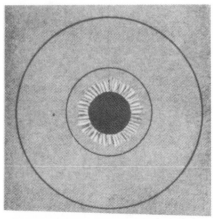

FIG. 71 (b).   Sub-acute Acid Stomach. Hypochlorhydria (insufficient Hydrochloric Acid) one-plus. Very little pain.

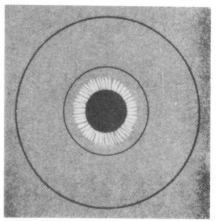

FIG. 71 (a).   Acute Acid Stomach. Hyperchlorhydria (excess Hydrochloric Acid). Pain, belching, heartburn.

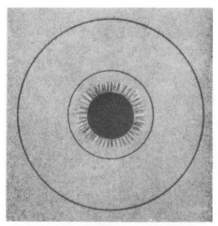

FIG. 71 (c).   Chronic Acid Stomach. Hypochlorhydria, three-plus; very little Hydrochloric Acid. No pain. Very poor protein digestion.

In about four out of five of the patients who come to you with stomach disorders, you will find the stomach to be in a chronic state, not secreting enough hydrochloric acid. I believe medical statistics substantiate that as many as eighty per cent of patients with stomach trouble do not have sufficient hydrochloric acid.

In most cases the lack of hydrochloric acid will be represented by a darker white throughout the stomach area. When the condition is chronic there will appear around the pupil a small, dark, ragged edge that follows the stomach area. When this becomes very dark brown, it signifies a marked lack of hydrochloric acid. If this dark area around the black pupil has not developed to the stage of a very dark brown, but is very light and seems to be active and raised, it indicates an excess of hydrochloric acid in the stomach. This small brown ring around the pupil can also be made dark through the continued use of drugs and refined and devitalized foods.

Catarrh is a condition of elimination of toxic acids through the mucous membranes of the nose, throat, bronchial tubes, and other organs. This process goes on when the body is overladen with toxic acids and they cannot escape sufficiently through the natural organs of elimination, i.e., the kidneys, skin, lungs, and bowels. When the individual lives and eats according to natural law, the eliminative organs are able to take care of ordinary elimination of the catabolic processes of the body.

We usually find a catarrhal condition somewhere in the body in acid cases because the body is unable to throw off the acids in the normal way. In highly inflamed acid conditions the nerves are very irritated and the autonomic nerve wreath in the iris appears very white. These acid cases are usually exceedingly restless, irritable, hard to live with, and their nerves are "on fire." Their metabolism is usually quickened and a hyperactivity can be found in nearly every organ, especially in the thyroid gland. The whole iris becomes

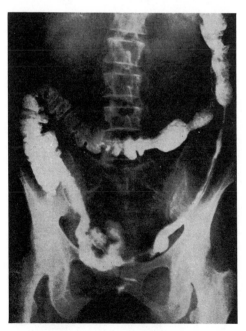

FIG. 72 (a). Marked spasticity involving the descending and sigmoid colon; incompetency of ileocecal valve

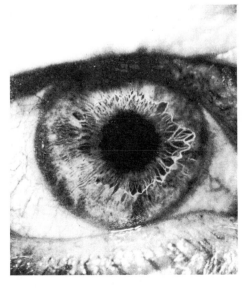

FIG. 72 (b). Spastic condition of descending and sigmoid portions of the colon as seen in the left iris.

white as the body attempts to eliminate these excess acids. The eye in cases of this nature can be termed a "rheumatic acid" eye and arthritis and neuritis develop out of this condition.

If these natural residues cannot escape through the organs of elimination, nature will come to the rescue of the individual and get rid of them the best way she can in order to keep the blood stream clean. When there is a discharge of phlegm or pus from the nose, throat, ears, or vaginal canal, this is nature's effort to rid the body of toxic acids that cannot get out through the natural eliminative organs. If the body is so filled with acid, it is coughed up in large quantities or discharged through the vagina in a concentrated form or it may work itself out through the ear canal.

The eliminative organs are vital and very powerful in getting rid of all harmful acids developed in the body, but for maximum health it is essential to eat and live in such a way that the production of harmful acids will be minimized; thus the

body will have a better opportunity to build up health. It has been demonstrated that dormant conditions in chronic diseases can be effectively changed by the nature-cure way, but when using this method in chronic cases one must not give up when the crisis sets in and pains and discomfiture are experienced.

A highly alkaline diet should be used in abundance in cases of high acidity. Large amounts of organic sodium and calcium are essential in the diet to replace that which is burned out by excess acids. When the sodium has been burned out, the calcium is thrown into the joints, as sodium, the youth element, keeps calcium in solution.

Arthritis, as such, is not specifically indicated in the iris. You can observe an acid condition developing and what it does to the joints, but you will recognize this condition more through the study of the chemical elements which we will talk about in greater detail in the chapter on The Sodium Story.

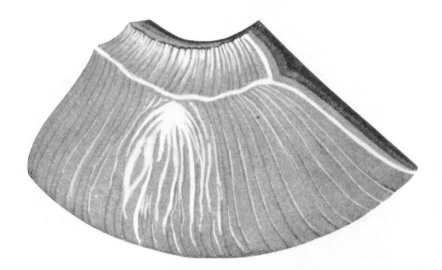

FIG. 73. Drawing of an acute open lesion that indicates the existence of a heavy catarrhal settlement in whatever organ area it may occur. The organ so affected will drain easily since the lesion is an open one.

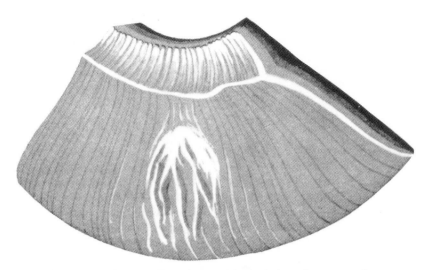

FIG. 74. A sub-acute open lesion. Catarrhal and toxic settlements have not drained well from the organ represented by the area in which this lesion occurs.

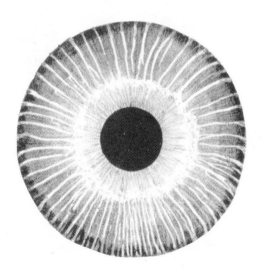

FIG. 75. Acute signs developed through the iris, which can be so prevalent that they show the whole body to be in an acute stage. Many times these white lines can be referred to as representing rheumatic acids. Invariably the patient exhibiting this iris complains of joint troubles.

D—TOXIC SETTLEMENTS

Toxic settlements can be found in any part of the body and are more than likely to eventuate in tumorous growths, especially if the toxins cannot be eliminated. There are other kinds of settlements that *flow through* organs. How fast or how slowly they circulate depends upon the type of toxic material. Each type plays its part in the symptoms produced.

The tissue condition is what you are reading in the iris. The tissue has become hypoactive in function when you see a dark settlement in any area of the iris, and you know the organ indicated has been overpowered and is not eliminating properly. This can occur if any one of the eliminative organs has to overwork in order to carry on the functions of the body. An organ overworked over a long period of time will eventually break down. Iridology will show you which are the broken down organs in need of care.

Keep uppermost in your mind, in caring for a patient, that the eliminative organs should be working properly at all times. Work toward correcting the metabolic forces so that diseased tissue structures

FIG. 76. The dark shading in the above diagram represents toxic settlement in the body. Those which are just beginning to irritate tissues are represented in white. This is the acute, eliminative stage. As they become less active and move along more slowly in the body, they become darker, as indicated by the shadings above. The more chronic a lesion becomes, the more you will see of the dark underlying pigment of the iris.

may be rebuilt through the right chemical processes. The correction can be accomplished through a program of proper diet and other right living habits. In some cases it will be necessary to assist nature, perhaps by natural diuretics and diaphoretics, to get the kidneys and skin to eliminate both the active and latent toxic poisons. See that the bowels properly evacuate themselves if the root of the trouble is to be cared for. Remember to apply this law: *The blood is as clean or as toxic as the intestinal tract, the lungs, kidneys, and skin.*

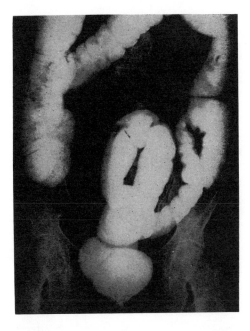

Fig. 77. Loops such as those in the above X-ray picture will not cause difficulty unless they interfere with the outward flow of toxic material. When the free flow of toxic material is blocked, a chronic toxic state is represented in the iris of the eye. The time required for ridding the bowel of toxic material depends upon how toxin free the bowel wall is. This can be determined by the extent to which toxic settlement is indicated in the iris. The older and more chronic it is, the slower it will move, of course.

The bowel is probably the root of most of our trouble and it is there we can almost always find the greatest amount of toxic material. There is usually no organ reflected in the iris that appears as dark as the bowel area. The bowel seems to be the center of importance in the body and when it is clean and in a healthy condition other organs are, as a rule, healthy. Every organ is dependent upon the intestinal tract. It is the center from which all organs extend; it is the hub of the wheel. A toxic intestine acts as a seat of infection, throwing out its toxins into the blood stream, and thus infecting other parts of the body. Infection in the body can be fed directly from the intestinal tract.

We have had X-rays taken after patients had been given barium meal, and, although it is said waste material should pass through the bowel in 16 to 24 hours, in many of these cases, the barium meal was still present in the bowel 72 hours after it had been administered. In a few cases, we found barium meal in the bowel weeks after it had been administered. In our detoxification therapy at the office, we even found grape seeds in the excrement from the bowels of a patient when it was verified he had not eaten grapes for many months.

In constipation, toxic material accumulates and develops in the bowel, finally to be thrown off into the blood stream to escape in whatever manner it can. It may settle in the leg area, or it may be thrown into any organ of the body. Nature will do her very best to rid the body of these harmful acids that are the result of our unnatural way of eating and living.

If you should find a lesion in the leg area in your examination of the iris, this finding would be no reason for treating the leg first. It would be better to trace the cause of the leg trouble and treat the cause—it might be a very bad bowel condition that is causing the leg trouble—and

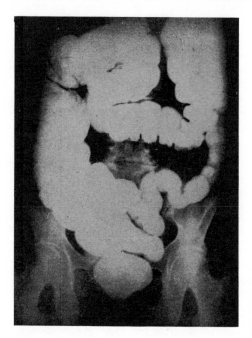

FIG. 78. Tendency towards atony involving cecum, ascending colon, and first portion of transverse colon. Such bowel conditions appear in the iris as chronic settlement in the intestinal area.

in this case it would be better to work on the bowel condition. There is no doubt you will see the leg lesion disappear as the bowel trouble is cleared up.

It is even more important to consider what damage has been done in the body when this toxic material settles in the liver, or in the heart or lung areas. In an examination, the vital organs should be given first attention so that you can give the patient immediate help in starting the reversal of the symptoms of which they are complaining. When the liver and bowels are functioning better, symptoms begin to disappear and the patient feels better because new life and energy are now flowing through the vital organs.

We know that we build new skin on the palm of the hand every day. We know the stomach walls can be made new again. We know the tissues can be repaired, built

over, and completely rejuvenated. With this in mind, let us note how the toxic material, which we are most interested in is found in the tissue structure itself. Our concern is not with what is in the bowel at the time of the examination, but rather with the condition of the bowel wall itself. This condition is determined by what has constantly gone through the bowel over a long period of time, as well as by all the other factors which influence good or bad digestion and assimilation of food.

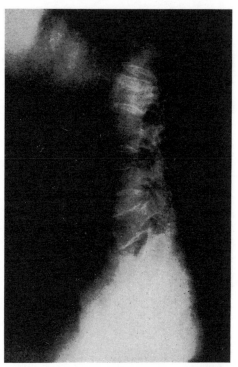

FIG. 79. A heavy white film over the iris of the eye represents rheumatic acid and arthritic tendencies in the body. These tend to produce spurs on the anterior portion of the spine if the spine area is the center of greatest weakness. From the iris we can detect these conditions coming on long before they become evident in an X-ray. In the above X-ray picture we see the development after many years of suffering with back ache.

The blood absorbs waste very quickly just as it has the power to absorb nutritive materials. This power of absorption by the blood can be demonstrated by putting a clove of garlic in your shoe. In less than thirty seconds it will be apparent in the breath. And if you put a clove of garlic under your tongue, the garlic odor can be detected in the soles of your feet in less than thirty seconds. It is said that 125 barrels of blood go through the heart every day. This is a big job for one organ but the heart is equal to it if the blood is clean and filled with nourishing material to keep the heart tissue healthy and strong.

The body has the wonderful faculty of spreading its problems throughout the entire organism. We find this to be true both from the standpoint of nutrition and from the standpoint of toxemias of various types. For example, it is impossible to have a toxic condition seeping into any one organ of the body unless it is carried there by way of the blood stream. We know the blood stream does not throw off toxic material in just one organ and leave every other organ clean. The same blood that feeds and bathes the spleen, also feeds and bathes the heart. The heart has its

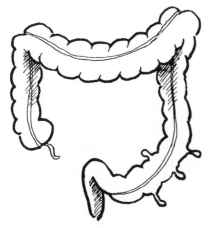

FIG. 80 (a).   Drawing illustrating diverticulitis.

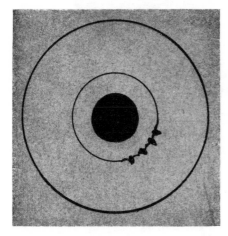

FIG. 80 (b).   Bowel pockets—which may represent diverticuli, chronic bowel stasis, chronic toxic settlements.

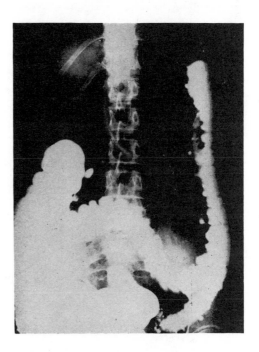

FIG. 80 (c).   X-ray photograph showing multiple diverticuli involving the hepatic flexure, the latter portion of the transverse colon, and the descending colon. In the text we refer many times to these diverticuli as bowel pockets. They are sources of infection and the seat of many of our toxic organic disorders.

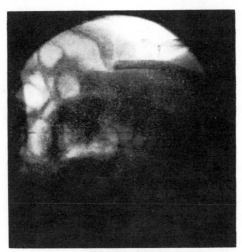

FIG. 81 (a).

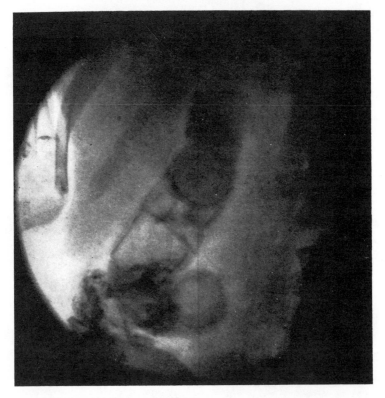

FIG. 81 (b). Toxic settlements such as are shown in these two X-ray pictures of gall stones are an accumulation over a period of years. Though we cannot determine the presence of stones from examination of the iris because any sign registered there is from the wall of the organ and not from stones, we should consider the possibility of stones in every chronic lesion.

toxic problems just as the spleen has, although the cause of that toxic material may come from the intestinal tract. Likewise, it is impossible to lack calcium in just one organ without lacking this mineral in every other organ as well.

Every organ in the body requires clean blood. An impu e blood stream will cause poor functioning ability in every organ because good tissue cannot be built from impure blood. There is a close interrelation among the organs, which is the body's way of balancing the health level in every organ. Oxygen, for instance, is necessary to the life of every cell, yet the cell can get its needed supply only when the body is toxin-free and the blood is circulating well. The circulatory tissues are poor in their functioning ability when circulation is not up to par. Remember, the blood gets its nourishment from the intestinal tract. To make good healthy tissue it takes good blood carrying all the best materials. One of the functions of the blood is to bathe the intestinal wall which makes it possible for both nutritive and toxic material to be picked up by the blood stream and carried into every organ.

To have a strong healthy bowel we must eat properly and exercise enough and have the right mental attitude. If we live in fear, or keep ourselves tense with rage or jealousy or other negative emotions, our bowels are going to feel as though ,they are tied up in "Chinese knots" as a result of our poor state of mind. This tenseness results in a gradual breakdown of the glands, as the suprarenals, the thyroid, or any gland, regardless of whether all other conditions, including diet and rest, are right. The best foods and combinations of foods will do little good if the patient is under nervous tension.

Toxic settlements do not necessarily have to be waste material absorbed from the bowel. There is a toxic reaction to drugs. There is a toxic reaction to carbon monoxide gas. There is a toxic reaction to breathing foul air. Toxic conditions also result when there is such inactivity of the skin that toxic material cannot be eliminated through it. This lack of skin elimination may be due to clothing which hampers circulation of the blood and elimination through the skin glands.

In a later chapter in this book we will discuss these toxic conditions in more detail.

E—NERVE RINGS

Nerve rings are represented in the iris, according to the chart illustration, by a ring-like indentation which follows the circumference of the iris. When you use your light in different directions you will notice the indentation produces a shadow. You can tell exactly how deep these nerve rings are by directing your light in various directions and positions.

These nerve rings can be very acutely white; they can be dark; they can be indented extremely or just slightly. Each nerve ring represents a particular condition in the body. As the fibres come from the wreath to the periphery, they should normally be in an even, straight line. If there is an extreme indentation or drop, it indicates a "cramp" condition and that the body is irritated mentally or environmentally. It could be indicative of a focal irritation, from toxic material where there is an acid condition, or from a seepage of acids from one part of the body to another. It could be a reflex condition from another organ. Consequently it is well to trace down the cause of the trouble in this particular nerve ring.

Drugs can cause a lot of nerve irritation in the body. Sometimes the drug cannot find a channel for elimination so it has to settle in one of the organs of the body. When this is the case a nerve ring will often develop and it will have its beginning where the drug has settled.

When the nerve ring goes only halfway around the iris, it shows that only certain organs are affected. It would be

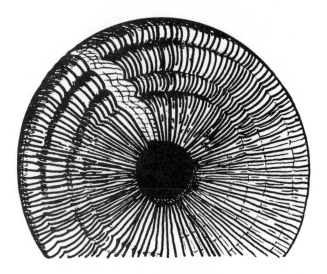

Nerve Ring Formation

FIG. 82. This illustration shows iris fibres contracted. Note the concentric furrows. These are
easily seen in the iris when light is directed
from the side, as a furrow makes a shadow.

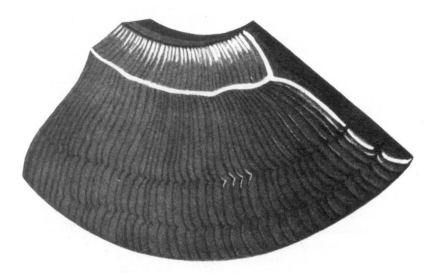

FIG. 83. This illustration of cramp
rings shows that the extent to which
the underlying pigment layer is seen
depends upon the depths of the rings.

well to examine the beginning and end of the nerve ring to see which organs are producing this nerve ring and which are receiving the irritation. It is at the extreme ends of the nerve rings, many times, that we must look for the beginning and the end of this "cramping," as mentioned above. And, as mentioned, drug irritation may be the seat of the trouble at the end of the nerve ring.

The organ at the beginning of this nerve ring may often appear much whiter than the rest of the organs. A nerve ring may often begin at the ovary and end, probably, in the pleural or breast area. Many conditions could exist within the ovary or they may originate from a mental situation, and a toxic settlement in either location could cause a reflex condition and a "cramp." It may be that overactivity is producing the cramped condition in other organs. One nerve ring doesn't mean there is too much trouble in the body but when there are four, five, and maybe six nerve rings, it is too much for the human body to stand. The person whose iris shows many heavy nerve rings, is either headed for a breakdown or is in one. Many nerve rings can develop in both hyper- and hypo-active conditions of the thyroid.

The brain is for our use and the Good Book says that we have dominion over everything on the face of the earth. Some people cannot always handle their own problems and the first thing you know their problems get the best of them. Some of us say that we have a job, but instead, our job "has us." And when we cannot "take it," the condition is represented in the nerve rings of the iris.

In many cases we need to be re-educated. We have to be taught how to attain peace of mind. We have to be impressed with the idea that quarreling, irritability, and chaos do not bring about peaceful actions and reactions in the body. Many books are written today by doctors and psychologists on how to relax. Many systems of

healing are now teaching us how to live in an entirely different manner than formerly. We are shown how to look at the world through different eyes, how to get along in the world and be successful, how to "make the grade" in this twentieth century while keeping our health and equilibrium, how to live in this atomic age just coming in. Many social and economic changes are being made and the individual who has a good nervous system is the one who will be able to make the adjustments, if given the proper tools with which to work. But the person with a poor inheritance, with a bad nerve ring reading, is going to have a harder time of it. Harmony is the order of the day.

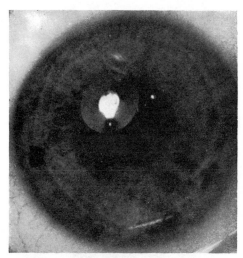

FIG. 84. In this photograph we see nerve rings which are the result of drug deposits in the body.

The state of tension the body is in is an indication of how the nervous system is being used. What affects the nerves, affects the glands, and vice versa, as the nervous system is very closely related to the glandular system. "The tight bow is the one that breaks" is an old saying. It is this tension we must avoid in the body, because, in cramped tissues the blood cannot properly circulate and toxic settlements are then locked in parts of the body by means of various types of nerve contractions. We see the nerve rings as contraction centers and as the nerves are drawn taut they develop contraction grooves which you will notice when you look at the iris with your light reflected down toward the side of the eye. When these nerve rings are seen in the brain area and sex centers, hallucina- tions can result. Insomnia can also be the result of an irritated nervous system.

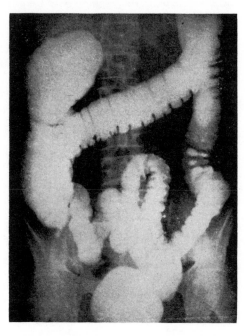

FIG. 85 (c). X-ray photograph show- ing multiple diverticuli involving the lower descending and the sigmoid co- lon. These diverticuli can be sources of enough irritation within the bowel that a stricture can develop or a nerv- ous contraction can occur.

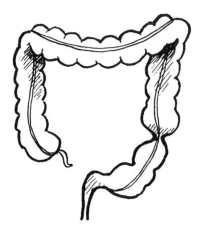

FIG. 85 (a). Drawing illustrat- ing stricture or spasm.

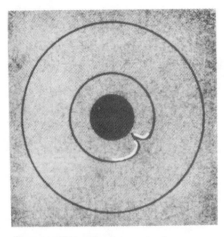

FIG. 85 (b). Drawing indicating stricture or spasm in the descending colon, as seen in the iris of the eye.

Although the emotional state is probably responsible for the nerve rings, there is also the possibility of an improper chemical balance that could cause the trouble. A lack of iodine in the thyroid gland, for instance, causes malfunctioning of this gland, thus producing hypertension of the nervous system. Excessive emotion can cause a hyperactive state for the moment but hypoactivity will be the final result. We now see more thyroid disturbances as a result of emotional upheaval than ever before. You will find more nerve rings in the irises of people who live in the fast, emotional life of our large cities than you will see in the irises of those who live in the quiet country districts. These nerve rings are very definite in the young business girl who has only ten minutes to eat and lives mostly on coffee, doughnuts, and cigarettes to "keep her going." The boys coming home from war have nerve rings in excess.

The nervous system of man was first given to him, no doubt, in the Garden of Eden where there was an ideal condition for relaxation and happiness, but in the hectic world we live in today, with often the wrong companionship and other chaotic conditions, the nervous system has much to combat to prevent tension. The food was also perfect in the Garden of Eden and everything was there for man's good and pleasure, but this is not so today. Many foods are now so denatured and refined that they are almost "foodless." The noise and confusion of factory and office life tells on the workers, resulting in occupational diseases.

We could go on in an endless chain describing the modern conditions that irritate the nervous system. We must do whatever we can to help combat these irritating forces of our present age. The high-powered electric current that flows over the nervous system today is affecting it and not helping by any means. We are breaking down the nerve structure faster than we can possibly build it up. Stop and think about the appalling number of nerve depletion cases coming into a doctor's office today as compared to 25 or 30 years ago. Just look at the figures showing the increase in insanity and look at the increase of doctors who are specializing in mental cases today. Look at the increase of drugs taken for mental and nervous disorders as compared to the past in amount and kind.

When a nerve ring has settled in the intestinal tract area of the iris, it is a sign of a condition we term "nervous indigestion." Nervous indigestion in most cases has to be corrected by a change of mental attitude as well as by a change of diet. We recognize more and more that many wrong mental attitudes are caused by a lack of certain vitamins and minerals in the diet of the individual suffering from a nervous condition.

The person who eats too fast, or overeats, suffers from nervous indigestion. He cannot seem to become satisfied with what he eats. He is always hungry. When we have a patient with nerve rings indicating nervous indigestion, it is best that they not be criticized while eating or the trouble will be made worse. And they should not be scolded. They need more time to eat, to joke, and to laugh while they are eating. This advice should be applied even to those of us with a "normal" digestion. Shocking news and disagreeable subjects discussed while eating could be responsible for many intestinal disturbances. Eating time should be a happy time.

A patient with nerve rings running through the intestinal tract area in the iris should be told that his intestinal tract does not have a strong nerve background and that insofar as possible he should eat slowly at all times in pleasant surroundings with pleasant companions. They should be encouraged to try to be in an atmosphere of good music while eating, because the right kind of music affects the nervous system favorably. Music therapy is now being used on the so-called "nervous diseases" in many hospitals to quiet and soothe the nerves and to bring about a joyous feeling.

Mechanical pressure is also a cause of much disturbance in our nervous system. A sedentary occupation can interfere with the proper nerve supply to the legs and to various other parts of the body, especially if the body is in a constantly twisted position. Neuritis and neuralgia often develop as a result of occupational conditions. Consistently carrying a heavy object in the right hand over a period of years can produce conditions that will irritate the nerves on the right side of the body more than on the left.

If you break down the word "emotion," you will find you have: "e" representing the word EGO or "I," and "motion" representing movement, and so we have "I move." If you could read the iris of my eye, you would discover how "I move"—whether in irritation or stimulation; whether by natural mental tendency or whether I am driving myself. Actually, you will be able to judge every motion of my body in every organ through interpreting the nerve rings in the iris. You would see white nerve rings in case there was an acute condition, and darker ones if the condition had become chronic in some areas. The nerve rings demonstrated in the accompanying drawings and protographs will help to show you how these nerve rings appear in the iris.

Through a study of the brain and mental faculties, we can somewhat control a good many of these nerve rings. It is truthfully said that we worry some of our troubles into existence. We do tomorrow's work today. Lately this has been demonstrated through experiments conducted in some of our larger universities. Professors tell us that our stomach disturbances come from a worried mental attitude. One said jestingly, "People are worrying a lot and trying to build a house on it."

It is difficult to say whether the nerve rings should be considered as due to pathology in the body or to the environment, which affects the nervous system. But whatever the reason, get right into your problem. Attack it either from the nerve standpoint or consider the toxic condition that may be aggravating the nerve condition. They are both vitally important and care is equally necessary in both cases.

This is a day of nerves, noise, warfare. We are in a so-called "civilization." In this era we are faced with a combat of nerves. You hear people say they want to relax but they cannot. They feel more like fighting. They are on edge and quarrelsome, cause or no cause. It is the nerves crying out against the conditions they are unable to meet. The body and nervous system of the average person simply has not been conditioned to cope with this atomic age. Harmony creates health while chaos destroys and is a disease producer.

F—INJURIES AND OPERATIONS

Operations and injuries are registered in the iris with some degree of accuracy unless the patient has been given too many drugs over a long period of his life.

In a case I once diagnosed through the iris markings, one marking appeared much like scar tissue. The eye showed there had been mutilation of the leg tissue in an accident. The injury had happened so many years before my examination that the patient had even forgotten about it.

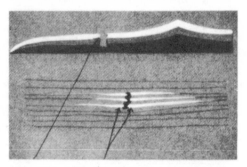

FIG. 86.   In this drawing a section of the upper layers is removed so that the bottom layer is visible. This is to simulate what occurs in the iris layers when tissues have been destroyed or injured.

In a healing crisis, when the reversal process is interrupted by an operation such as the removal of an ovary, sometime or other that body will have to finish this reversal process before it can completely normalize itself. A highly acid and toxic condition of the body, such as exists in ovarian and tonsil trouble, cannot be corrected by an operation. If discharging, infected tonsils are removed from a body filled with toxic waste, removing the tonsils will not remove the waste material in the other tissues of the body. This can only be done by nature in what we call the cleared crisis, at which time every organ and tissue is being changed, renewed and rebuilt. But nature cannot do this colossal job on the high-starch diet of a

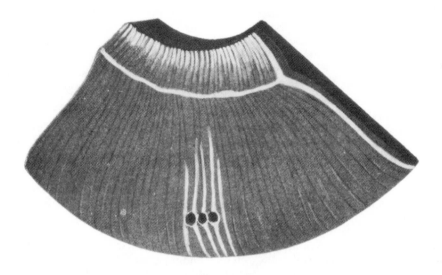

FIG. 87.   The above drawing is intended to indicate broken fibres such as would be seen in the iris in case of a broken leg.

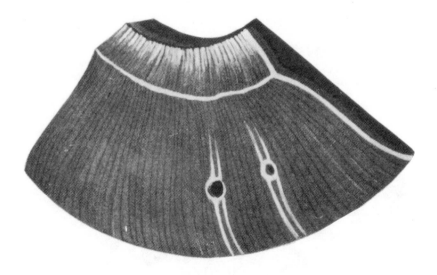

FIG. 88.   This drawing indicates the iris appearance of a bullet hole, and of a healed bullet hole with scar tissue around it.

coffee and doughnut routine. The vitamin-mineral foods are the real cleansers and tissue builders.

As a rule, operations are performed to remove decayed tissue which is in a part of the body that has been fed by a poor blood stream. A healthy body has clean, firm tissue and needs neither doctor nor operation. When an operation seems necessary I usually recommend that the patient first go on a strict blood-cleansing and body-building program. The patient usually finds that at the end of this cleansing-building regime he does not need the operation.

People who have come to me after having ten or twelve operations are often impatient, wanting me to cure them of their troubles in the same period of time that it takes to operate. Nature cures in her own time and in her own way. If people do not want to take the time or experience a little discomfiture in getting their health back, they should not expect to rid themselves of disease by the nature-cure method. But if they could learn to be faithful to the health-way, they are bound to experience very fine results. I believe there are emergencies when surgery is indicated, but after an operation, the health-way regime, with special attention to diet, should be followed for as complete a return to health as possible.

When an injury is not healing the way it should, we often discover in the iris what is the cause. It may be that the blood chemistry is out of balance or there is an acute acid condition of the blood or a toxic settlement which is interfering with the healing process in the injured part.

When a person dies in an unconscious condition, as following an injury, and is unidentified, the medical history of the life of the deceased could be of great value in helping to make an identification. Here again is where iridology could be very helpful and effective in giving information to departments of justice. I believe there is a large field here for effective work in the science of iridology.

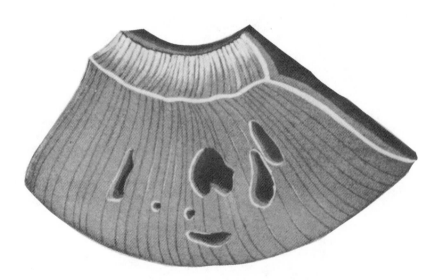

FIG. 89.   Closed lesion indicating that tissue has been destroyed or that degeneration has set in,—resulting from injuries, operations, amputations, bullet wounds, etc.

G—THE LYMPHATIC ROSARY

The lymphatic rosary in the iris appears only when there is an excessive amount of toxic settlement in the lymph system. It shows up in the iris as small, white congestive spots on the inside border of the scurf rim or skin area. Although this rosary is usually found very close to the periphery of the iris, it can be scattered in any area throughout the iris. Under close scrutiny you will see the fibres so enlarged and congested that they will lie very close to each other and are raised up toward you. With this congested condition very little pigment can be seen from underneath.

The lymph system is just as important to take notice of as are the venous or ar-

Fig. 90.   The lymphatic rosary.

terial systems for the lymph fluid is very precious and not easily produced. The distribution of this lymph fluid is very necessary to the economy of the body. When the lymph is filled with toxins, the body will be filled with acids and catarrh. It is like a log that has become waterlogged and is trying to go downstream but is too heavy to remain afloat and is finally submerged. The patient with a lymph system loaded with toxins is in about the same condition as the log.

It has been established that catarrh and acids are the beginning of many diseases. Lymph goes into tissue where blood cannot penetrate and picks up toxic material in the form of acids and catarrh that must be eliminated. These toxins are then passed through the eliminative channels of the lymph glands.

The tonsils are at the terminus of the lymph system in the throat. The toxic material that is eliminated through this terminus is often swallowed and, with the lymph fluid, is reabsorbed into the system and carried to the bowel. There, the toxic waste is separated from the lymph, and the waste is eliminated while the lymph fluid is picked up again to continue on in the system. I am sure this is the reason why the lymph terminus for eliminating toxins is placed where it is—at the entrance to the alimentary canal.

People with toxic lymph streams are always spitting and complaining about excess amounts of acids and catarrh. They are constantly having discharges and colds and complaining of poor elimination and they pay very little attention to their diet and the type of foods eaten.

Arsenic seems to have an affinity for the lymphatic system and iris discoloration there may represent poisoning by this drug from sprays used by paper hangers and painters and other sources.

You will find the lymphatic rosary illustrated in the iris chart.

H—THE SCURF RIM

The scurf rim is a darkened circular area beginning in the skin area of the 7th zone and spreading in toward the pupil, the darkness depending upon the amount of toxins and drugs in the body. It can spread as much as half-way from the periphery of the iris to the pupil, while the toxic material indicated in the bowel area of the iris seems to work from the center out to the periphery. It has been said that when these two toxic rings meet, death results. I do not believe you can tell death from the iris. Many persons, however, walk around "half dead" from toxic body conditions, and these toxic conditions can be read in the iris. A scurf rim does not always make a completed circle around the periphery of the iris but when it does, the wider its appearance, the more indicative

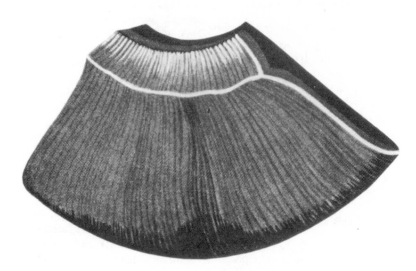

FIG. 91. This drawing illustrates a portion of the scurf rim. The wide portion indicates suppression of foot perspiration.

is this of toxic poisoning of the body. The above drawing illustrates what we mean by "scurf rim."

The presence of a scurf rim shows under-activity of the tissues involved—mainly the skin and circulatory systems—and shows the patient to be sluggish and filled with toxic waste, particularly in the bowel, and many times in the lungs. The scurf rim indicates, particularly, a backing up of toxic material from a poorly eliminating skin.

Our mode of living today does not pro-vide for an adequate care of the skin. We are no longer "children of the sun." We are children of apartment houses. Our skin becomes very inactive when we do not take the time to give ourselves plenty of air and some sunlight. I do not advise people to become nudists or to run around without clothes in public, but I do tell them to find a way to get more air and sunlight to the entire body. If they do

not their toxic troubles will be multiplied. One of the most important changes you will note in the study of disease through iridology is how the darkened area of the scurf rim becomes lighter when the skin is well brushed each day and given care which will develop its best functioning ability. Those with the poorest skin elimination are found to have a very dark scurf rim. We see in these cases an almost black rim around the outside of the iris. A very dark, wide, and dense scurf rim indicates an excessively toxic, waste-laden body. One could almost compare such a rim to the "scurf" rim found in some bath tubs. And, just as important as the elimination of the scurf on the outside is elimination of that on the inside of the body.

When the scurf rim appears darker over the lung area, it shows that in all proba-bility the skin is not eliminating as well as it should, and the lungs have become overloaded with toxic waste in the body's effort to eliminate it. If the skin is not eliminating well, you will find other organs loaded with "backed up" toxic waste. This waste is thrown out of the body through a series of pimples and skin rashes, or even psoriasis, but if the whole body is functioning adequately the organs of elimination carry off these waste products in such a way as to be hardly noticed by the individual. When you have these toxic cases, treat the *whole* body, and the local eliminative conditions such as "pimples" will disappear.

Dr. Henry Lindlahr had a case at one time of a tiny baby whose scurf rim was very heavy and dark. This baby could not gain weight after birth. Upon examining the irises of the baby, Lindlahr said: "You are killing this baby with these clothes you have on him. Put him in the sun and let the air get to his skin and you will see wonderful changes." The mother did as advised and in a period of a few months, the baby had gained normal weight and looked so well, it was almost unbelievable.

When the scurf rim appears very dense, dark, and wide, we know the tactile sense in the skin has been lowered. A person with this condition cannot seem to get "all the joy out of life," because he is not feeling well. Over a period of consistent corrective skin treatment you will have a wonderful revelation in even three months' time as to what skin therapy can do to change a scurf rim and thus rid the body of stored-up toxins.

The blood is closely related to the skin. Certain odors come from the skin that are brought there by the blood for elimination. These odors disappear when the blood stream becomes clean through a suitable diet and a more particular way of living. It is more difficult to work with some of the toxin-filled organs because a toxic blood stream is constantly pouring more waste materials into them in the blood's effort to keep itself purified so that it may nourish the tissues with clean, nutritive material. This process is very necessary for effective body metabolism.

I believe that in the future we will be able to test the toxicity of the body by our skin reactions. Waste acids of the body are eliminated directly through the four eliminative channels, but the skin is one organ which we can touch and otherwise test directly with our senses and with instruments.

Wherever there is a heavy scurf rim, this signifies a retention of morbid waste in the body. When there is a wide, dark, deep scurf rim opposite any particular organ area, that organ has the greatest amount of acid, catarrhal, and morbid waste retention. It is also a definite sign of a suppressed condition in that organ.

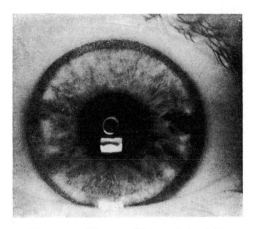

FIG. 92.   The scurf rim of the iris.

A dark scurf rim in the area of the feet, for example, probably is the result of having suppressed chronic perspiration of the feet. The scurf rim becomes darker in the brain area through the suppression of scabies. The areas of the generative organs become dark and the scurf rim wider and darker with the suppression of gonorrhea, leucorrhea, etc.

The scurf rim is a definite sign that we have acquired toxic material through our living habits. It is possible to have a congenital scurf rim, but in this case it will extend completely around the iris.

Many of the cycles or cyclic symptoms which occur in the woman patient are brought on or aggravated by the amount of toxic material settled in the circulation or represented in the scurf rim. For example, when a heavy scurf rim extends inward to the ovarian area, the ovary cannot function properly until this scurf has been eliminated. This is one of the many reasons for "hot flashes." A variety of symptoms may result from suppression of toxic material in the ovaries. I believe that the amount of toxic waste stored in the body is in direct relation to skin activity.

Further, a hypoactive condition of the thyroid gland (which can be a toxic condition), can be demonstrated by lifting a bit of skin—that on the back of the hand, for example—and noting how slowly it goes back into place. It is well to know that when you supply iodine to the body, which is needed specifically by the thyroid gland, the skin resilience will be increased. Thus we see the relationship between the skin and the chemical elements specific to some organs; a dry skin indicates a lack of iodine in the body.

In studying the depth of darkness of a scurf rim, we find it sometimes becomes darker when vaccines, injections and drugs are used. This fact was brought out in the published work of Liljequist, one of the early discoverers of iris diagnosis.

Many oils and deodorants used on the skin help build a scurf rim. They actually impede the action and defeat the function of the skin. The more encumbered the tissues become with toxic waste, the darker, wider, and denser the scurf rim is. The skin is one of the most important organs of absorption and excretion in the body.

I—THE RADII SOLARIS (SPOKES)

The radii solaris in the iris appear somewhat elongated. They take their shape from a separation and bending of the topmost fibrous layers, giving the appearance of a deep trough or funnel. They may be likened to the spokes of a wheel and are called "spokes" by some authorities. They often look like the rays emanating from the sun and truly are the dark rays or toxemia rays issuing from the intestinal tract. Some authorities claim that the radii solaris coming from the nerve wreath are the pupillaris minores and those radiating from the pupil outward to the various organs, severing the autonomic wreath, are the pupillaris majoris.

As we mentioned in the discussion of toxemia from the intestinal tract, these radii solaris increase in number and darkness as the toxic material builds up in the body. The darker their appearance the more toxin-laden is the body. These signs are a definite indication that there is stagnation and a very toxic condition of the gastrointestinal tract. They also help you to determine which organs are receiving the toxic waste. You may find these radii solaris in any of the iris areas where organs in the body are grossly affected and where toxic material is continually pouring into the organs from the gastro-intestinal tract through the avenue of the blood stream. The presence of these so-called "spokes" in the iris are a definite sign that the toxemia is interfering with the cleanliness and normal function of the body.

Where these signs are quite numerous in the iris, you will find an accompanying breakdown of the nervous system. You will probably find the characteristic nerve ring indicating a poor nerve quality which means a breakdown, or near breakdown, of the nervous system. If nerve rings are found in the presence of the radii solaris, elimination is usually very poor and rejuvenation difficult because of this weakened nerve function.

In a tired body, especially in the brain areas, gravity impedes perfect circulation of the blood. When we think of the gravitational pull man has to work against to get clean blood into the brain areas for good functioning ability, we can see why

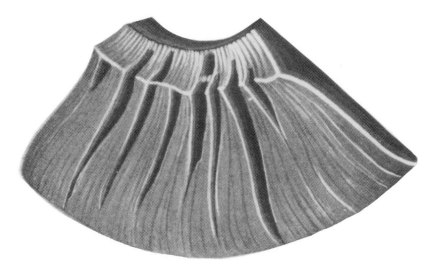

FIG. 93.   Drawing to illustrate *radii solaris*.

there is more toxic material settled in the brain areas than in the other structures of the body. In a tired body activity above the heart is usually the slowest and a sluggish brain will not al'ow any organ —pancreas, lungs, heart—to function adequately. If the brain functioned perfectly at all times we would live a long life, think more clearly, and every organ in the body would work more efficiently. Digestion, circulation, in fact, every action in the body, is dependent upon the nerve force coming from the brain. In my personal practice I have found the *radii solaris* appearing mostly in the brain areas of the iris.

J—PREGNANCY

Although many claim that pregnancy can be determined from the iris of the eye, I do not believe this can be done. The iris seems to reveal the more abnormal manifestations of the physiological processes and, as pregnancy is a normal process, I do not believe it is recorded there. However, any abnormal results of pregnancy or abnormal deliveries, such as abortions, can definitely be told from the iris by a complete break in any of the fibres in the uterine area.

These breaks appear as little black spots, but magnification shows them to be definite breaches in the fibres.

K—DEATH

In my practice I have not found that the approach of death can be told from the iris of the eye.

It is not for man to set the time of death or even to know when the time of passing is upon him. Our concern should be with how we spend the time while we are here and how we use our bodies. It is the amount of cigarettes we smoke, the number of cups of coffee we drink, and the doughnuts we eat that help to number the days in our lives. Those born with strong constitutions are able to handle wrong diet and other poor habits of living much better than those born with inherently weak constitutions, but eventually, all wrong living habits will take their toll.

We know it is these habits that pile up toxic waste materials in the body and it is the strong constitution that can throw off the toxins easier than those with inherently poor functional ability. This accounts for the reason why some people who seem to break all the rules of health "get away with it" and live so long.

L—TUMORS

Tumors are very difficult to detect through the iris. However, many times closed lesions represent a tumorous condition. This means there is an encapsulation of the toxic material; that wastes have gone into the tissues with insufficient outlet for elimination.

A tumor is simply walled-off fluid or material that has been localized to save the life of the patient. Even the smallest tumor could be just as important in its being walled-off from the blood stream as a larger one would be.

There will be times when you will suspect tumors, especially so in the uterus, but it is better to depend on other forms of diagnosis rather than iridology to determine their presence and size. I have handled many tumor cases and in my experience I find that if the iris shows a response in healing signs within the closed lesion, then the fairly certain prognosis is that the tumor will grow smaller and eliminate itself.

At the menopause period, when a tumor has been developing over a period of years and it shows up very dark in the uterine area it can often be reduced to the size of a walnut and will dry up, if the patient goes through the right living program. This means, of course, that she must restrict her diet to adequate cleansing and building foods—must stay away from the toxin-forming, refined and adulterated food products, such as macaroni, doughnuts, white bread, etc. If an operation can be avoided by living a health-building program, I believe this is far better than to resort to surgery with all the attendant complications and shock.

There are some tumors that develop very quickly causing pressure symptoms where immediate care becomes necessary and the slower method of "eating the way to health" will not meet the emergency quickly enough. This type of tumor must be handled in other ways.

M—THE SODIUM RING

The appearance of the sodium ring in the iris is usually due to the excessive use of table salt, bicarbonate of soda, and drugs such as sodium salicylate, which have overloaded the body with inorganic sodium. Most of our foods are far too heavily salted both in cooking and at the table. Too much bicarbonate of soda is used to neutralize the acids in foods, to sweeten sour milk, to preserve bottled and canned food, and to help maintain the green color of vegetables while cooking. It has been said that we use very little salt in America, but in some instances, as much as twenty times too much salt is being consumed daily. This overload is certainly more than the body can take care of, which is evidenced by the sodium ring in the iris.

Oversalting of food is a habit from childhood and some people do not seem to realize how much salt they have put on their food, and they keep on salting. They even season their food, as a matter of course, before tasting the food for its flavor. When salt has settled in the brain, the brain tissue becomes hardened and inelastic. In this state there is a lack of power of expression and an underactivity of mental processes, which includes a poor memory. Very often, when these heavy salt users have a change of environment they do not use as much salt as previously but unless they first go through a definite cleansing of the body to remove this stored-up sodium a marked sodium ring will be found in the iris.

The sodium ring is a little different in its relation to the iris than most of the other deposits. It does not start in the seventh zone, which is the skin area zone, but in the sixth zone, which is the artery and vein zone. It seems to be a part of the sclera, following or covering the cornea and overlying the tissues of the iris without touching the iris. It seems to be *in* the

Fig. 94.   Illustration of how an ulcer
of the stomach may appear in the iris.
Sodium ring is also shown.

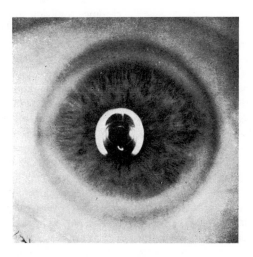

Fig. 95.   Heavy sodium ring.

cornea but *over* the iris of the eye without being a part of the iris fibre itself as are the lymphatic rosary and darkened lesion areas which we have been discussing. The ring can be narrow or it can spread over as much as half the iris, and the heavier it gets the more of an opaque white it becomes. The sodium ring may be one of many shades of white and may be opaque, translucent, or transparent.

The differentiation between the sodium ring and the white sclera coming up over the iris (the anemic sign) is that the sclera is very transparent; you can actually see the iris behind the sclera. The degree to which the sclera is drawn over the skin area in the iris signifies the degree of anemia.

Where tissues have become hardened and inelastic, the flow of blood is naturally somewhat impeded, and many symptoms of poor circulation, such as cold feet and hands, are the result. Because the blood vessels cannot contract enough to force the blood through as fast as it should move, the blood cannot get into the small arterioles and into the cell life in many parts of the body, and especially in the extremities. The brain is also seriously affected. Its tissues will become inelastic when sodium has settled in them. This condition has a serious effect upon memory.

Many symptoms that doctors cannot find any cause for can be traced to the use of salt. Poor circulatory conditions of the legs, especially bad feet, bunions, arch and knee disturbances, can be influenced and made worse through the use of too much salt. Often a good deal of salt has been found to settle in the lower extremities, especially in those whose occupations allow for little body movement. The circulation of the blood is impeded and the veins and arteries become less elastic. People with these conditions will tell you their legs have been giving them trouble for years. Many of them have gone from doctor to doctor wondering why these leg conditions cannot be cleared up.

Highly saturated solutions of salt will settle in the tissues, making those tissues hard, and causing hardening of the arteries and high blood pressure symptoms. Salt will also make red blood cells smaller which limits the amount of necessary nourishment they can carry to all the cells of the body. In many cases no examination or laboratory test reveals the condition of the veins and arteries until it has become serious. The sodium ring in the iris will show such developments as hardening of the arteries long before symptoms appear.

A person who suffers from an ulcerous and acid stomach and has been a consistent user of sodium bicarbonate will develop the sodium ring, especially if he has a poor circulatory system.

The sodium ring can also be developed through excessive use of sodium salicylates used for the many rheumatic conditions. We have made it our business to investigate cases where it was said the patient was "turning to stone." Nearly every one of these cases had been given sodium salicylate, an inorganic compound of sodium. They were treated for different symptoms such as rheumatism, neuralgia, neuritis, or arthritis. I am sure that the sodium salicylate treatment was a suppressive method which made the rheumatic conditions more chronic, resulting in a state of "turning to stone." Now, this calcified condition interferes with and disrupts the proper chemical balance of the body. The extreme acids would have been broken up and neutralized, the rheumatism and the pain would have left, had these persons been treated with foods rich in organic sodium, such as celery juice and whey. Organic sodium can break up much of a calcium fixation and neutralize an over-acid body condition.

Science is also finding out that salt is the cause of many skin disturbances. In one of our own cases, for instance, we had a woman patient who had a very marked sodium ring. Her history revealed that she had been employed at a salt works where she had to have her hands in salt all day long. The salt had been absorbed through the skin and was the main cause of the sodium rings in the irises of her eyes.

I consider salt to be a drug and an irritant to the body. It is one of the greatest offenders to humanity. Practically all commercially prepared food is salted for flavor. Even considerable salt is used in the bread we eat daily. It would be so much better for each individual to salt his own food to keep it at a minimum. Its overuse can cause many disturbing results.

N—DRUGS AND CHEMICALS

Medical records now show at least 1800 symptoms of disease and approximately 35,000 remedies to offset these symptoms.

Drugs do what is claimed they do. They get rid of pains and they suppress disease, but they do not "cure." Drugs do not help the body replace old tissue or cleanse it. And they are usually found in the body years after their administration, which can be shown by the study of the iris.

Inorganic drugs taken into the system are not absorbed. If they cannot be eliminated through natural channels, they will settle in tissues and organs of the body and will remain there unless changed living habits and proper treatment enable the body to eliminate these foreign substances and toxins.

Much can be said against drugs, but we are not here to criticize any more than is necessary. With the natural healing methods, however, drugs are not needed at all in cleansing and building new tissue and in exchanging old tissue for new. When nature is given all the natural elements for life she is supposed to have to work with she is well able to build or rebuild a body when unnatural methods do not interfere.

If the drug sign in the iris indicates settlement in any one organ of the body, you will find that particular organ will suffer the most. Usually, when a drug has been taken it filters through the blood stream and lodges in some inherently weak spot or organ. There are some drugs that have

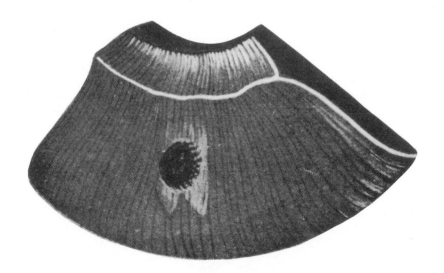

FIG. 96. Drawing to illustrate drug settlement in iris tissues.

an affinity for certain tissues in the body, as sulphur has an affinity for the skin. When a patient is ridding his body of poisons through discharges, you can often find, by testing these discharges, drugs he had taken years previously.

A drug made up of certain chemical elements usually has an affinity for the organ which seems to want most to repel that specific drug. Drugs of an inorganic nature cannot be used by the tissues of certain organs and whenever they settle in these organs they become a source of irritation. This can be proven to you if you will note the many cancer signs in the iris. In studying them you will see that many of these cancer signs have a drug base.

We are discovering how many new treatments being used for cancer today are actually only driving the disease to another part of the body. I do not say that drugs produce all cancers but a few years back I had an opportunity of going over more than 300 cases in a cancer institution. In every case of cancer diagnosed from the iris there was a drug base. I definitely believe cancer can be produced in the body through certain types of drug irritation.

Harsh drugs and treatments divert the natural body processes away from their functional activity and deter elimination, suppressing nature rather than assisting her. Often, a simple, chronic disease is made more chronic and complex through the use of drugs and accompanying treatments. In using the nature cure way, when you see drug signs in the iris along with the disease signs of the organs, you will not only have to treat for the disease but you will have to eliminate the drug also.

In the nature cure way of treating, a discharge that is dormant in the body may again become active, and the patient may become alarmed, but when nature is cleaning house she stirs up latent, encapsulated conditions that will gradually eliminate

themselves through the blood stream and the eliminative organs. In the process of

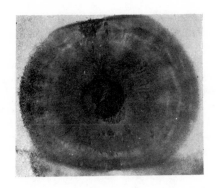

FIG. 97.   Photograph showing drug settlements in iris tissues, producing rings which indicate nerve irritation.

cleansing, nature is breaking down the stored-up toxic material that has developed in the body from the use of drugs, vaccines, injections, and generally bad living habits. Those who do not understand nature's way of ridding the body of toxins through a discharge, do not understand that when a drug is given to suppress this discharge they are interfering with nature's way of ridding the body of toxic waste. This elimination of toxins by the body is referred to as, "the healing crisis."

The American people are taking more drugs today than is generally realized. We all hear so much about vitamins and how good they are for us that some of us become so conditioned to advertising we try every product we hear about or that is recommended to us. Some of these products have coal tar in them—one of the most deadly, insidious poisons—the same material used in paving our streets. This certainly is not meant to go into the body and cannot possibly add to the health of the person taking it. Persons with strong constitutions do not notice the ill effects from the drug as do the weak, but weak or strong, these poisonous drugs are not good for the body and sooner or later it will break down.

The following is a table I developed to illustrate how drug and chemical signs appear in the iris, how they are eliminated, and the symptoms they produce in the body. You will easily come to recognize these signs if you study the chart often and thus help to acquaint yourself with them. You may be sure that any unusual discoloration of the iris, or any spot or unnatural marking will be a sign of a deposit of some kind and does not belong to what we call a "normal" iris. It is well, therefore, to have a vivid picture in your mind of the "normal" color and appearance of the blue, brown, and gray eye.

If you will look over lists of drugs to see what has been given in the past and what is being given today, you will notice many additions to the medical pharmacopoeia. This is mentioned because eventually you will have to recognize the signs of these drugs in the irises of patients. This is especially true of the synthetic drug preparations, such as atabrine which is used as a substitute for quinine. Modern prescription druggists do not carry simple, crude drugs as in the past; drugs are now considerably changed and highly refined. We no longer have what I term "pure" poisons to deal with; we now have much more potent and poisonous poisons. Some of the newer poisons are so highly refined that they do not even leave a characteristic color impression in the iris. This is not to be wondered at since now so many different drugs are combined that it will be some time before we can possibly differentiate a compound in the iris coloring. Comparative studies could not keep pace with the frequent changes in drug mixtures. We have in mind such drugs as the sulfonamides, the antihistamines, veronal and barbiturates, salvarsan and arsenicals, carbon tetrachloride, ethylene cyclopropane,

atabrine and other antimalarials, para-aminosalicylic acid, decholin, thiouracil and dramamine.

Drugs in high dilution, as administered homeopathically, do not leave their mark in the iris. Here, we are dealing with a highly active, vibratory force for healing rather than the effects of a crude drug.

Some drug signs in the iris appear in the same color found in the crude state. When these poisonous drugs have settled in any organ of the body, and remain there for a long time, they can cause so much irritation in the nervous system that the resulting damage may be indicated by the appearance of characteristic nerve rings. The discoloration seen in the iris is part of the fibre; the fibre itself has become discolored. The drug spots you see are the colored fibres.

A drug spot can be spread over many different areas, every fibre can be colored, and minutely you can see the underlying pigment showing between the fibres. On the other hand, the iris can appear so dense that you will be unable to detect the fibres. When drug upon drug has been taken over a long period of years, these appear very dark in the iris and are considered as chronic settlements in the body. As these markings become darker and darker, the patient develops what is called psora or "the itch." These psora spots can be very dark—almost black.

When a seriously toxic body shows psora spots over a long period of years, I believe there can be so much irritation and disintegration of tissue that there would be only the poorest functioning in the organs involved. This can so influence the development of the fetus or certain tissues and glands in the fetus that the resultant development could be idiocy.

The lymph system tries to carry all the poisons and foreign matter out of the body through the organs of elimination, but when the functional ability of the body is much below par and under a heavy dosing

DRUG AND CHEMICAL CHART

Drug Name	How Gotten Into Body	Organs Settled in Most	Organs Eliminated Through	Appearance of Drug in Eye	Medicinal Uses	Symptoms
Arsenic	Salvarsan. Accidental Poisoning: Paris Green Spray. Fowler's Solution. Dyes, Cosmetics.	Circulatory area.	Lymph System. Kidneys. Bowels. Skin. Mucous Membranes.	Tiny White dots occurring singly or in groups in Lymph System.	Heart Stimulant. Gastric Disorders. Used with sulphur internally to suppress skin eruptions.	Abdominal Cramps, General Edema, Boils, Emaciation, Skin Eruptions, Weakness, Falling of Hair and Nails, Irritability.
Bismuth	Bismuth Subcarbonate. Bismuth Subnitrate.	Digestive Tract.	Mucous Membranes.	Dark Metallic Grey, irregular circle.	Coats Mucous Membranes and acts as a mechanical protection. For Syphilis.	Skin Discoloration. Frequent Urination. Blue Line on Gums. Black Patches on Buccal and Rectal Mucosa. Angina.
Bromides	Bromoseltzer. Sedatives.	Brain area.	Skin and Eliminative Organs. Mucous Membranes.	Bluish White Crescent in Brain Area.	Antipyretic. Epilepsy. Neurasthenia.	Neuromuscular Weakness always in Legs. Orange or Yellow Skin Eruptions. Violent Headaches.
Coal Tar Products	Aspirin, Acetanalid, Saccharine, Patent Fever Remedies, Some vitamins.	Brain area and Nerve Tissue.	Skin. Kidney. Mucous Membranes.	Dark Steel Gray.	Pain killer. Fever breaker. Hypnotic.	Easily Fatigued. Loss of Memory. Epilepsy.
Creosote	Cough Remedies. General Nerve Sedative. Acetanalid. Antipyrin. Phenacitin.	Stomach and Intestines.	Kidneys. Catarrhal discharge through Mucous Membranes.	Dirty Gray color. White specks in Gastro-Intestinal Tract.	Respiratory Diseases. Tuberculosis. Coughs. Stimulant. Painkiller. Antipyretic. Purgative.	Mental and Nervous Disorders, Fear, Loss of Memory, Excessive Urination.
Ergot	Eating rye containing ergot. Drug preparations.	Generative organs and Stomach.	Mucous Membranes.	Lighter Red than Iodine. Spot in Uterine and Stomach areas.	Given to hasten delivery. To cause contraction.	Difficulty in Breathing, Numbness, Nausea, Vomiting, Diarrhea, Dizziness, Gangrene.
Glycerin	Chiefly through remedies in which used as a Carrier.	Skin. Kidneys. Lungs.	Mucous Membranes.	Large White clouds in Skin, Kidney and Lung areas.	In rectal suppositories. Solvent and sweetening agent in medicine.	
Iodine (Iodide)	Iodine Antiseptics. Iodine Douches. Patent Remedies for Goiter.	Settles everywhere. Often in Liver, Bowel, Kidney, Stomach, Lungs, Pancreas.	Mucous Membranes.	Red and Yellowish Red spots surrounded by White borders.	Antiseptic. Injections for Pleurisy. TB of Glands, Goitre. Inflammation of Glands, Joints.	Inflamed Gums, Colds, Frontal Headaches, Frothy Expectoration and Cough, Diarrhea. Skin Eruptions, Atrophy of Glands.
Iron	Water containing Iron. Blood Tonics. Iron Bromide.	Settles anywhere.	Bowel. Mucous Membranes.	Dark Rusty Brown spot. Much darker in Brown Iris.	Anemia. Antidote in Arsenic Poisoning, Iron Sulphate to Counteract Diarrhea, Iron Bromide for Amenorrhea.	Abdominal Pains, Black Stool, Stubborn Constipation, Relieved by Pressure, Tooth Decay.
Lead	Lead in drinking water from lead pipes. Workers handling lead, type, paint, tin foil. Coloring and canned goods.	Stomach and Intestinal area and Nervous Tissue.	Skin. Bowels. Mucous Membranes.	Lead Gray or Lead Blue. Perfect circle around Pupil in Stomach and Intestinal area.	Skin Disease. Inflammation or discharge from ear or urethra. Douches.	Wrist drop, Dizziness. Neuro-muscular Pains in Arms, Shoulders and Neck. Malnutrition. Blue Lead Line on Gums. Paralysis.

DRUG AND CHEMICAL CHART

Drug Name	How Gotten Into Body	Organs Settled in Most	Organs Eliminated Through	Appearance of Drug in Eye	Medicinal Uses	Symptoms
Mercury	606, Hydrargyrum. Amalgam Tooth Fillings. Mirror Platers. Mercury Miners.	Circulatory area of Brain. Bones.	Difficult to eliminate. Skin. Mucous Membranes. Hemorrhoidal Discharge.	Whitish or Silver Gray. Metal Lustre. Bluish in Brown Eye.	Antiseptic Dressing. Ringworm Lotion. Disinfectant Douches. For Syphilis. Blue Ointment to suppress Parasites.	Tender swollen Gums, Loose Teeth, Deep Ulcers, Hutchinson's Teeth, Locomotor Ataxia, Mental Degeneration, Metallic Taste in Mouth.
Opium (cocaine)	Laudanum. Paregoric. Morphine.	Stomach. Intestines. Sympathetic Nervous System.	Mucous Membranes.	White or Whitish Grey lines radiating straight out and around Pupil.	Sedative. Hypnotic. Sweat producer.	Stimulation mixed with Depression. Mental and Physical Fatigue. Chronic Constipation.
Phosphorus	Inhalation by workers in match factories. Medicines. Vermin Poisons.	Diaphragm and heart. Angle of the jaw.	Skin. Bowel. Mucous Membranes.	White flakes anywhere in Iris, especially in Muscle and Bone Structure areas.	General Nerve Tonic. Softening of Bone. Sexual Impotence. Pulmonary Disorders. Some Skin Diseases.	Chronic Diarrhea, Constipation, Later Chronic Headaches, Ulceration of Gums, Pyorrhea, Skin Itch, Necrosis of Jaw.
Quinine (alkaloid of) (salts of)	Bromo-Quinine Malarial Preventative. Appetizer Tonics. Hair Tonics containing it.	Stomach and Intestinal Tract. Chronic Use Spreads Throughout Body.	Mouth, Skin, Kidneys, Bowel, Hemorrhoidal Discharge, Mucous Discharges.	Yellow or Yellowish Green in G.I. Tract and all over the Iris.	Fever Breaker. Tonic during Convalescence. Rectal Injection against Amoebic Dysentery. Painful nervous conditions.	Ringing or Roaring in Ears, Deafness, Disturbed Vision, Quinine Taste Mouth, Mental Depression, Itchy Skin Eruptions, Perspiration.
Salicylic Acid	Food and drink preservatives, Aspirin, Cold remedies, Oil of wintergreen.	Brain area, Stomach and Intestines.	Bowels. Skin. Mucous Membranes.	Whitish Grey to Dirty Grey cloud. Shown mostly in upper part of Iris.	Fever Breaker. Night Sweats. Inflammatory Rheumatism. Chronic Cystitis.	Headaches, Loss of Hair, Dullness of Hearing, Ringing in Ears, Dimness of Vision.
Sodium	Table salt, Bicarbonate of Soda (Baking Soda). Salty food. Sodium Salicylate. Sodium Benzoate.	Circulatory Area.	Skin. Mucous Membranes.	Dull White arc or circle in Circulatory area.	Saline Cathartics. Stomach Acidity. For Rheumatism.	Eczema, Boils, Pimples, Dyspnea, Arteriosclerosis, Angina Pectoris, Constriction of Pupil, Poor Memory.
Strychnine	Tonic Stimulant. Nux Vomica.	Stomach.	Mucous Membranes.	White to Whitish Yellow wheel of perfect proportions around Pupil.	Stimulant. Appetizer. Heart and Nerve Tonic.	Constipation, Fermentation, Emaciation, Indigestion, Unnatural Hunger, Weakness of Heart, Paralysis, Anemia.
Sulphur (sulfa)	Sulphured Foods. Sulphur Water and Baths. Inhalation of Sulphur Gases. Medication.	Bowel and Stomach.	Skin. Bowel. Mucous Membranes.	Dark Brown Cloudy Discoloration.	Packs, Salves, Bowel Cleanser. Preservative. Scalp Ointments, Water, Bacterial Infections.	Boils, Pimples, Eczema, Rash, Eruptions, Nausea, Vomiting, Fever.
Turpentine	Accidentally absorbed through inhalation by turpentine distillers, painters, artists.	Genitourinary organs.	Genitourinary organs. Kidneys. Mucous Membranes.	White in area of Genitourinary organs. Dense Gray clouds.	Antisepsis and diuresis of genitourinary organs. For colds.	Suppression and Retention of Urine.
Vaccines	Injections or through skin.		Skin. Mucous Membranes.	Black to Dirty Murky Brown spots with White borders. Deposited superficially on Iris surface.	For immunization.	Skin Eruptions. Fevers.

of drugs, their elimination cannot be accomplished. They become stored in the tissues and organs, and once they have become lodged in the system, there is hardly anything that will move them except a thorough cleansing of all the tissues and organs of the body, by natural therapy and the "healing crisis."

Suppressing acute or sub-acute symptoms of the body processes produces a light brown coloring around the pupil and if this suppression of symptoms is continued, the coloring deepens and the scurf rim on the outer edge of the iris becomes blacker and broader. So-called children's diseases, as measles, scarlet fever, mumps, etc., should be regarded as "suppressed" conditions of normal elimination, especially by the skin. Improper treatment of these skin manifestations produces a yellowish coloring around the pupil inside the stomach area which later darkens the scurf rim. Signs of scabies are sharply bordered with coarsely-marked spots appearing about the size of "pin pricks." They may spread, appearing as large as the head of a match. As they become larger and darker, we can tell at about what age the disease occurred and whether unnatural treatment was used. In fact, these signs indicated that the original disease was made dormant by suppressive treatment.

Salves, ointments, soaps, etc., containing tar, sulphur and mercury used in skin treatments, introduce poisonous matter into the system which always settles in the weakest part of the body.

I believe each drug has its own avenue of elimination. Individuals who have an excessive amount of sulphur in the system usually eliminate it through the skin. Sulphur seems to have a skin affinity, and as you know, has been used by the medical profession in most all cases of skin diseases. Boils, pimples, skin rashes can be the result of sulphur elimination through the skin.

When you find a drug settlement, do not stress this too much in dealing with your patients. In most cases, they do not know or have forgotten what drugs they have taken in the past. Many of the drug signs in the irises of patients today are from remedies taken when they were children, especially quinine and sulphur. But there are many unusual signs and discolorations in the iris that are not due to drugs taken for various ailments. They may be due to chlorine in the drinking water or iron from old rusty pipes used for drinking water; or discolorations may come from mineral waters such as we have in Colorado Springs and in many areas of Arizona.

To demonstrate a sulphur spot, let us refer to the colored iris plate which refers to a much distressed woman with a sulphur spot in the breast area of her iris. This drug settlement is very definitely a source of much dis-ease, in whatever area it is found. And this condition is found all too often in our so-called "age of efficiency and advancement of medical science."

Preservatives can be considered in the classification of poisonous drugs because they have the same ill effect on the tissues in which they settle. Many of our canned foods are being preserved with drugs. In the past, arsenic was used in the canning of peas. We find that some companies are using certain poisonous fluids and drugs to preserve canned meats. Soda is frequently used as a preservative. Coal tar products often are used for coloring and flavoring.

Table salt is also considered a drug and produces irritation in the body. Our discussion of the sodium ring demonstrates that. Pepper acts as an irritant to the body. Vinegar destroys the red blood cells.

Iodine is recognized in the iris by sharply bordered red spots, turning to dark brown and growing darker as absorption of the poison increases.

Arsenic settlement in the system is usually indicated by whitish flakes in the circulatory area of the iris. This seems to be more pronounced in the blue than in the brown eye, where the settlement seems to appear more as flakes of a very light amber. Sometimes these flakes also appear in the scurf rim when arsenical medicines have been given through the skin and have not been carried off by the circulation. They can be found deposited in other organ areas, too, when arsenic has been used over a long period of time.

Besides drug treatment, there are other ways in which substances poisonous to the body can enter it. Painters and printers acquire lead poisoning from their occupations. Insurance companies recognize this, as they also recognize certain types of disease in persons working with X-ray where they do not use a screen to protect the body from constant bombardment of rays.

In the early days of X-ray, operators became sterile, but now protective equipment is used to prevent this. We definitely know from the statements of medical authorities that X-ray and radium can cause cancer. However, I do not know as yet how X-ray and radium burns will show up in the iris.

Symptoms of gas poisoning can be detected in the iris. For example, some thirty workers in a factory at San Leandro, California, were poisoned by tetraethyl chloride gas used for cleaning tractor parts. The symptoms were vomiting, loss of control of the mental faculties, memory failure, and speech difficulties. All their senses were dulled and they lost interest in their surroundings. It was extremely difficult for me to find the signal in the iris, but I found a marked darkening throughout the lung area, and many of the brain areas were also inflamed from the irritation.

The iris showing was the same in the case of a man who did not get enough oxygen when poisoned by gas from a motor in a shiphold. The iris showed a very darkened condition in the whole lung area.

In the case of a man who had been heavily gassed with chlorine in the war, there was a dark yellowish discoloration in the entire lung area only.

At one time I treated a man who had taken sulphuric acid to commit suicide. We found the esophagus area in the iris quite darkened and lined with white on the inside, which indicated the tissues had become scarred by the sulphuric acid. Many drugs and fumes will cause scar tissue while there is no sign of the drug showing.

Acids, other than those developed from foods, are distributed by the blood stream and absorbed throughout the body, acting as an irritant in the system and causing the whole iris to become darker.

That vaccination and serum inoculation does affect body tissue is evidenced by the fact that the blue and brown pigment of the iris becomes much darker afterwards. From the time vaccine therapy was introduced into the world there has been a division of opinion among medical minds as to the ill effects of this therapy. Even as great a medical authority as Sir William Osler quoted a Doctor MacFarland as saying that he had traced ninety-five cases of tetanus as an aftermath of vaccination. In his practice of medicine, another authority stated that he believed latent maladies such as syphilis and tuberculosis may be reactivated with fatal results following vaccination. The celebrated English physician, James J. Garth Wilkinson, stated: "Vaccination is a homicidal insanity of the whole profession" and is "blood assassination."

Vaccination was denounced by an M. D. in an article in Physical Culture magazine for May, 1921. This physician claimed his two healthy sisters had never enjoyed another well day after they were vaccinated, and died after "successive crops of ulcers and abscesses sapped their vitality," eventuating in acute miliary tuberculosis.

A highly recognized bacteriologist, Professor Edgar M. Crookshank, who first had become a great believer in vaccination, later denounced it after an exhaustive investigation of its bad after-effects.

These are not isolated and limited cases of the effects from inoculation of serums and vaccines. There is a long, long list of fatalities resulting from the use of these therapies and thousands upon thousands of patients give a case history of bad health after serum inoculation or vaccination.

In 1919, by a record count of inhabitants of the Philippines, out of 107,981 persons vaccinated, 59,000 died after vaccination. So it is not unreasonable to insist that no arbitrary rules or laws be made requiring citizens to be vaccinated or inoculated. Children should not be kept from school because their parents will not allow them to be vaccinated. Let those who want vaccination have it, but since they believe they have been immunized by this, why should they then be afraid of "catching" the disease from someone who has not been vaccinated? No one should have his freedom taken from him and be forced to have vaccination or inoculation.

People who live in such a way as to build a strong resistance to disease are not afraid of epidemics. Those who are learning the natural way of living and healing and keeping the body well, should especially adhere to the natural laws during an epidemic: Keep up the life force by strict adherence to the nature cure health way. If a cold or a discharge of any kind develops, this elimination of toxins should be encouraged and not suppressed. All that can be done should be done to cleanse and build the body. Few of us are born with strong constitutions and sometimes we do not gain the knowledge of this nature cure health way until we are broken down in health. A "cure" is not accomplished except through patient, persistent effort in adhering to the laws of nature.

We do not wish to go into argument here as to whether drugs do all that is claimed for them. What place drugs may have in our lives as individuals and as a nation is yet to be determined. But people are realizing more and more that there is a place, and a great need, for nature's way of cleansing the body and building vital tissues. Nature's way is the replacing of old tissue with new and maintaining a clean, healthy body. *This is something a drug treatment cannot do.*

O—ANEMIA IN THE EXTREMITIES AND IN THE BRAIN

Anemia in the Extremities

You will find reflected in the irises of the eyes a half dozen conditions which affect everyone. This fact has proven itself to me by every patient I have diagnosed.

In the iris I have found anemia in the area of the extremities and the word "anemia," I feel, best describes this condition. Every patient I have had in my office has shown a lack of blood flow to the extremities. This lack is due to a tired and enervated body. A sick or over-tired body does not have the power to maintain a normal pace or to move the blood as rapidly as is necessary. The blood should travel approximately thirty feet every second to keep the cell life of the body well for the cells must have enough blood in order to function at their best. The parts of the body that suffer most are the extremities and the brain, due to gravitation and enervation. This condition, which shows up in the irises, is a natural consequence and exists in everyone, but in some more than in others.

We make the greatest improvement in health by taking care of this anemic condition and there is no better method than by walking in the sand on the beach. Walking in the dewy grass before breakfast in the morning helps the blood to circulate in the extremities, while at the same time the circulation in the organs in the central part of the body is also benefited. Barefoot walking is the best method of developing the small muscles which help to return blood to the heart, and keeping the leg tissues healthy. Hot and cold foot baths also can be very beneficial. Any time the heart or any of the organs are given such assistance, they have a better chance to recuperate and regenerate because these tissue processes take place when the body is working under the least strain or is in a state of rest.

When the body has suffered over a period of years with anemia of the extremities, you know that toxic material has settled in these tissues. The joints have hardened, the arteries have become inelastic, the veins have less contractibility and break down, and they soon become enlarged. Gout and phlebitis are good examples of this, as are rheumatism and arthritis. No organ of the body should receive greater care than the veins. The venous blood is not propelled by the action of the heart; its relatively slow rate of flow is made possible by a combination of factors, including pressure of the surrounding muscles. The pressure of every muscular contraction upon the soft veins pushes the blood toward the heart. We may wonder why it is propelled toward the heart only and is not forced back into the tissues. It is because many veins, especially those of the legs, are equipped with elastic valves which can act as pockets which will completely close the veins if necessary to prevent blood from flowing back into the tissues. This is an important reason why physical exercise, and especially walking, increases blood circulation and thereby stimulates all tissues of the body.

The sodium ring, when found in the iris, is a sign that the blood will not circulate freely throughout the body. Whenever there is a sodium ring present the arteries are hard and have lost their elasticity and ability to contract.

It is necessary to take care of the feet as they are the first to give trouble signals in the person who has a poor circulating blood stream. The shoes worn today are not conducive to good foot circulation, and arches fall as a result. Few people can say they have perfect feet. The Seminole Indians, according to U. S. Government figures, have the finest arches and yet they have no arch supports in their shoes; they wear moccasins. It is only civilized people with arch supports in their shoes whose arches are becoming weaker from lack of use. I know from experience that going barefoot improves the circulation in the legs; it also improves the eyes. I could seat you thirty feet away from a headline in a newspaper and you would be unable to read, but through rubbing your feet and increasing the circulation there, I could help you to read the headings which you could not read before. We have been able to help people discard their glasses by improving the circulation in their feet.

The following should be a part of everyone's pattern of living: Walk barefoot a little every day. Follow the laws of nature in the use of heat and cold. Cold drives the blood into the body while heat relaxes, and the tissues are allowed to fill with blood again. Make a daily habit of the hot and cold foot baths. If possible, walk through the heat of beach sands and alternate with the cold ocean water. The blood will then circulate sufficiently in the lower extremities and your health will improve. This treatment is wonderful in heart troubles but is also a health-building measure in general. It is not a treatment for any one disease.

One of my own personal experiences taught me how valuable these natural treatments are. I had heard about the Kneipp water cure in Germany—running in the damp, cool grass before breakfast—but I was not impressed to any great extent. I had read of this cure in books and I had seen 150 people doing this at one time, but my only thought was that they were extremists in the health work. My personal experience, however, proved to me that there was something to this cure.

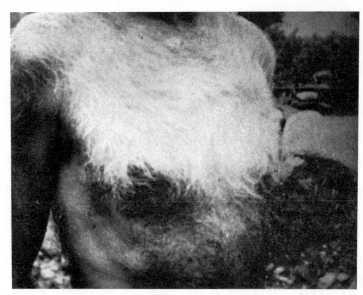

FIG. 98.   This photograph shows an example of graying of the hair above the heart line,—in this case following an extreme shock in an accident. It demonstrates that an enervated body cannot force the blood into all of its parts, and especially into the brain area. The pigment of the hair is dependent upon a good blood supply, and if the supply above the heart is inadequate, the hair may quickly become gray. The hair of the man in the photograph remained dark in color below the heart line, where the blood supply was adequate.

FIG. 99.   This is a photograph of Joe Tonti, who was considered the world's greatest upside-down athlete. At one time he had considerable trouble with his complexion and hair. This difficulty was completely corrected when he started doing his work upside down and getting more blood circulating in the upper extremities. He has been featured in Ripley's "Believe It Or Not" pulling a five-ton truck with his teeth up a 3 per cent grade while walking on his hands.

Sometime ago I had guests at my home for an early breakfast; the party included men of dignified positions. We decided to go on a hike before eating, and ended, barefooted, at the golf course nearby. It was a sight to see these dignified men, acting like children, dancing up and down, running through the cold, wet grass with their shoes in their hands rather than on their feet. We were enjoying our "cure" when a caretaker came along in his car and asked us what we were doing. One of the men told him we were curing our rheumatism although he, of all people, had no rheumatism! The man asked, "Do you see the sign down there? TRESPASSERS NOT ALLOWED."

We left, but five years later I had a letter from the caretaker stating he had taken our remarks seriously. He told how he had cured his rheumatism by walking in the wet grass in his own backyard.

When your feet feel good, you feel good all over.

Brain Anemia

Through the science of iridology I believe I have made one of the most important discoveries I could make—brain anemia. I have coined this term because there is no other that can better describe the condition, and I use it constantly in my practice. Is it possible, you may ask, that the brain, the garden of the body and the one organ we cannot do without and would not trade for all the money in the world, can suffer from anemia?

The brain is the one structure in the body that needs to be nourished and fed more than any other part. The finger moves by the brain. We walk by the brain. We play the violin, speak, love by the brain. We taste by the brain. Every-thing we do comes through the brain first. The digestive juices from the stomach or intestinal tract cannot be secreted without the brain and this is why we should first think of treating the head area for diges-tive disorders before treating the intestinal tract itself.

Brain anemia comes as a result of fatigue, enervation, and worry. Man was given the privilege of walking on two legs and can do so hour after hour, the only symptoms of over-activity being fatigue, a lack of vivacity, animation, and life force. When man becomes enervated, power wanes. His alertness and his ability to remember, judge, and reason weaken and become underactive. He complains, feels mean, and is irritable. It is difficult for him to live harmoniously with others, as well as with himself.

It is not enough to have a normal blood count with the proper hemoglobin level; for regenerative purposes, we also need a sufficient quantity of that blood in the tissues. Any organ or tissue which receives only half the amount of healthy blood required, will starve to death.

Arcus Senilis

The arcus senilis comes from the word "arc," meaning part of a circle, and "se-nilis," meaning senility or old age. This arc of old age is found in the brain areas only, appears in the upper part of the iris, and is a sign of an anemic condition of the brain. Geriatrics, the care of elderly people, is a vital problem in the general field of healing. In this day and age there are more factors than ever be-fore which can produce anemic conditions in the brain. And the ability to regener-ate these centers is less today because of refined foods, city life, lack of outdoor activities, etc.

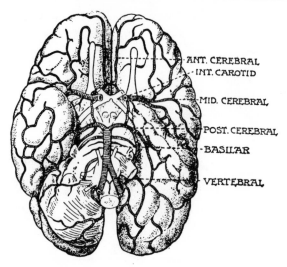

FIG. 100. The blood vessels of the brain.
Many nervous diseases can be directly traced
to changes in the brain blood vessels and an
insufficient blood supply is responsible for
many symptoms, especially in later life.

The arc is formed when a portion of the sclera is pulled down over the upper part of the iris. In some cases it appears like a transparent membrane, but in others is colored, or it can be an extreme white. Alkalizers and bromide headache remedies can settle in the arcus senilis and cause a more opaque white. A bluish white color, depending upon the amount and kind of drugs taken, may also develop. Bromides are one of the main causes of brain and nerve disturbances in the head. A headache is a reflex symptom. To get rid of it through a suppressive method may cause developments of a more serious nature.

Many drugs settle in the brain and nerve tissues of the head, often causing headaches of a more serious and chronic nature than the original headache for which the drug was taken. A hardening of the brain tissues, which can interfere with the memory and decisive powers, can be brought about by the overuse of such drugs. With these conditions in the brain areas we cannot be complacent or peaceful, but rather, we become chaotic and develop complexes and manias.

P—MECHANICAL SIGNS

In most of the preceding chapters, we have discussed the chemistry of the various tissues. We stated that the condition of a tissue is judged by its toxic settlement, and by its acute, sub-acute or chronic stage of disease. We will now discuss some of the mechanical factors which can detract from well-being. When tissues have good blood to work with but not enough because of interference due to pressure, they are in *mechanical distress*. We must remove the mechanical pressure by mechanical means before the blood can repair these tissues properly.

The most recognizable mechanical sign in the iris of the eye is that of prolapsus of the transverse colon, which is illustrated in the diagram in Fig. 101. Any other mechanical sign which may have developed in the iris does not reflect the physical position of an organ unless that organ is causing pressure or is undergoing tissue changes which interfere with its blood supply or that of some other organ. Transverse colon prolapsus is one of the most

Normal

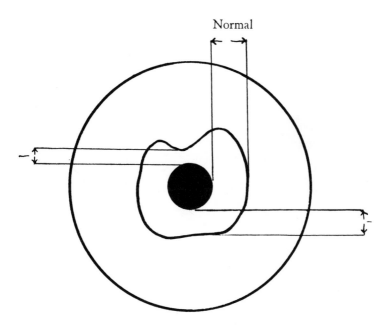

FIG. 101.   Normally the autonomic nerve wreath forms an
even outline equidistant from the pupil, but when there
is prolapsus the distance between the wreath and the
pupil is decreased.   A dropped transverse colon will cause
the wreath to dip down toward the pupil and narrow the
distance superiorly.   When this prolapsus is causing extreme pressure symptoms, there will be narrowing of the
distance inferior to the pupil (a rising up toward it)
in the areas of the cecum or sigmoid colon.   The more
pressure there is from the transverse colon, the closer the
autonomic wreath in the sigmoid area will be to the pupil.
In other words, the narrowing that exists below is because
of that above.

important factors to consider in assuring
an adequate blood supply to the abdominal
organs. It may cause prolapsus of the
stomach also ("fish hook" stomach). This
prolapsus is not due to pressure from some
other organ or organs, but to lack of
essential elements, especially calcium, and
possibly to fatigue.

When there is extreme pressure on the
prostate gland, the ovaries, or the uterus
from prolapsus of any kind, toxic material
can settle in these organs because of restricted blood flow. This condition will be
one of your best studies in this science.
Symptoms can develop in the patient that
are due to mechanical pressure, and may
be difficult to differentiate from other
causes. A rectal disorder may not be a
chemical problem at all. Prolapsus often
causes rectal pressure, which may be seen
in the iris. Usually, however, in cases of
rectal pressure, where hemorrhoids have
developed, look for a reflex chemical disturbance in the liver and a toxic condition
in the sigmoid colon. When mechanical

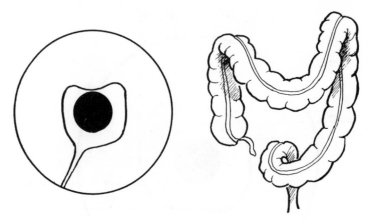

FIG. 102 (a).   Illustrating dropped transverse colon as it will appear in the iris of the eye and as it may exist in the patient.

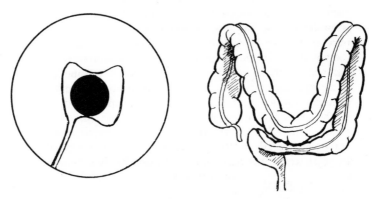

FIG. 102 (b).   Diagrams to illustrate dropped transverse colon with sigmoid colon pressure.

pressure such as that of prolapsus is added to this condition, the elimination of toxins from the rectal tissues is inhibited. These tissues become weak and the added strain may result in bleeding and rectal pains.

Disorders which are reflected in the iris may have developed because of one organ pressing against another. Prolapsus of the abdominal organs can bring on pressure

symptoms affecting the uterus, the prostate, the ureters, or ovarian tubes, preventing adequate drainage. Prolapsus can also interfere with a sufficient amount of fluids entering the blood stream from the intestinal tract.

Some toxic materials and the formation of gas may cause definite pressure symptoms in certain organs, which produce a reflex activity. This is the case in many

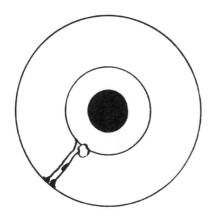

FIG. 103. Internal and external hemorrhoids. The white portion in the drawing represents acute inflammation at the site of the Valve of Houston. The two black spots half-way down in the rectal area represent internal hemorrhoids, and the two spots in the anal area represent external hemorrhoids.

heart disturbances. Gas pressure against the heart can create serious complications. The many persons who die of "heart failure" between two and three o'clock in the morning, after a heavy evening meal, suggests that the "heart attack" resulted more from gas pressure than from some other complication. I believe more persons die from a bloated condition caused by gases from decomposing food than die from actual abnormalities of the heart itself.

In cases where we have relieved the gas condition, the heart symptoms, such as flutter or extra fast heart beat, have often disappeared. Gas pressure can cause disturbance in any organ of the body, which may seem to be far removed from the seat of the pressure symptom. Gas pressure causes trouble in remote parts of the body reflexly, including headaches. Reflexly the pain of a toothache can be reduced by pressing on a finger; then instead of the aching tooth, we feel the finger pain. Pains are produced in parts of the body remote from the source not only from pressure caused by gas or prolapsus, but from se-

dentary occupations which force one organ against another.

In the normal iris the autonomic nerve wreath and the intestinal tract area should encircle the pupil in even outlines. If there is a closing-up of the wreath toward the pupil in the sigmoid colon area, you will usually find that what is causing the sigmoid colon to close up is prolapsus. When this condition exists in the sigmoid colon area, it usually exists also in the area of the cecum in the other iris. When the wreath extends towards organs in this manner, the trouble usually is due to pressure on these organs.

Mechanical pressure results when the law of gravity is violated. When we live a fatiguing and exhausting existence, every organ becomes prolapsed and remains in abnormal position. Pressure symptoms can be due to curvatures of the spine, to improper chemical balance which can produce drooped shoulders, or to occupations which necessitate constant sitting or standing in one position. A person who sits and holds his arms in one position while driving an automobile over long periods can produce anemic symptoms in his body that actually cannot be remedied unless postural positions are assumed which will overcome this mechanical abuse. Mechanical pressure on any organ can produce tissue degeneration just as readily as chemical imbalance, because mechanical pressure interferes with the blood supply.

When you find tissue depletion for which you cannot find a reason, it is well to check the environment of the patient for enervating conditions. Examine the spine and determine whether there is weakening of nerve tissue or of nerve force. Treatments by chiropractic, osteopathy and various mechanical techniques will help to maintain a normal flow of nerve force, and are the finest means of releasing the right amount of energy to the various organs, because these treatments help to relieve the mechanical pressures of the body.

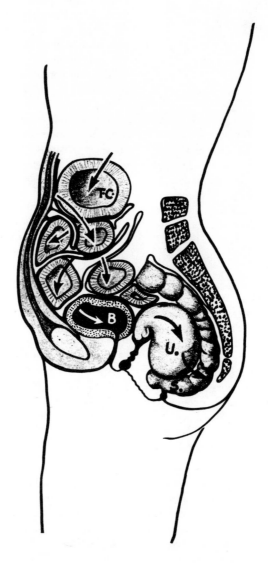

FIG. 104.   Cross section of the body
showing dropped transverse colon causing pressure on lower organs, such as
ovaries, uterus, bladder and rectum.
The transverse colon (T.C.) has prolapsed and is exerting the greatest
pressure on the bladder (B), the uterus
(U.), and the sigmoid colon (S.).

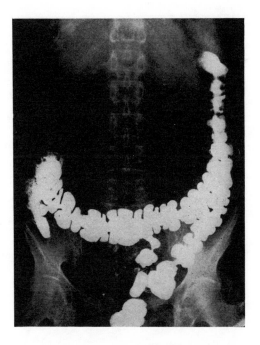

FIG. 105 (a).   Twenty-four hour film
showing prolapsus.

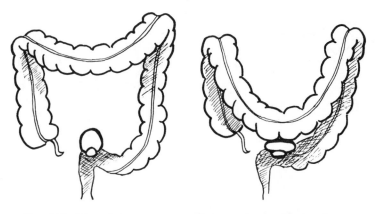

FIG. 105 (b).   It is easy to see why a patient with the above
condition would be complaining of bladder pressure symptoms. In a case like this the symptoms disappeared when the
mechanical pressure from the transverse colon was removed.

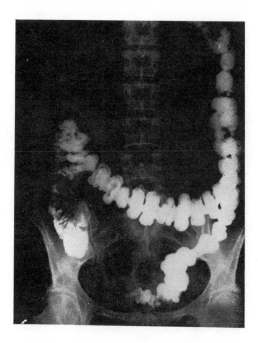

FIG. 106 (a). Twenty-four hour film
showing prolapsus.

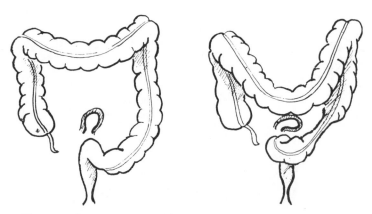

FIG. 106 (b). A patient with the condition indicated above
consistently complained of left leg and groin pain. The disorders of the uterus and the leg were due to this prolapsus.
There was more pressure on the left side than on the right.

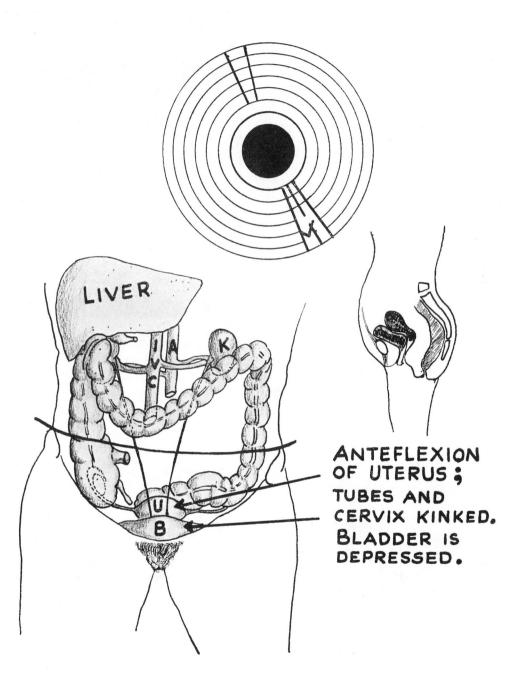

LIVER

ANTEFLEXION
OF UTERUS;
TUBES AND
CERVIX KINKED.
BLADDER IS
DEPRESSED.

FIG. 107.   In the above diagram, note that the prolapsed transverse colon causes protrusion against the uterus and bladder. Sterility can result from prolapsus. A cyst will not drain properly in this kind of prolapsus. Acute inflammation can result from constant irritation of one organ pressing against another.

Habitual posture of course must be considered, for this is important. If we are considering an inanimate structure such as a bridge, we can readily understand that if it were ever so slightly out of proper alignment, the resulting stress would cause deterioration. It is more difficult to realize that the body must surely suffer and degenerate from strain when its structural parts are out of alignment so they cannot properly carry out their function of weight-bearing. The person who habitually uses his organism in such a manner that there is constant tension in his neck and head, or any other part of the body, is causing interference with proper drainage, blood and lymph circulation, and flow of nerve force in these parts. A person who has developed a large abdomen cannot have a normal blood supply in the legs because of pressure on the veins and arteries leading to the legs. The nerves will also be compressed.

The colon and intestinal tract areas in the iris have a direct reflex relation to the organs represented opposite them. In cases

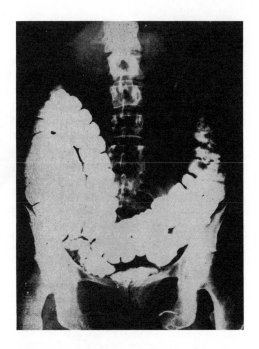

Fig. 109.   X-ray picture showing dropped transverse colon.

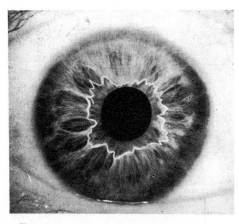

Fig. 108.   Dropped transverse colon.

of dropped transverse colon there usually are reflex conditions in the brain. Defective functioning of the transverse colon is reflected in defective memory, judgment, and concentration; it may influence the development of an inferiority complex. We see,

therefore, that it is important to remedy mechanical sources of disturbance in the body.

Q—FURTHER DISCUSSION OF LESIONS

In order that you may know the extent to which symptoms can develop, it is well to present the symptomatic approach to all the known organ areas in the iris. We have learned already that when examining the iris we often see evidence of a chronic condition in some organ or organs which may not be expressed symptomatically for years to come. With this valuable technique of predictability we can enlighten the patient as to where his weakness lies, and can launch a program for regeneration of the tissues.

Consider the value of having detected iris signs of ataxia in the area of locomotion. Many lower back and leg conditoins have been treated locally when the trouble actually was coming from the center of locomotion in the brain. In cases of varicose veins in the legs which recently have become ulcerated, what you will see in the iris are acute active white lines. If the condition is chronic with little vein contraction, the leg area in the iris will be darkened. As we mention in later chapters, an important consideration is that mechanical pressure from the transverse colon can interfere with circulation of the blood to and from the legs. This can be offset to a great extent by having the patient lie with the feet above the head.

Pressure symptoms can cause acute inflammation in the uterus, which will appear as white lines in the iris. Menstrual disorders, especially if accompanied by pain, will also be evidenced by white lines, but if the condition is chronic, the area will turn dark. If the uterus is overactive and the menstrual periods occur too frequently, an acute sign will be represented as white lines in the uterine area of the iris.

Lesions of the prostate gland may be revealed in the iris when by finger examination they would be missed. You will of course know the size of the prostate by palpation, but many times its size is dependent upon inherent structure. And you cannot determine the inherent vitality of the gland by feeling it. The prostate may be chronically enlarged, but this does not necessarily mean that it is overactive. Furthermore, you cannot always determine by palpation whether the gland is cancerous, but through the iris we have the opportunity of seeing whether there is a cancerous base and the constitutional possibilities the patient has of overcoming the problem in that particular area. You can go even further. From the iris you can tell whether the prostate gland is causing any sexual disturbances by checking the gland area opposite the sex life and mentality areas. A man goes through the climacteric, as does a woman, and many of the altered conditions are reflected to the

mentality area. When looking at this area for physical causes, see the relation between brain and sex gland areas. By means of iridology, anyone adequately trained to handle these conditions, whether physical or mental, can go directly to the basis of a problem and deal with the cause immediately; not the effects.

When there is a lesion in the visual center, the environment must first be corrected. If the patient cannot change his occupation or tissue structure sufficiently to carry on his activities without inordinate strain, we should see that he is helped with glasses. If the condition is very acute, the white lines will be in evidence, but if there has been deterioration over a period of years and a chronic condition has developed, the visual area in the iris will appear darkened.

With an acute condition in the speech center of the iris, the patient's problem may be stuttering or stammering. The appearance of the speech center area tells us its condition with respect to thought and speech coordination. If a person cannot speak normally, look to the causes behind the speech defect. This may be difficult since there is still so much research work to be done in this field. One of the causes may be the forced use of the right hand in a person whose tendency from childhood was to use the left hand predominantly. If there is a weakened speech center on one side of the brain, we should attempt to develop the speech center on the other side. This can be accomplished to a marked degree by developing the use of the opposite hand and eye insofar as possible.

The auditory center can break down from an excess amount of catarrhal settlement or from shock, which will be evidenced in the iris by a white line. If this white line is being developed there because of nerve irritation from some other part of the body, we then look for an acutely irritating, emotionally stimulating circumstance that may be producing this auditory condition. When the hearing has become defective and there is a chronic dark latent sign in the auditory centers, determine whether wax is settled in the ear which may be causing the poor hearing.

A catarrhal settlement can cause inflammation in and around the nose, the pharynx, and the larynx. If it has been there for a long period, the patient may not be complaining of any discharge at the present time. Affected areas are chronically laden with toxic material, and an eliminative process will have to be induced in these particular organs in order for it to be thrown off. An old dry mucous membrane will be made active again when you bring the patient through such a cleansing crisis. When the tonsils have been removed there is very little you can do in this particular area. It is interesting to note, however, that although healing signs cannot be made to appear in the area of the tonsils if they are no longer a part of the body, signs which show healing in associated organs will appear in the corresponding iris areas. It is these organs which will have to do more than their share in order to compensate for the lack of tonsil tissue.

Acids and catarrh, or mucus, as catarrh is often misnamed, cannot be eliminated by an inherently weak organ. Catarrh cannot be eliminated if there is not enough blood in the tissues to maintain sufficient strength. In addition to adequate circulation of blood to these tissues, there must be the right chemical balance in order to eliminate catarrh.

We are less interested in the waste of the body than we are in the power and strength of the tissues to cope with this waste material. When we speak of resistance to disease, we speak of the power of the body to overcome disease. We know that germ life exists throughout the world and must find its host to live on, and that bacteria are necessarily here to stay. But if the body is strong and has power, then no destructive germ life can settle in any

organ. Likewise, we are not so interested in acid body conditions as we are in the ability of the body to get rid of the acids. Whether the body tissues are overladen with lactic, uric, or sulphuric acid, we know that sufficient power in the body can overcome any of them. If the body is weak, however, then the acids may alter body chemistry and undermine health.

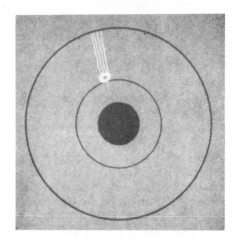

Fig. 110. This drawing illustrates an acute lesion, which is one of the many signs that may appear in the ego pressure center.

If you see a black line or spot in the ego pressure or apoplectic center, interpret this as forewarning of an impending stroke and act accordingly to prevent this if possible. With the development of high blood pressure the patient is in a state of tense emotional strain which is reflected as a white line in the brain area of the iris. If the area is already a dark shade, this indicates that the stroke already has occurred.

In cases of dizziness, the cause may be an acute condition in some part of the body. If it is a chronic problem, there will be a chronic sign in the iris. On the other hand, if the dizziness is due to menstrual disorders, the dizziness center in the brain area will show up more at this particular period than during the rest of the month. You may not detect this condition, however, if you diagnose a woman patient in between her periods. During an epileptic spell you will find more acute lines in the iris than when the patient is not under this stress. Hysteria, which may come in cycles, can be compared to the menstrual periodicity. The signs will appear in the hysteria center and in the sex life and mentality areas more acutely at these periods than at other times.

As we have mentioned before, you cannot determine from the iris the presence of gallstones or kidney stones, but you can judge whether stone formation is likely since you can tell from the iris whether these organs are too inactive to eliminate stone-forming material. Likewise, you cannot tell the amount of catarrh settled in the bronchial tubes or lungs, but you can tell the ability of the lungs to get rid of the accumulated toxic material.

In reviewing the above conditions, do you see the relation between changes in the fibres of the iris of the eye and the changes in bodily organs? If there is an overactive condition in any organ of the body, there is also an acute white line appearing in the iris of the eye indicating this overactivity. When a latent condition exists, with no pain and no discharge, the iris appears dark or gray in that particular area.

Let us always remember that in iridology we are reading the tissue signs of the body, the chemical balance, and the amount and kind of blood in the tissues. We are also reading the constitutional ability of a particular organ to get well, or to develop a disease. The iridologist can lift his patient's mental level by showing that it is not necessary to fear disease. He has a basis upon which to assure his patient

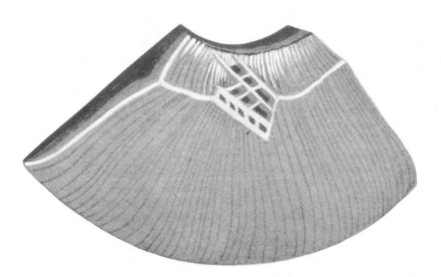

FIG. 111.   This drawing illustrates how coronary occlusion looks in the iris of the eye. The autonomic nerve wreath is involved and usually is very white. The dark portions of course represent chronicity, inactivity and destruction of tissue, and the inability of tissue to withstand strenuous physical exertion.

since from the iris he can determine what organs need to be strengthened—what tissues are in greatest need of repair, and can supervise a health-building program for the patient.

In collaboration with iridology, natural methods build good health. Nature cure doctors are not concerned with the negative aspects of disease or how to fight a disease condition. Rather than giving attention to factors such as those which disturb mental equilibrium or instill fear of what may happen next, they are interested in teaching how to live healthy, positive, peaceful lives. A healthy body is necessary to complete peace of mind.

The power of will is related to the response of the body tissues. Without the power of the body to carry through our ideas, accomplishment is difficult, so we must consider will power a physical, as well as a mental, faculty. It is extremely difficult for a sick person to direct his will one way or another. We can evaluate the power of will in his body by his muscle tone. Educating the will is one of the most important factors in educating the mind, and as we build the whole body, the will power becomes stronger.

After you use iridology time and time again, on problems such as these described above, you will see its advantages. You may have a discharge analyzed in a laboratory, but to know that the cause may have a mental basis or that it is due to nerve tension is a big step toward putting you on the path toward the accomplishment of "cure." What laboratory test could be made to reveal nerve tension in any organ? It is not possible to learn from laboratory tests whether the trouble is due to environment or is arising from within the body itself. Although iridology is not all-inclusive, and other forms of analysis have important applications, much information which laboratory testing fails to provide, only iridology can supply.

R—THE BRAIN IN IRIDOLOGY

In spite of the great importance of our brain, in the growth of the science of iridology less has been discovered in connection with these areas than any others in the body. Modern life compels us to expend a great deal of brain energy in order to survive the tempo and complexities of our civilization—speed, noise, insecurity, anxiety, financial problems, hectic marriages, divorce courts.

How important is the brain? We know that in it every gland has its center of activity; that there every action starts. The brain is the organ of psychic, telepathic, and spiritual activities. Through it we experience our feeling world, our anxious moments, our fleeting perceptions, our egotistic ambitions. Surely we should look first to the brain in our search for means of correction. There must be a way of determining whether a patient is becoming psychopathic, so that he may be counseled and his condition brought under control.

Iridology has the greater part of the answer. With this key we can unlock the cause of many a difficulty—whether internal or external; whether direct or reflected. If it is necessary to handle an emotional problem, to alter the environment, to outline a new diet or suggest supplementary feeding, or to advise exercise,—iridology can be used as your guide or used in conjunction with any other diagnostic methods.

The brain substance which we inherit has the potentiality for extensive development as we go through life. We cannot acquire knowledge without the necessary foundation—good brain structure. An idiot can be developed to only a limited extent during his lifetime.

The development of psychosomatic medicine shows the extent to which we now recognize the inseparability in the mind-body relationship. Thus the organ of the mind, the brain, now receives more attention than in earlier times. The doctor of the new day will recognize that a man's most important workshop is not the physical body but the mind that controls it. He will see that the sustaining attitudes and the mental equipment we possess are most important in the proper balance of body functions.

Besides the sensory activities which are expressed through the physiological side of the brain, there are the senses which function through our psychological brain. These senses—which have to do with deep reflex feelings, impressions of heat and cold, etc.—often are distorted before there has been time for reasoning to produce positive feelings, final impressions, logical conclusions. We can base our psychological counseling upon the findings in this five-sense area of the brain in the iris.

Even though we can define a certain area in the iris as a blood pressure center, we must consider additional factors. After considerable study and deliberation, I firmly believe that this brain area is the "ego center." The person whose ego is under stress can raise his blood pressure. He may be trying to strengthen his ego by boasting and "putting on a false front." He increases the pressure in proportion to the intensity of his thought activity; in proportion to his degree of fear and anxiety and the degree to which he forces his ego to the fore. "Elephantitis" of the ego can put the organism under considerable strain. In explaining to such patient about the condition of his ego pressure center, we will of course emphasize the importance of having toxin-free blood to nourish the brain centers, but we will also go further and point out that he must develop control and direction of energy in coping with life's problems.

To some patients we will need to explain that the inharmonies of fear, hate, anxiety, contention, disrespect, etc., produce a kind of tension attitude within the body-mind, the expression of which finds its way to physical cell structure and results in irritation and possibly in pain and dis-ease. The victim may set up a resistance which is even more painful to the mind, and which will be reflected in tension and physical abnormalities. If the patient's hate complex, for instance, stems from some childhood experience, we can help him to allocate the hate; we can help him see that it is not necessary to feel hatred toward the whole world because he felt it toward some individual in the past. After it has been allocated to that one person, even that eventually can be neutralized. Our compassion for him will help to release his tension. While hate expressions can cause a condition of hyperactivity in the brain centers, those of love can reduce this hyperactivity. The patient may be brought to understand that love is more potent in combating these particular mental acids than alkaline broths, etc. taken into the stomach to neutralize acids.

Evolution has brought changes which have to do with man's finer forces—forces so sensitive that their vibratory patterns are affected by our mental attitude in every word we express. A person who feels blue is temporarily influenced by something just as tangible to him as the man who is sculpturing, painting, or playing a violin. The cells of his body will be affected in an entirely different manner from those of a person who is in a joyous mood.

Wonderful possibilities for getting to the bottom of complex problems are offered by iridology. By examining the brain areas in the iris and determining the strength or weakness of the inherent structure, we know the capabilities of the patient. If we find hypoactivity in an inherently weak structure, we may assume that the person does not have inner control. Possibly this hypoactive condition has gradually developed, through toxic engorgement, to the point where he is no longer himself. In contrast to the hyperactive patient who has a disease, in this case the disease has him.

Transmitted through the brain is the very spiritual essence that animates every cell of the body. The brain is the first organ to register fatigue, and the faculty that controls fatigue is animation. Consider the effect upon these important centers when not enough good blood is supplied to them and they become clogged with toxic settlement. All parts of the body will be affected. If the faculty of animation is not functioning well, we feel languid; the energy mental center becomes under-active, the entire eliminative system becomes sluggish, and the whole glandular system becomes less responsive. The pituitary gland, which is considered to be the master gland, is a part of the animation center, a part of the ego center, and is also a part of our five-sense center. The animation center and the spirit within need to be more closely allied with the physical body.

S—PUPILLARY REACTIONS

The pupil of the eye is in constant motion. The orifice contracts in accordance with the nerve tone and with the light intensity to which it is subjected. You will be able to determine the normal tension of the pupil only after analyzing many eyes.

When the pupil is relaxed and has poor tone, the condition of the fibres is flaccid. On the other hand, when the pupil is contracted, it puts tension on the fibres all the way to the periphery of the iris. This tenseness represents the tone of the whole body. The orifice of the pupil is influenced to dilate or contract by mental and physical reactions to stimulation, animation, etc. Fatigue and the general tone of the body can be determined from the tone of the pupil. All orifices work in direct relation to that of the pupil.

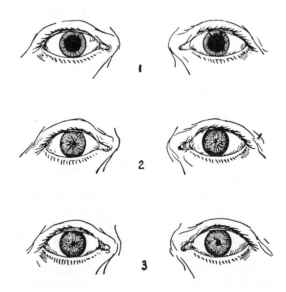

Fig. 112. Diagnosis from the eye-pupils. The eye-pupils are (1) dilated in alcoholic intoxication; (2) contracted (to "pin-points") in opium poisoning; and (3) insensible to light and may be contracted unequally in a case of stroke. By observation of the pupil you can differentiate between brain concussion and compression. In concussion the pupils may be either dilated or contracted, but usually are even. In compression they usually are uneven.

FIG. 113.   Diagram illustrating degrees of pupillary tonicity
in relation to tone of fibres in the iris.
A—represents atonicity.
B—represents hypotonicity.
C—represents normal iris fibre tone.

The pupillary border may be drawn toward the area representing the lesion of greatest irritation in the body. As to whether the direction of the pull is inward or outward will depend upon whether the stimulus is from the central nervous system or from the autonomic nervous system. We have described the iris plexus which makes up the autonomic nerve wreath encircling the intestinal tract, and now wish to mention that encircling the pupil is a plexus representing the central nervous system.

When there is a strong pull from nerve rings within the iris, you will find corresponding stress and strain in the organs represented in the areas through which the nerve rings pass. If any particular organ is reflecting an extreme amount of irritation and its iris area includes more than one nerve ring, the pull will be greatest on those particular fibres. The autonomic nerve wreath will be drawn toward that particular organ area involved in this extreme nerve tension. When this condition exists, the parasympathetic nervous system is under a greater strain than the central

nervous system and the pupil is drawn toward the affected organ.

When there is a great amount of strain on the central nervous system and a pull toward the pupil, the pupillary border will be flattened. This flattened surface indicates a lack of tone, a lack of function, and the incapability of the organ opposite the pull to recuperate.

The pupillary border can become like leather. From the coloring of that leathery edge, we can determine whether the stomach is in a chronic or a sub-acute stage of inflammation. When it is light brown, we know that the inflammation is in an active stage; when it is a very dark muddy brown, then we know the condition has existed a long time and is in a chronic stage. A person whose living habits have been poor and who has abused his stomach dietetically over a period of years may have a stomach that has become toughened, scarred, hard, and inactive. This chronic state of physiological function is represented in the iris by a dark brown circle around the pupillary edge of the stomach area.

16

THE HEALING CRISIS IN PRACTICE

A healing crisis is an acute reaction resulting from the ascendance of Nature's healing forces over disease conditions. Its tendency is toward recovery, and it is, therefore, in conformity with Nature's constructive principle.

—From a catechism of Naturopathy

A healing crisis is the result of an industrious effort of every organ in the body to eliminate waste products and set the stage for regeneration. Through this constructive process toward health, old tissues are replaced with new. A disease crisis, on the other hand, is not a natural one; every organ in the body works against it, rather than with it as in the healing crisis.

The signs of the healing crisis in the iris are the reflection of an acute eliminative process taking place in all the organs of the body. You have already learned about the appearance of disease signs in the iris. The one way to tell whether the crisis is a healing one or a disease one is that in a disease crisis only part of the body shows marked changes. The white lines in the iris are confined mainly to one or two organ areas. The reason for this is that the strong organs, which are working against the disease, will not show crisis signs in the iris. Disease does not have the support of the whole body. In a healing crisis there is usually a fever or catarrhal elimination; and every organ area in the iris will have healing signs in it since every organ is working for the health of the entire body.

The experience of going through a healing crisis will seem very much like having disease because of re-experiencing disease symptoms; but there is a very important distinction—elimination. In the healing crisis, the elimination is perfect. The bowel movement is natural. All eliminative organs are doing their part. Right up to the time of the crisis all elimination is regular. But in the diseased state elimination usually stops or is unsatisfactory, which adds to the trouble. In the healing crisis the eliminative processes have become more acute because of the abundance of stored-up energy. Whatever catarrh and other forms of waste have been stored in the body are now in a dissolved, free-flowing state, and a cleansing, purifying process is under way.

When healing lines appear in the intestinal tract area of the iris, every organ begins to show improvement. These healing lines—or *calcium luteum* lines, as Liljequist describes them—may be likened to strong pillars used to bolster up a house which probably has been abused for some time. By putting in new timber, a stronger foundation is provided. And so it is with the body; new tissue replaces the old. This

191

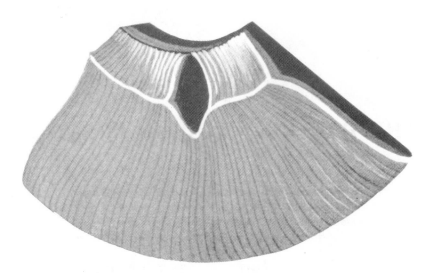

FIG. 114.   This drawing illustrates the chronic toxic lesion before
any healing signs have appeared. This is where the doctor starts
with the average patient. His job is to handle the patient so that
the lesion is filled with new healing lines.

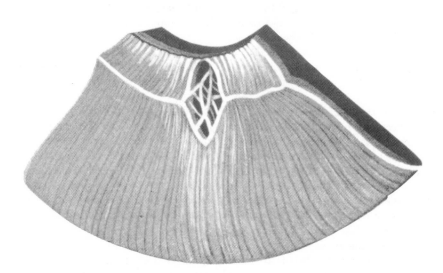

FIG. 115.   This drawing represents a pocket or lesion in the iris,
which appears black because the dark pigment layer underneath is
exposed. In the healing process, white lines fill in this hole and the
black disappears. When in a crisis the network of white fibres has
been completed, this indicates that the organ represented by that
area now has the strength necessary for normal healthy functioning.
It indicates that the weak organ has built up as much strength as
it is possible for it to have; now it is toxin free.

replacement is represented by the healing lines in the iris. In time, the new tissue becomes strong enough to take its place in the various activities of the body. What becomes of the old tissue? It is not absorbed immediately; nor is it eliminated from the body immediately. It is exchanged by the blood stream over a period of months in a gradual process of reabsorption. This process of building up new cellular structure has been accomplished through good blood and through the circulation of the blood where it is needed. The real cure has taken place when new tissue is exchanged for the old by the blood stream.

The health routine outlined by the doctor may extend for varying lengths of time before the crisis is reached. In a child it may be only a seven- to fourteen-day period. In adults it occurs usually after the third month. Some cases work out in cycles of seven and therefore reach the crisis on the seventh, fourteenth, twenty-first, twenty-eighth, etc., day.

The crisis can come without warning, but generally you will know it is close at hand by the patient's telling you how wonderful he feels. The final day of the eliminative period comes as an explosion, so to speak. The vital force and energies have been turned loose. This explosion, or exchange of new tissue for old, comes only when there is power from this new tissue which has come into activity. The old has spent itself and the new, built from life-giving foods and health-building processes, has grown stronger than the old, abused tissue. Tissue that has been built from poor food and bad living habits will some-day have to wrestle with the tissue created from natural foods. It is plain to see which will dominate. That is why we say a crisis is a blessing in disguise. Most persons cannot realize that they have passed through a "knothole," so to speak, with the new now asserting itself.

There are three stages through which a person must pass in getting well. They are the eliminative, the transitional, and the building stages. The crisis usually occurs during the transitional period, which is the time when the new tissue has matured sufficiently to take on the functions of a more perfect body.

A healing crisis usually lasts about three days, starting with slight pains and discomfort which may become more severe until the point of complete expulsion has been reached. Following this the pains diminish. If the energy of the patient is low, the crisis sometimes lasts for a week or more. The stronger the vitality and the greater the power of the patient, the more profoundly will he be affected by the crisis.

Although there are many paths which lead to a crisis, fasting will bring healing lines into the iris quicker than any other method. Fasting alone is not enough, however, for complete recovery from all ailments. The chemical elements that are necessary for rebuilding the body and instructions for proper living should be given by the doctor following the fast.

Through the iris, you will see how the healing signs represent a fairly normal chemical balance. A person taking calcium only, for instance, would not show the healing lines as they would appear if the right balance of sodium, silicon, iodine, and the rest of the necessary minerals were included. Healing lines appear only when healing begins, and when the blood is carrying all required elements.

Many times during a fast a crisis does not occur. If this is the case, a short time on a health-building program will be necessary before the crisis will develop. All conditions must be in its favor—climate and altitude, the right mental attitude, healthful eating habits and good elimination, etc. Think of the whole body getting into action and correcting conditions.

Although a crisis cannot be brought about without proper diet, or fasting, the best diet in the world is ineffectual if the patient needs corrective exercises. If there is a mental state causing a great deal of irritation or colitis in the bowel, the best colonic will not cure it—nor even the best of any other physical method. Proper diet and a good bowel condition can accomplish a great deal, yet with a heavy catarrhal condition in the body, there may be many small crises to go through before the final one is possible. Everything must be considered and given its proper place in the build-up to a healing crisis.

A lady patient I had been treating for some time was about due for her healing crisis, I thought, when one morning about two o'clock she telephoned to say she was suffering from excruciating pains in the stomach. When I arrived at her home, she was in the process of using a stomach pump. Upon questioning this patient I found she had changed her diet somewhat, but not enough to prevent the healing signs from being present in her irises. She had previously asked if she could have pumpernickel bread. Since she was seventy-five years of age I did not want to make too many drastic changes or omit bread from her diet entirely, which I would have done had she been younger. I had agreed to the pumpernickel bread in her diet, therefore, assuming the intake would be moderate. Needless to say, I was surprised to learn that she had been eating a full loaf of bread with each meal—breakfast, lunch, and dinner. Then I realized, of course, that her pain and distress had nothing to do with the healing crisis. The bread eating had slowed down the process.

The iris gives you a wonderful check on the patient. If he has been following your instructions the evidence will be there. The type of healing crisis we have been discussing is only for certain persons however—those who desire to live in accordance with natural laws.

Years ago I put a man, almost blind and with heart trouble, on a regular health routine of diet, exercise, and rest. About three months after starting treatment, I was called to the house. This man was having a heart crisis. His heart was beating so forcibly that his bed was moving on its casters. I knew this was a crisis and that he would come through all right. His crisis lasted twelve hours. Almost immediately afterward he was able to read the newspaper for the first time in years. Later he was able to read fine print, and in about two months he attended a motion picture show. His heart condition was not entirely cured but the crisis brought him to the stage of eliminating the toxic material from his body, and the building process which followed restored him to fairly good health.

Remember that when the healing crisis is in progress there is under way an acute stage of what previously occurred during the course of a disease process. While eliminating the trouble there is a step-by-step retracing. "All cure starts from within out and from the head down and in reverse order as the symptoms have appeared," as Hering states. In order to get well, the patient must go through the crisis. You must expect it, look for it, and work toward it.

A lady patient I had one time had spent three years traveling to various doctors and sanitariums throughout the country in an effort to obtain the healing of fourteen leg ulcers. These healed in three weeks' time due to her cooperation in taking nothing but a broth made from the tops of vegetables. No crisis occurred during this three-week period, but after about three months under my care, this patient lost her sight for two days. At first she could not understand why this should happen and then she remembered an incident a number of years before, when, as a piano teacher, she had worked so intensely in preparing for a recital that she lost her sight for two days. After this lapse of time her sight was restored to the state when the disorder began.

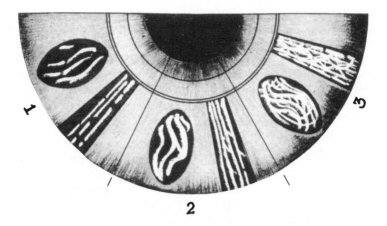

FIG. 116. The time required for the healing crisis to come to fulfillment depends upon how chronic are the lesions, and also upon the patient's living habits and the recuperative power of his tissues. As illustrated in the three stages above, you will note certain changes during the first month, more healing lines during the second month, and so on to completion.

Depending upon the length of time required for the formation of healing lines equal to those shown in the above sections representing each month, you will be able to judge the probable length of time which will be required to precipitate a crisis. For example, if a particular patient requires two months in stage 1, it may require six months for him to reach the crisis at stage 3. If the patient's progress is so slow that he requires four to six months' time in stage 2, this may be due to poor recuperative ability. If this is not the case, either he is not cooperating or you are not instructing him correctly.

Usually people forget what diseases or injuries they may have had in the past, but during the crisis are almost always reminded of what they had forgotten. The eye never "forgets," as all injuries are registered there.

This same patient had an extreme curvature of the spine. As her healing progressed, she developed a severe "cold" which lasted fifteen or twenty days. It was necessary to assist her eliminative process with frequent eliminative treatments. During one of these treatments, she underwent the retracing of an experience she had gone through in an accident fifteen years previously. For a few moments, she seemed to go all to pieces. Her tongue swelled and she could hardly talk. For fifteen minutes or so her body shook all over and she seemed to be in a critical condition. But after this experience was over, the spinal tension disappeared, the curvature was decreased, and there was constant improvement in the spine throughout the following year. She felt better than she had in many years.

These case histories are presented because we want to verify the rule that there is a step-by-step retracing, in the reverse order, of the disease conditions experienced through life. The retracing process is justified when we stop to think that a person's living habits and the food he eats determine the kind of tissue he has. In order to rid the body of the tissue built from injurious living habits,—tissue that holds disease symptoms lying latent in chronic tissue,—the retracing process, the healing crisis, is necessary. "We suffer the sins of our flesh." We suffer these during the processes of the healing crisis, which is the absolute purification process.

We should not force a tissue into an acute condition unless the whole body is ready for it. The eliminative processes of the kidneys will be more active and the results more permanent if the other eliminative organs are functioning adequately. The stomach can better overcome its problem if the bowel is working normally. If there is a bronchial discharge and elimination, the bowels will aid in this, the elimination becoming more complete as the patient goes through the crisis. In producing a crisis, as much help as possible is needed from every organ. This is why a healing crisis is more successful when the doctor has been treating the "organism-as-a-whole-in-the-environment" rather than only certain organs, as is so often done in ordinary office practice. The doctor who understands the healing crisis knows that it progresses most satisfactorily when a complete right-living program has been followed.

We can almost always predict the approach of a crisis through iridology. We know that when healing signs develop in the iris the organs under observation now have not only improved circulation, but are supplied with a superabundance of clean, healthy blood. It is this surplus blood in the area that is going to build better tissue. Under high power magnification you can see small white lines appearing in a deep hole, finally building up to the surface. When these lines come to the surface and become very white, the crisis point has been reached. An inherently weak hole in the iris can be compared

to a hole in a sock. When darning this hole, you start with a coarse weave of cross fibres, and finally fill in with a finer weave. Healing signs do not follow the fibres of the eye; they can go crosswise, sideways, or in any direction.

Since healing signs are dependent upon the degree of chronicity, the patient's living habits, and tissue response to these habits, you cannot predict from the iris the exact time when a patient's crisis will occur. Keeping in mind the conditions just mentioned, judge when you would expect crisis signs to appear, and then tell your patient you think that within a certain number of weeks he may expect his crisis if he continues to follow the health-building program you have outlined.

You can help to bring forth a reaction in any organ of the body through stimulation, and there are many methods for this purpose. An organ whose processes have been thus speeded up will absorb more nourishment etc., but such stimulation to individual organs does not produce lasting effects. The reason for this is that there isn't healthy support from the other organs of the body. This is one reason why we do not believe in specialized treatment of any one organ when the condition requiring correction is constitutional. In a complete healing crisis for the good of the whole body, every organ manifests changes for the better. In this way whatever change has come about will remain because the whole structure has been strengthened enough to maintain the revitalized condition.

No doubt you will handle many unusual crises in your practice. I am reminded of the case of a man with stomach trouble. After treating him for some time the stomach condition was cleared up, but during the crisis he developed a very severe backache. When I questioned him he could not recall having had any backache in the past, but after he completed the crisis he came in to see me. He reported that now he remembered a fall from a porch when a child, following which he had the same kind of back pain that he experienced during the crisis.

Another patient, who came to me from Fresno, California, was suffering from ulcers of the stomach. From the iris I found that this young man had sulphur deposits in his system and, although he said he had never taken sulphur into his body, it was there. Upon further questioning I learned that he had worked in a fruit drying or packing plant where sulphur was used. He had breathed the sulphur into his system. There are many ways of taking things into our systems as we see from the example of this young man who took in sulphur by inhaling it.

At the time of the healing crisis, this patient broke out with a skin rash. We must always expect some kind of skin rash or eruption when there is sulphur in the system. In an experiment once tried in an Eastern University, a number of boys were each given one-fourth teaspoon of sulphur. Within thirty days they all broke out with boils.

There is not only the physical healing crisis, but the mental crisis as well. As an example, in one of my cases the physical improvement which resulted from fasting, etc., enabled a tissue response in the brain area. I noticed a change in the sex life area, where healing lines were developing rapidly. I asked the patient whether there was something bothering her sexually or mentally and would she like to talk things over with me, but she replied that there was nothing on her mind. Two or three days later she asked to talk to me and went into a prolonged crying spell. She unravelled quite a story, telling me she had lost a child because the doctor who delivered the baby was under the influence of liquor at the time. The baby was born dead and the doctor said it was because she had contracted a disease from her husband, which I later showed her was not true, but probably was stated by the doctor to cover his own indignity. This information had tormented her for many years, and as a result she had developed a complex toward her husband and toward the sexual act which finally reached tremendous proportions in her mental make-up. In my talk with her I cleared up the problem by suggesting that she had a false conception of what had happened, and by pointing out that even if she had the disease, the fast would overcome it through the healing crisis. I pointed out that there are others who have had still-born babies and have not developed mental complexes, and that it was to her advantage to clear up this mental situation. After our talk she seemed like a new person mentally. Eventually she passed through her mental crisis, and after she returned home it was gratifying to receive a letter telling me how happy she was and how her married life had been practically made over because she now believed in her husband's innocence.

To have mental fixations and complexes cleared out of the mind is just as important as cleaning out the bowel or any organ structure of the body. In the process of trying to heal people through fasting, you will find that in many cases a long fast results in a phychic crisis. These psychic crises are very difficult to handle, and it takes considerable patience and understanding to carry the patient through. At this time the patient is in a mental state of reviewing the past. He will respond only to one in whom he has confidence and faith, and the person who is taking care of him must have a harmonious association with him. He will divulge many things from his subconscious mind which he will deny after the crisis is over. We know there are many memories and complexes buried in the mind that can be the cause of serious difficulties. I have heard patients undergoing crisis relate incidents that happened twenty or thirty years previously.

FIG. 117. Like the darning of a hole in a sock, the black-appearing hole in the iris is woven across with fibre threads until the white network completely obliterates the dark. This marks the point of the healing crisis.

Some of them bring up experiences in their sexual past which they would not reveal under other circumstances. This is one of the best housecleaning processes that could ever come to a patient. I do not advise prolonging a fast for the purpose of developing a psychic crisis, however.

On occasion I have used the assistance of a surgeon in a crisis. One such case was that of a male patient who had an inherent weakness in the right groin with lymphatic involvement. Catarrhal congestion was present throughout the body. As the result of treatment the catarrhal settlement was being eliminated through the glands in the groin. A swelling the size of a grapefruit formed. It seemed foolish to allow this mass to be absorbed and carried through the body for ultimate elimination, possibly through the lungs, kidneys, and bowels. Without an anesthetic, it was lanced and a quart and a half of pus was drained out.

Since the patient's body had brought on the crisis I believe it would have handled this eliminative process, but considering that the groin is not a vital organ, we decided in favor of draining the toxic material out through the skin. If a vital organ such as the bowel or the kidney had been involved, we would have left it to be eliminated through the natural channels. The surgeon working with me was an osteopathic physician who knew what a crisis was and understood what I wished to accomplish. The patient's psoriasis cleared up after this crisis.

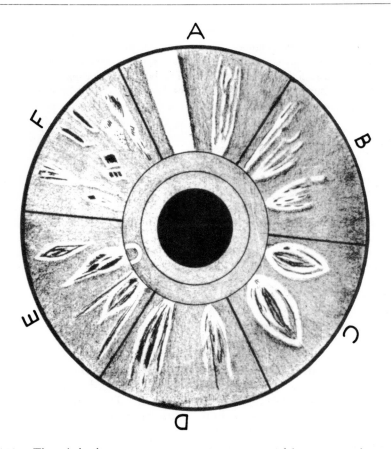

FIG. 118. Though healing signs can occur in any type of lesion, some lesions are more difficult to bring through a healing crisis than others. This drawing shows the white lines that indicate healing in various organ areas you may see in the iris. If you see acute white signs in any one organ area in the iris and none in the others, this signifies a disease crisis. These may be pain signs, but the pain will be that of disease rather than that of a healing crisis.

What is illustrated in section A of the above drawing may represent the first stage of acute elimination. All diseases that are being eradicated must be brought back to this stage. All diseases in this acute stage are painful, active, and eliminative. The healing crisis represents the acute stage of disease, a return to the first stage, and overcoming this is the healing. As long as any signs of coloration remain in any lesion, as indicated in sections B and C, there will be no healing crisis. In sections C and D the acute white lines may indicate the presence of pain in the corresponding organs. The lesions in C may represent cyst formation and those in section D a rheumatic condition in the leg. Section E contains lesions which may occur in the glands, showing overactivity but no pain. In the lesion markings of section F, which represent injuries from accidents, the dark portions indicate destruction of tissue, and the acute white lines around them indicate pain which may accompany this condition. These are not always a sign of healing. If instead of an intense transparent white the whiteness is opaque, this can indicate scar tissue.

The healing crisis might be called a purifying process. White (symbol of purity) will be found in the iris areas representing organs that are undergoing the purification process.

No two cases are alike. Because everyone lives his life unlike his neighbor's, has a dissimilar occupation, an environment he may be subconsciously fighting, an attitude of tension and pressure, there may be fifty different causes starting fifty different diseases.

During the time of crisis there is absence of appetite. One should follow the body's natural cravings. At this time the body needs water to help carry off the toxins that have reached the elimination point and this is a time for rest. "Rest it out," is an expression I use during the crisis period, and I mean mental as well as physical rest.

The patient should be advised not to overeat during a crisis and to eat foods which will assist the eliminative process. During the height of the crisis have the patient abstain from eating for the most part, to give the body a chance to work on the healing processes, or suggest that he eat only a very small quantity of food. Consider the body as being like a bank. If there has been a consistent deposit in the bank during the building process, there will be enough strength to draw upon when needed. If the patient is on a fast at the time the crisis comes, you might have him continue to the next period of seven days before breaking the fast. If he is feeling fine, however, and everything seems to be favorable, you may break the fast.

The crisis is not the accomplishment of the doctor, nor that of the patient, directly. The body processes accomplish it. The intelligence within the patient's body knows more about tissue structure repair and regeneration than any doctor could possibly know, regardless of the system of healing in which he believes.

The crisis time usually is the time when the doctor does the least for the patient. The effort is wholly that expended by the body to normalize itself, and in most cases it should be left alone to do this job. The doctor should be alert for fears that may develop, however, and should avoid treatments which either suppress or stimulate. The body that is capable of producing this healing is making a normal readjustment and needs no outside help. In most of these cases, it is not what we do for the patient but what we do not do that is important.

There does not seem to be the incentive to prevent disease that there should be today, nor do we have adequate education or the health ideals each individual should strive for, to carry out his own health program. It is regrettable that some persons are merely interested in getting by and seem unaware that they are committing slow suicide every waking moment. They are not interested in health until they lose it, or until their work is hampered; then they start looking for something to remedy their condition. When such a patient has been given up by his doctors, he at last awakens to the seriousness of his problem and is frightened enough to do something about it. The nature cure doctor often gets this patient when his hope is almost gone.

It is up to you as a doctor to bring your patient through the crisis for a cure, but do not always promise a cure because there is no such thing as absolute cure for everyone. It is for the doctor to decide with the patient just how a condition should be cared for, and the doctor should tell the patient exactly the way he works so he will know what to expect.

Do you see now what I mean by the healing crisis? Relatively little is generally known about it, or written about it, so far. Few doctors know very much about it. I feel fortunate that I have been able to observe all that I have concerning the healing crisis, and I have done my best to analyze and catalogue this information. The body could manifest no greater proof of its ability to be self-adjusting, self-regenerating, and self-healing than it does through the retracing of disease and the production of a healing crisis.

17

THE IRIS REVEALS THE CAUSES OF DIS-EASE

Let us first understand the facts,
and then we may seek the cause.
—Aristotle

What's in a name? So far as doctors are concerned, the answer to this question depends upon the training and the philosophy of the doctor. Those who have been thoroughly indoctrinated in a method which requires the name that applies to a patient's symptoms before therapy can be instituted, are necessarily very much interested in the names of diseases. But the name is comparatively insignificant to the doctor who recognizes symptoms as mere effects, and knows the basic importance of getting to the bottom of disease conditions by cleansing the entire system and eradicating the *causes* which underlie symptoms. Regardless of the label generally attached to a syndrome of symptoms, he knows that in all cases the dis-eased body will have to go through certain healing processes in order for health to be restored. Every organ responds, in minute detail, to the health or the disease in every other organ.

In iridology, therefore, we do not work with the expectation of being able to see in the iris, signs which represent conditions that have been given numerous names in the system referred to. Instead of becoming so lost in a forest of symptoms that we cannot see the trees, or causes, we may diseregard the name which describes the breakdown symptoms of some particular organ, and try to understand the language of the patient's entire organism—as it is ex-

pressed in a diagnostic field such as the iris of the eye.

If we attempted to diagnose cancer from the iris, for example, what would we find? In cancer we find all stages of inflamation. How could there be any one sign in the iris for cancer when there are so many things that can cause it—among them being malnutrition; coal tar and other poisons in drug products, in artificial "foods," and in synthetic vitamin and hormone products; radiation from X-ray and radium treatments; local irritations; fear campaigns; emotionally disturbing environments; lack of spiritual values? Of the cancer cases I have examined, about 50 per cent show a drug settlement, which I believe is the underlying cause of the cancer in these patients. The iris also usually shows broken fibres surrounded by a jelly-like substance.

As another example, in the condition called asthma there is no one iris sign. A combination of glandular conditions may be involved, which can be different in every individual. It may be bronchial asthma, or it may be heart asthma.

In previous chapters we have discussed iris markings in the various organ areas. We are dealing with causes whose nature can be judged by the degree of inflamation

201

which the iris shows is present in an organ, and by additional signs such as drug deposits, with possible accompanying pressure from gas or from prolapsed organs.

Regardless of how extensively this newer approach is described or how thoroughly and repeatedly it is discussed, I feel certain there are bound to be some doctors who will ask me, "Now how can I determine this disease and how can I diagnose that disorder from the iris of the eye?" In answer to such inquiries, let me say first that those disorders which, instead of being reflex in nature, have their cause at the site of manifestation, can be determined specifically from the iris. Examples are diverticulitis, colitis, gas pressure, slow bowel movements, lack of bowel tone, traumatic conditions, extreme spinal subluxations, etc.

We have already stressed the importance of carefully examining the autonomic nervous system wreath in every case. If it shows acute inflamation coming from the spine, we know that mechanical therapy is indicated. In every organ area that registers a dis-ease manifestation, we always seek the reflex source that is causing it— which usually can be found in the intestinal tract.

From what has been presented, you already know how definitely you can detect abnormalities in any part of the body from iris analysis. And the findings regarding each patient will be different. You also know that you can detect from the iris incipient conditions which can then be prevented from developing.

As we are going to bring out in the Pictorial Section which follows, microscopic studies of other minute structures, besides the iris, give us invaluable information about interior conditions without cutting into the body to explore them. Consider how many doctors would like to know the degree of inflamation and abnormal activity in some organ such as the kidney from minute study of certain external structures. The time is coming when precision instruments will prove to their satisfaction the value of what I am teaching regarding the information we can obtain from study of the iris.

When you have come to appreciate fully the value and advantage of being able to determine from the outside of the body what is occurring within it, you will see how superior this method is in many ways to the laboratory diagnostic practices in common use, and you will no longer search feverishly for the appropriate *name* for a condition. Also, you will no longer try to treat the symptoms represented by a name, because you will be able to discover something far more important—the sources of these symptoms.

Part IV

PICTORIAL SECTION

18

IRIDOLOGY ILLUSTRATED

Introductory Remarks

In the following photographs we illustrate various problems and both normal and abnormal iris signs. After you have learned the combinations of these different signs, they will enable you to look at the patient as a whole. Since bodily organs are so inseparably interrelated, it is necessary to have both right and left irises completely represented in order to make a complete iris anaylsis.

At the beginning of this undertaking we did not realize that so much time and money would be involved in developing these plates for practical use. It is difficult to realize that over two thousand photographs were taken, from which these were selected. Little did we realize there would be such variation in patients' patience and in cameras, color, films, techniques, etc. This work is the result of my own research, ever keeping in mind the importance of clearly teaching and demonstrating this subject. We have employed the best in camera techniques and the best printing facilities available to date. I believe we are presenting a good all-around picture of the various iris manifestations.

The photographs have been made large so the markings can be seen with the naked eye, and they represent what would be seen under high magnification. The composite charts are presented in order to show the greatest variety of comparisons, individual lesions and colorings, etc.

In studying the Color Plates of the iris it will be necessary to become photograph minded and to apply this in analyzing the iris of the patient. It is also necessary to become clock minded so as to locate organ areas according to clock numerals.

It is well to consider comparing one iris area with another, noting its density and the depth of lesions. Also, it is well to locate the autonomic nerve wreath if possible; this is the most important landmark.

Rather than reproduce the entire iris of each one selected to illustrate various iris signs (lesions, colorings, shadings, density, etc.), it was decided to present only portions of each. It is these portions which compose each Color Plate. In other words, the composite plate was not made with the idea that a complete diagnosis can be made of the patient whose iris section is presented.—For example, one of the sections in Color Plate No. 3 is from the iris of an epileptic patient. The section we chose from that particular iris, however, had other signs which were considered more valuable, especially since the epileptic lesion was rather indistinct. In eye photography, the amount of illumination required sometimes makes it practically impossible to see the translucent fibres. You will see these in your practice, however. Furthermore, the underlying and accompanying conditions which are indicated in this section (discoloration, inherent weakness, bowel disorders, drug poisoning) no doubt were more responsible for the epileptic conditions than the small degree of irritation that was indicated by the actual lesion in the epileptic center. In such an indistinct lesion, healing signs would be hardly noticeable and it would not be a good example of an epileptic patient.—Therefore, those sections were selected which contained the clearest examples of lesions and other signs, regardless of whether all the symptoms mentioned in connection with a case (left-hand page) were represented therein.

In order to show these signs still more clearly, a composite line drawing has been placed below each composite Color Plate, representing its various sections and showing the iris markings in bold outline. The lettering corresponds to signs which are worthy of study.

Superimposed upon the drawing in Color Plate No. 3, with the proper portions to fit each section, is a composite of parts of my iris chart. This combination outlines particular lesions and shows the organ areas in which they are located. I wish to explain that the parts which make up this composite of my chart are of necessity out of the positions they occupy in the regular complete chart. This of course is because each chart section must correspond to the iris section reproduced in the drawing beneath it. For example, in Color Plate No. 3, Section 3, the animation and life center is not in the regular location at 12 o'clock. If it is easier for you, you can turn the book so that this center is at 12 o'clock and so that any center at which you are looking is in the regular chart position.

In the material on the left-hand pages, comparisons of special interest are called to your attention, details are given of the symptoms represented in the Color Plates, etc. This was planned so that all aspects can be studied in one place rather than requiring constant referral from text discussion to iris plates elsewhere.

We include a number of black and white photographs which contain certain markings we wish to illustrate, but which are difficult to photograph, require special lighting, etc. Also included are some unusual photographs, which should be of interest to you, of another minute structure besides the iris: the capillaries under the tongue and in the lips.

The first two Color Plate photographs show irises which are very close to being the normal blue and the normal brown. We would be able to find but few normal blue eyes today. Some iridologists consider hazel as the normal iris color. Iris coloring can no longer be what was considered normal in the past because the iris becomes darkened by the many poisonous irritants involved in modern industry and modern life in general. Besides examples of irritants already given, there are the effects from cotton dust, aluminum dust (as in airplane manufacture), dry cleaning fluids such as carbon tetrachloride, and the use of coal tar products for food coloring, flavoring, and "enriching" purposes. Wars also are bound to result in eye changes. The prevalent use of coal tar for synthetic vitamins and drugs as well as its many uses in foods, is conducive to cancer. We could not expect to find normal iris coloring under these conditions.

Twenty-five or thirty years ago, when crude drugs were used, it was much easier to detect individual drug signs in the iris than it is today. Modern drugs are so complexly compounded that it is difficult to discern individual drug signs in the iris. Arsenic, for example, which used to be given in crude form, now is more volatile and refined and is combined with many other drugs. The whole iris has been discolored more than ever by the constant use of these complex drugs.

It has been difficult to bring the science of iridology up to date, but we are greatly aided by photography, which is far superior to drawings and paintings. Nothing in the past could compare to what is possible now through the improved methods of photography, printing, etc.

With enlargements of iris photographs such as are presented here, doctors who would not have thought of attempting to diagnose from so small a field will now find it practical. The microscopic capillary photographs which are included here show that those of us who are enthusiastic about iridology are not the only ones making use of what minute external structures can tell us about the inner functioning of the body. We should not neglect to investigate any method which offers a means of gaining valuable information about a patient's difficulties. Study of such structures provides us with data besides that which can be determined from the laboratory techniques in general use.

Certainly many doctors would like to know—tangibly, visibly—the condition of vital organs without resorting to exploratory operations. And certainly many doctors would like to know the degree of improvement in a patient's internal organs as a result of therapy. Through iris analysis and photographic studies of the iris, we are enabled particularly well to determine these very conditions, and without any shock or harm to the patient.

In the accompanying pictures of lungs we see how healthy pink lung tissue becomes darkened from breathing polluted air. This is included here because we can liken it to the gradual darkening of the iris of the eye, where the structures of the entire body are represented.

We start in infancy with the cleanest body possible, but we contaminate it through abnormal living conditions—including smog, vaccinations, coal tar products and other drugs, synthetic vitamins, devitalized foods, preservatives, too much clothing, etc.— all resulting in heavy toxic absorption over a period of years. As cellular structures become altered, the iris changes accordingly.

I have seen iris darkening occur in the children born to some of my patients. Although an infant started off with perfectly blue eyes, by about the third month the living habits were evident in irises practically as dark as those of the parents. It is well to study the clear iris of an infant whenever there is an opportunity, for the iris is then the cleanest it will ever be during its lifetime. Note that in Color Plate No. 8, Sections 1, 2 and 3 are marked blue.

Note the irises in Color Plate No. 3, showing eyes that originally were blue but which became darkened by the living habits of their owners, who acquired toxic settlements throughout their bodies. Section 4 in this Plate probably shows underlying color which is as close to normal as you will see, while Section 6 would be next. Section 3 would follow that. The iris shown in Section 1 is becoming darker, and in Section 2 there is a very heavy settlement of acquired poisons and disease. Section 5 is very heavily encumbered with toxic settlement.

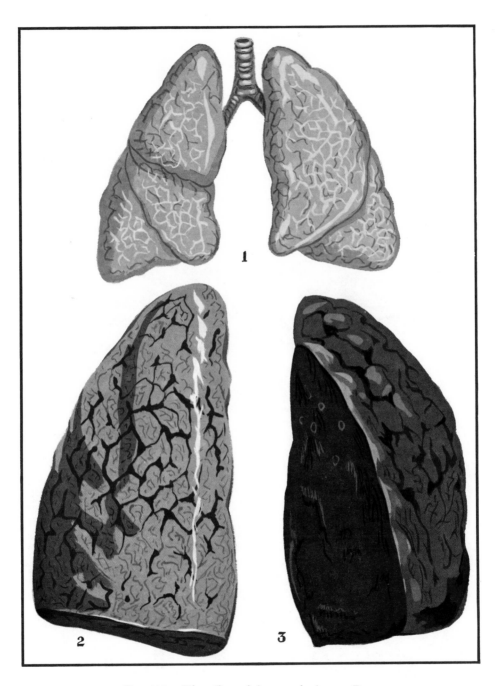

FIG. 119.   The effect of dust on the lungs. Drawings taken from actual specimens, showing the
lungs of — (1) An infant. (2) An adult town
dweller. (3) A coal miner.

Die **Untersuchung** des Haargefäßnetzes (Kapillaren) an der Lippenschleimhaut ermöglicht wertvolle Einsichten in die Verursachung von Kreislaufstörungen (Blutstauungen) und die sich anbahnende Heilung.

Fɪɢ. 120. The examination of the capillary system on the salivary tissue of the lips makes possible valuable insight into the causes of circulatory disturbances and the ensuing cure. (Picture taken at Dr. Bircher Benner's Sanitarium in Zurich, Switzerland).

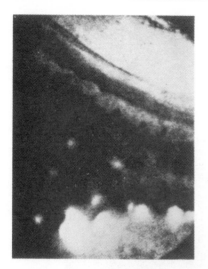 

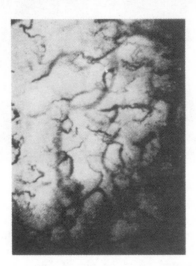

FIGS. 121 (a) (b) (c). It is interesting that if we find capillary changes in a certain organ, these are indicative of changes in other parts of the body. The above photographs show capillaries under the tongue and in the lips. It is also interesting to observe capillaries that were fragile and permeable becoming strong, with change of diet (including supplementary vitamins and minerals) and living habits.

Similarly, the iris mirrors bodily conditions and contains healing signs when the body has been properly fed and cared for.

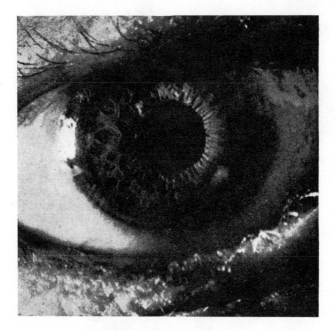

FIG. 122. Questions I am frequently asked are: how I know that various layers in the iris actually exist, whether research has been done on this, and whether they have been measured. Although I have never measured goose pimples, I know they rise above the surrounding skin and have depth.

Since the above photograph was taken with the illumination extremely to one side, the layers in the various lesions are visible—proving the existence of depth. Experience teaches the iridologist to recognize these layers.

FIG. 123. This photograph is of a model representing a section of the iris. It demonstrates the fibres of the top layer that are white, of the next layer that are gray, and the black underlying pigment layer. Microscopic study of the iris reveals this kind of fibre separation, distortion, and discoloration, depending upon the conditions which they denote.

FIG. 124. This three-dimensional drawing of a section of
the iris shows its layers, how it is constructed, and how it
is placed in the eyeball.

FIG. 125. Photographing the human eye so that the minute fibres can be seen and studied has been a difficult problem. Many persons have been able to photograph the eye, such as the whole eye of a beetle pictured at the left above, but very few have been able to show individual sections such as those shown in the highly magnified picture at the right. I have succeeded, however, in taking photographs of the human iris which show individual fibres.

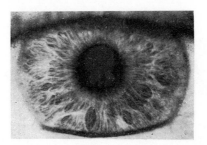

FIG. 126. This photograph shows healing of lesion in upper spine, between 8 and 9 o'clock. This occurred after body chemistry had been normalized. Mechanical adjusting and exercise will now be more effective than would they alone have been without chemical normalizing.

The inherent kidney weakness can be kept free of toxic encumbrance if the skin is kept active and the bowel clean.

This iris shows very little scurf rim, and the healing signs that have developed in the bowel pockets indicate healthful living.

The acid stomach ring is quite visible in this iris. A clean body, even though it may have many inherent weaknesses, can have more strength and endurance than an inherently strong body that is heavily encumbered with toxic waste.

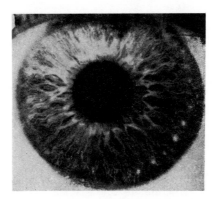

FIG. 127. In this photograph the lesion near 9 o'clock indicating in-herent weaknesses shows numerous healing lines. This shows that the body has the power to utilize vital elements if they are provided. Regardless of the disease state of the patient, the prognosis usually is good if the body has been remineralized, for then the blood-making organs have the energy to repair tissue as evidenced by these healing lines.

This iris has a typical lymphatic rosary, clearly visible on the right, looking like beads, between the areas of the intestine and the skin. The lymphatic system, which is greatly neglected in the healing arts, I believe is largely dependent upon the skin and intestinal tract.

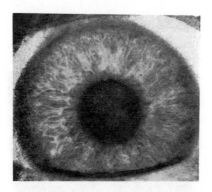

FIG. 128. In the above iris the scurf rim shows the greatest amount of encumbrance to be settled in the central part of the body. In such cases the lung structure usually is underactive. Since the body from the neck to the knees usually is well covered with clothing, acids cannot be eliminated through the skin in this area. A heavy scurf rim opposite the thyroid gland, as seen here between 2 and 3 o'clock, produces a toxic thyroid. Enlargements, growths, and overweight can develop. While the administration of iodine and thyroid preparations is the accepted therapy, it is a shame not to see the rest of the picture —the need for cleansing and elimination. Measures which improve the skin area and lighten the scurf rim always help thyroid activity.

With a toxic bowel there could be an extremely toxic condition of the lung area where the inherent weakness exists at 3 o'clock.

With a scurf rim like this, all kinds of eruptions may develop. When it is opposite the liver area it may indicate a torpid liver or cirrhosis. Any organ whose iris area is penetrated by the scurf rim will be benefited by skin therapy.

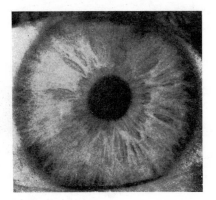

FIG. 129.   The above photograph and Section 1 of Color Plate No. 8 both show the heavy overlying whiteness which signifies the extreme acid condition of rheumatism or arthritis.   In these cases the body is "on fire."   Sodium, potassium, silicon, and calcium have been burned out of the body.   Under these conditions, lung cavities develop, the nerves become oversensitive, and the whole body is overactive.   All metabolic processes are increased.

These conditions are aggravated by acid fruits, especially when they are immature, and are soothed by vegetable broths.

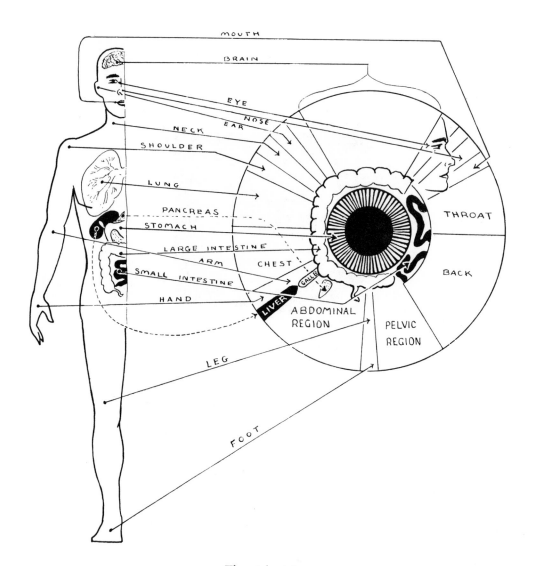

The right iris.

FIG. 130.   Diagram showing schematically
how organ areas are placed in the chart
to correspond to those in the body.

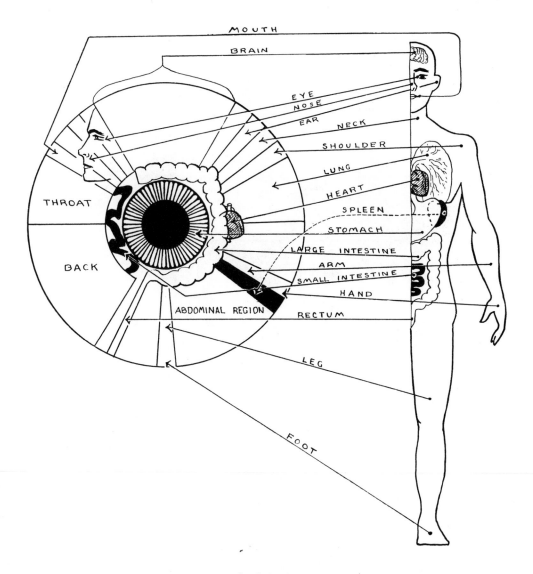

The left iris.

FIG. 131. The left iris holds the story of
the left side of the body. Right iris holds
story of right side of body.

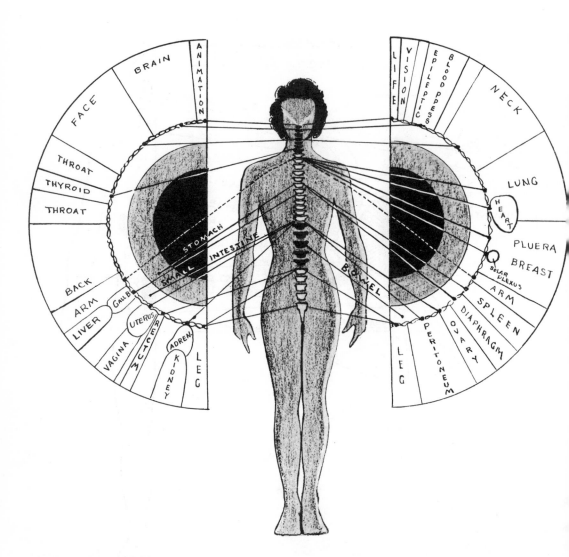

FIG. 132. This drawing shows the relationship between the spinal nerves and the various parts of the body as represented in the iris of the eye. This relation is of special interest to practitioners using nerve therapy, mechano-reflex therapy, chiropractic and osteopathy because they are familiar with pressure techniques in connection with "hot spots" along the spine which involve terminal nerve-end reflex areas in various parts of the body, with percussion of spinal areas which will stimulate or inhibit remote portions of the body, etc. A great deal can be determined about the spinal nerves and the organs to which they ramify by studying the autonomic nerve wreath in the iris.

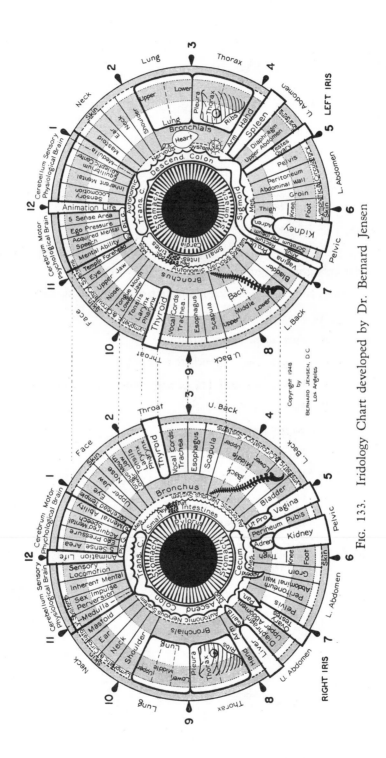

FIG. 133.   Iridology Chart developed by Dr. Bernard Jensen

Color Plate No. 1

Left iris; normal blue. Density 3½. Heavy catarrhal congestion. Lymphatic glandular enlargement (groin and breast). Nervousness.

This plate provides a good illustration of the lymphatic rosary (zone 6).

A. Open lesion, thyroid gland area.

B. Autonomic nerve wreath.

C. Closed lesion, bronchial area.

D. Pocket in bowel (¾ of way down descending colon).

E. Heavy scurf rim.

F. Nerve rings.

G. Sulphur settlement.

H. Reflection from light bulb.

I. Heart weakness.

J. Lymphatic rosary.

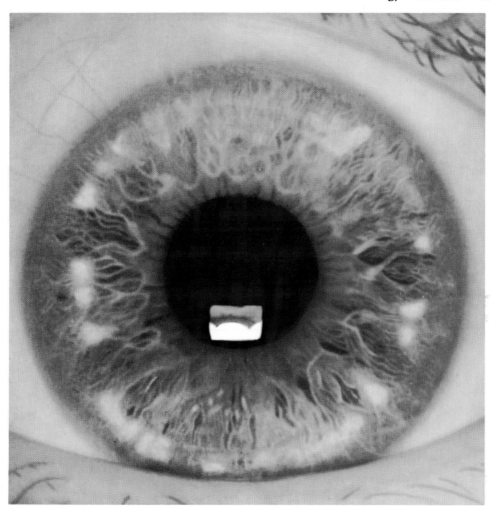

Color Plate No. 1

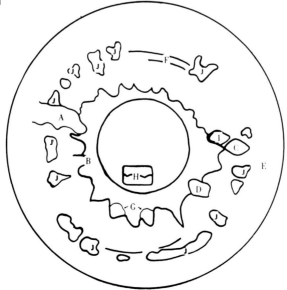

Color Plate No. 2

Right iris; normal brown. Individual fibres are not easily discernible in brown iris; they seem to be diffused with the pigment. Density 2½. Gastro-intestinal disorder (constipation). Poor skin elimination. History of skin eruptions.

A. Autonomic nerve wreath.

B. Gastro-intestinal area.

C. Heavy scurf rim.

D. Upper spine disturbance.

E. *Radii solaris.* (Spokes).

F. Neuritis, right arm.

G. Chronic inflammation, gall-bladder.

H. Chronic inflammation, pancreas.

I. Reflection from light bulb.

In Color Plate No. 3 which follows, compare stages of healing: first degree in Section 1, second degree in Section 3, and third degree in Section 4.

Note discoloration due to suppression of disease. When we suppress natural eliminative processes, the iris becomes darker. Accumulations of drugs, etc., over the years irritate the sexual system, and the mental and nervous systems, giving rise to many obscure pathological conditions for which a direct cause cannot be found. With that underlying condition, only a minor local irritation may precipitate a serious condition. In my opinion, conditions suppressed with drugs result in the worst kind of blood poisoning. If operations and surgical work are performed upon encumbered tissues, healing may be retarded. There will be cases in which you will look for a definite iris sign to diagnose cancer. I consider it a disease of the blood rather than a local disease. An accumulation of encumbrances develops the underlying cause of cancer.

The only way to lighten the iris and restore the body to normal is to remove the heavy catarrhal encumbrances through healthful living. I want to show that the greatest hope we have is the right-living program—including pure air, pure water, sunlight, exercise, natural foods, and wholesome mental attitudes. Discharging encumbrances and normalizing the body through application of these principles is the strongest proof that natural healing is the correct way.

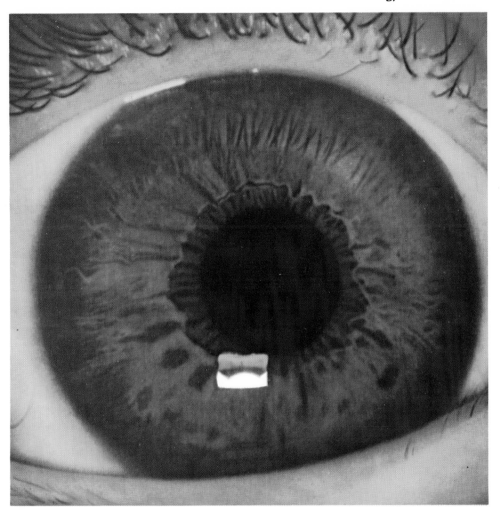

Color Plate No. 2

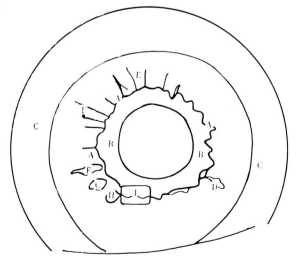

Color Plate No. 3

Composite chart containing sections of both right and left irises. This affords a wonderful opportunity to compare the structure of one iris with another.

Section 1—Right iris; blue. Density 4. High blood sugar; diabetic tendency. Chronic constipation.

    A. Inherently weak pelvis and groin.
    B. Inherently weak pancreas.
    C. Chronic toxic settlement upper abdomen and diaphragm.
    D. Irritable autonomic nervous system involving duodenum and gall bladder.
    E. Inherently weak gall bladder with inflammation extending to liver.
    F. Ovarian inflammation.
    G. Acute inflammation of upper abdomen and diaphragm.
    H. Heavy scurf rim; anemia.
    I. Lack of bowel tone from chronic toxic settlement, preventing elimination of waste.
    J. Chronic ring inside pupil bordering stomach area (drug deposit).

Section 2—Left iris; blue. Density 4. Epileptic patient. Heavy drug user.

    A. Sulphur, iodine, iron settled in intestinal tract (constipation).
    B. Heavy drug discoloration of entire iris (originally blue).
    C. Bowel pockets.
    D. Inflamed autonomic nerve wreath.
    E. Acute lesion in upper lung. (Frequent winter colds).
    F. Density 4.
    G. Large pupil (extreme enervation).
    H. Scurf rim.

Section 3—Right iris; blue. Density 3. Emotional thyroid case.

    A. Sulphur settled in intestinal tract (sulphur and molasses in childhood).
    B. Density very good.
    C. Inflammation, sex mental area. (Marital upheaval; impending divorce).
    D. Lower back pains; pains throughout hips from locomotion center of brain.
    E. *Radii solaris.*
    F. Depleted animation and life center. Waning of all life interests.
    G. Scurf rim; anemia in extremities.
    H. Pupil contracted from nerve tension.

Section 4—Left iris; blue. Density 3½. Rheumatic and arthritic patient. Heavy catarrhal discharge throughout body—sinuses, lymph glands, vagina, ears, nose (post nasal drip).

    A. Left breast slightly enlarged.   B. Extreme acid and catarrhal settlement.
    C. D. Two pockets in colon area.
    E. Upper bronchial closed catarrhal lesion, acutely eliminating.
    F. Acid irritation causing constant pleural pains.
    G. Lymphatic congestion.

Section 5—Right iris; blue. Density 3½. Poor circulation (anemia in extremities). High blood prsesure. Extreme pains, hands and feet. Heavy drug settlement throughout iris (especially quinine, giving its green discoloration).

    A. Greenish discoloration from use of quinine.
    B. Heavy chronic toxic settlement in bowel.
    C. Originally blue eye heavily encumbered from bowel toxins and drugs.
    D. Sodium ring.   E. Black scurf rim.

Section 6—Left iris; blue. Density 4. No calcium reserve due to tissue weakness. Poor alkaline reserve. Heavy catarrhal congestion. Constant backache. Persistent lower jaw pain and lateral slipping. Joint and muscular pains. Circulation very poor; extremely cold hands and feet. Palpitating, slow heart. Neuritis in left arm past 15 years.

    A. Inherent weakness in pleura, extending into left breast.
    B. Heart weakness and chronic underactivity.
    C. Acute inflammation, left arm and hand.   D. Irritable nervous system.
    E. Chronic acid stomach.   F. Anemia in extremities; scurf rim.

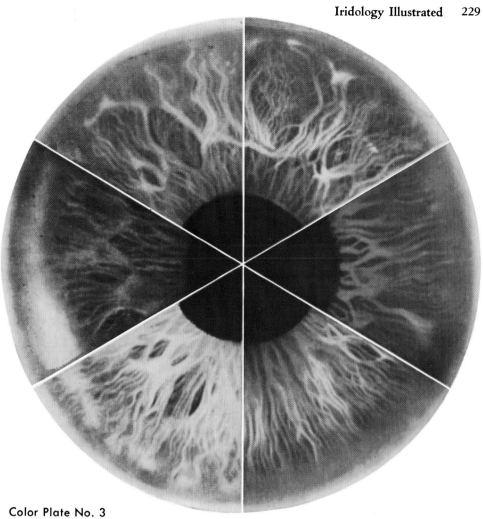

Color Plate No. 3

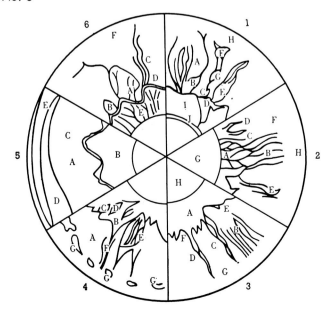

Color Plate No. 4

Section 1—Left iris; brown with some blue showing through. Density 3. Colitis. Boils. Gas. Mental retardation.
   A. Psoric itch spots.
   B. Scurf rim.
   C. Heavy catarrh.
   D. Gaseous bowel pockets.

Section 2—Left iris; blue. Density 2. Lymphosarcoma of bronchial tubes.
   A. Murky blue—cancer background.
   B. Drug spot (sulphur and iron), bronchial tube.
   C. Drug settlement, gastro-intestinal tract.
   D. Heavy congestion, intestinal area.
   E. Black scurf rim.
   F. Good texture.

Section 3—Left iris; blue. Density 3. Extreme gas pains half-way down descending colon. Heart flutter and arythmia.
   A. Chronic acid stomach.
   B. Very toxic bowel.
   C. Bowel adhesion.
   D. Closed lesion, lower lung.
   E. Heart lesion.
   F. Bowel pockets, causing heart pressure.
   G. Scurf rim.

Section 4—Left iris; blue. Density 4. Vaginal and sinus discharges. Glandular enlargements in groin.
   A. Lymphatic congestion throughout (zone 6).
   B. Inherently weak bowel structure.
   C. Settlement of sulphur and iron in bowel.
   D. Heavy acidity.
   E. Scurf rim.

In Section 1 of Color Plate No. 4 the white part of the brownish discoloration shows extreme acidity. This is the acute sign of acidity and catarrhal settlement.

In Section 3, discoloration of inner ring shows that acid condition of stomach has been there many years, aggravated by taking certain drugs. Autonomic nerve wreath shows up extremely well; you can differentiate the gastro-intestinal tract area from the organ areas. There is a direct relation between the large closed lesion and that portion of the intestinal tract area opposite the lesion.

Become well acquainted with the autonomic nerve wreath because it is one of the principal landmarks in learning to diagnose from the iris.

Section 4 shows clearly the 6th zone, containing the lymphatic rosary, and the 7th zone on the periphery, which is the area of skin and circulation. Note that the lymphatic rosary goes through the circulation area.

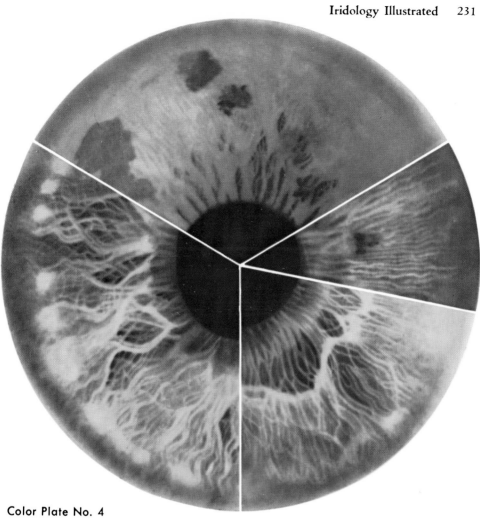

Color Plate No. 4

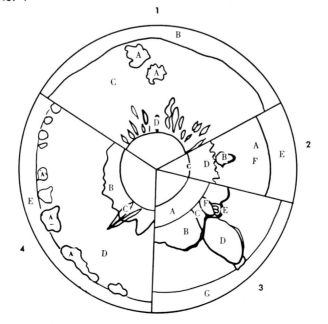

Color Plate No. 5

In this composite chart, notice difference in size of pupils. In Section 1 the desnity of 5 accounts for the lack of tone in the pupillary muscles.

Section 1—Left iris; blue. Density 5. Cancerous skin condition aggravated by scar tissue, etc., from X-ray treatment. Skin constantly peeled instead of healing. Many vaccinations and drug injections received in Navy; never well since. Nervousness. Stomach cramping.

    A. Chronic acid stomach.

    B. Scurf rim.

    C. Highly irritated autonomic nervous system.

    D. Large pupil.

Section 2—Left iris; blue. Density 4. Neuritis, left arm.

    A. Neuritis, left arm.

    B. Bowel irritation opposite this.

    C. Acute signs within closed lesion.

    D. Healing signs.

    E. Chronic acid stomach.

    F. Scurf rim.

    G. Bowel gas.

Section 3—Left iris; blue. Density 2½. Extreme acidity and discharges throughout body.

    A. Sulphur spot; cancer in breast.

    B. Pleural irritation.

    C. Bowel pocket.

    D. Scurf rim.

In Section 3 note the dark pocket in the intestinal tract area opposite the area for the breast. This is darker than the rest of the intestinal tract because it is responsible for reflex trouble in the breast. (Described more fully in chapter on Reflex Areas).

In Section 2 note both an open and a closed lesion.

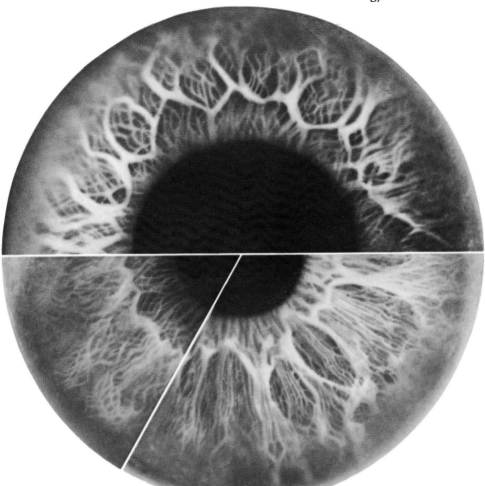

Color Plate No. 5

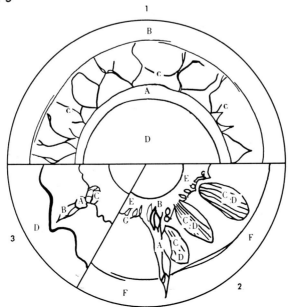

Color Plate No. 6

Section 1—Right iris; blue. Density 2. High blood pressure. Poor circulation. Stiffness and hardness in joints. Constant lower back and leg discomfort. History of sodium salicylate treatments for rheumatism (many years). Memory very poor.

    A. Sodium ring.

    B. Nerve rings.

    C. Acutely irritated autonomic nervous system.

    D. Inherent bowel weakness.

    E. Anemia, extremities.

Section 2—Right iris; brown. Density 5.

    A. Poor constitution.

Section 3—Left iris; brown. Density 2½. Leg pains. Bunions. Callouses. Fallen arches. Dry joints; grittiness in knees. Poor memory. Loss of alertness. High diastolic pressure; blood pressure 198/110. (Worked in salt factory for 15 years).

    A. Sodium ring.

    B. Anemia.

    C. Inherently weak intestinal tract.

In Section 1, the deep pigmentation of the iris makes it difficult to distinguish individual fibre lines. Note the nerve rings. Compare the structure of the fibres in the three sections of this Color Plate.

The structure in Section 1 may be compared to the oak, and represents vitality and recuperative power, but from the emcumbrance we see that even the best body so far as structure is concerned can be encumbered with toxic material.

The structure in Section 2 may be compared to the pine, and denotes comparatively low vitality and recuperative power.

The individual with strong tissue but containing toxic settlements may be weaker than the person with an inherently weak but toxin-free body.

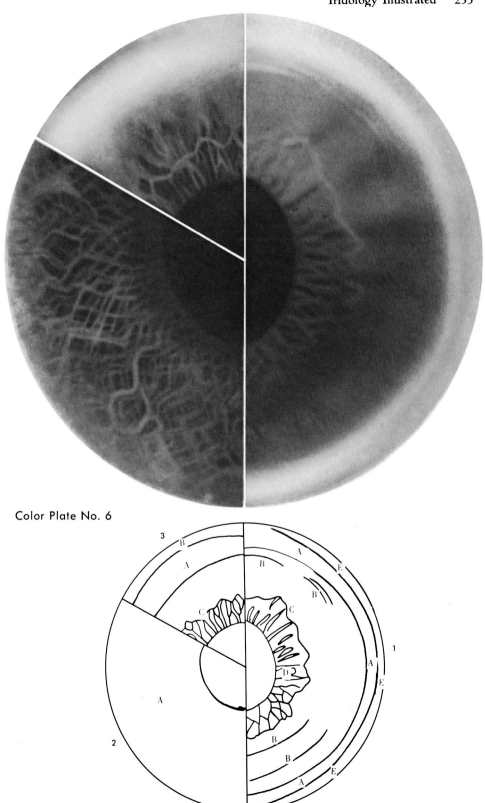

Color Plate No. 6

Color Plate No. 7

Rheumatic and arthritic acids are very heay in Sections 2 and 5 (need for alkaline elements).

Section 1—Left iris; blue. Density 3½. Bronchitis.

    A. Closed lesion, inherent weakness, bronchial tube.

    B. Bowel pockets.

    C. Healing signs.

    D. Scurf rim.

    E. Sub-acute acid stomach.

Section 2—Left iris; blue. Density 3½. Asthma patient.

    A. Bronchial lesion with healing signs.

    B. Two bowel pockets.

    C. Anemia, extremities.

    D. Scurf rim.

    E. Extreme acidity and catarrh.

Section 3—Left iris; ¾ blue, ¼ brown. Density 3. Cold extremities. Rheumatic pains. Foul breath.

    A. Anemia, extremities.

    B. *Radii solaris.*

    C. Sluggish, pocketed bowel.

    D. Heavy acidity throughout.

    E. Psoric "itch" spot.

Rarely do we see an iris which is partly blue and partly brown. Though these colors in the accompanying photograph are shown in two separate sections, they belong to the same iris. This is especially valuable in illustrating the ease with which we can distinguish fibres in the blue iris and the difficulty in segregating individual fibres in the brown iris.

Section 4—Left iris; blue. Density 4. Chest pains. Dyspnea. Belching.

    A. Inherently weak pleura.

    B. Closed pleural lesion.

    C. Bronchial weakness.

    D. Gas pockets causing heart pressure and extreme bowel disten-
tion.

    E. Chronic acid stomach.

Section 5—Left iris; blue. Density 3½. Rheumatoid arthritis.

    A. Acute activity, nerve wreath.

    B. Bowel distention.

    C. Bowel gas.

    D. Colitis.

    E. Bronchial weakness.

    F. Acid stomach.

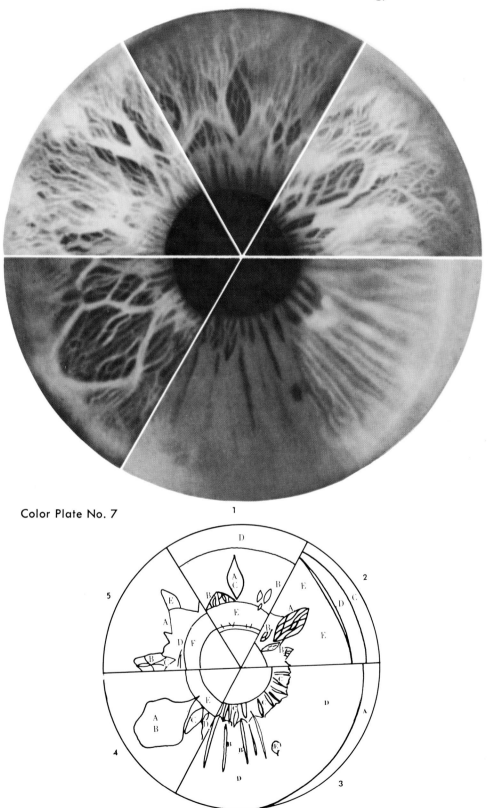

Color Plate No. 7

Color Plate No. 8

Section 1—Right iris; blue. Density 3½. Eight year old patient. Discharging ears. Tonsil and adenoid enlargement. Pronated ankles. Joint pains.

    A. Lymphatic congestion.

    B. Extreme acidity and catarrh.

    C. Acid stomach.

    D. Scurf rim.

    E. Calcium fixation.

Section 2—Right iris; hazel blue. Density 3. Dry skin. No perspiration. Scanty hair growth. Dandruff. Muddy complexion. Pains in right breast at time of menstruation.

    A. Open lesion, right pleura.

    B. Extremely heavy scurf rim, extending into pleural and ovarian areas.

    C. Heavy acidity and catarrh.

    D. Sulphur and iodine deposit.

    E. Poor bowel elimination.

Section 3—Right iris; hazel blue. Density 2½. Yellow jaundice.

    A. Inherent weakness and acute inflammation, liver area.

    B. Drug deposits throughout iris.

    C. Toxic intestinal tract.

    D. Scurf rim.

Section 4—Righ iris; hazel. Density 3½. Hyperthyroidism. Mental disturbance and irritation. Periodic headaches. Discharging sinuses. Hay fever. Uterine irritation. Moody during menstrual periods.

    A. Lesion, uterine area.

    B. Acute inflammation, vaginal tract.

    C. Intestinal congestion.

    D. Bowel pockets.

    E. Sulphur and iron deposits throughout iris.

    F. Scurf rim.

    G. Lymphatic congestion.

    H. Nerve rings.

Section 1 shows extreme rheumatic and arthritic acids.

The patients represented in Sections 2, 3 and 4 had blue eyes for two or three generations back, but the pigment changed to the extent that the iris appears brown to the ordinary observer. Mixtures of color, such as those producing the hazel eye, result from inherent taints, drugs, etc.

Note the structure in Section 3. There is a possibility that the heavy drug settle-ment could develop into cancer of the liver. The constitution is cancer liable. There is fair density and indication of good resistance and recuperative power; therefore the extremely white acute lesion in the liver area.

In Section 4, notice lack of coloration on outer margin, which is sign of anemia. Sclera is drawn over the edge (this also appears in Section 3). Patient complains of feeling cold; discomfort during cold or damp weather; "goose pimples" appear from slightest temperature changes; even emotional changes result in skin temperature changes. Healing signs only three-quarters completed due to imperfections in living conditions (climate, mental attitude, emotional control). Organs starving for adequate blood supply. In spite of normal blood count, in cases like this the tissues are starving for proper amount of blood.

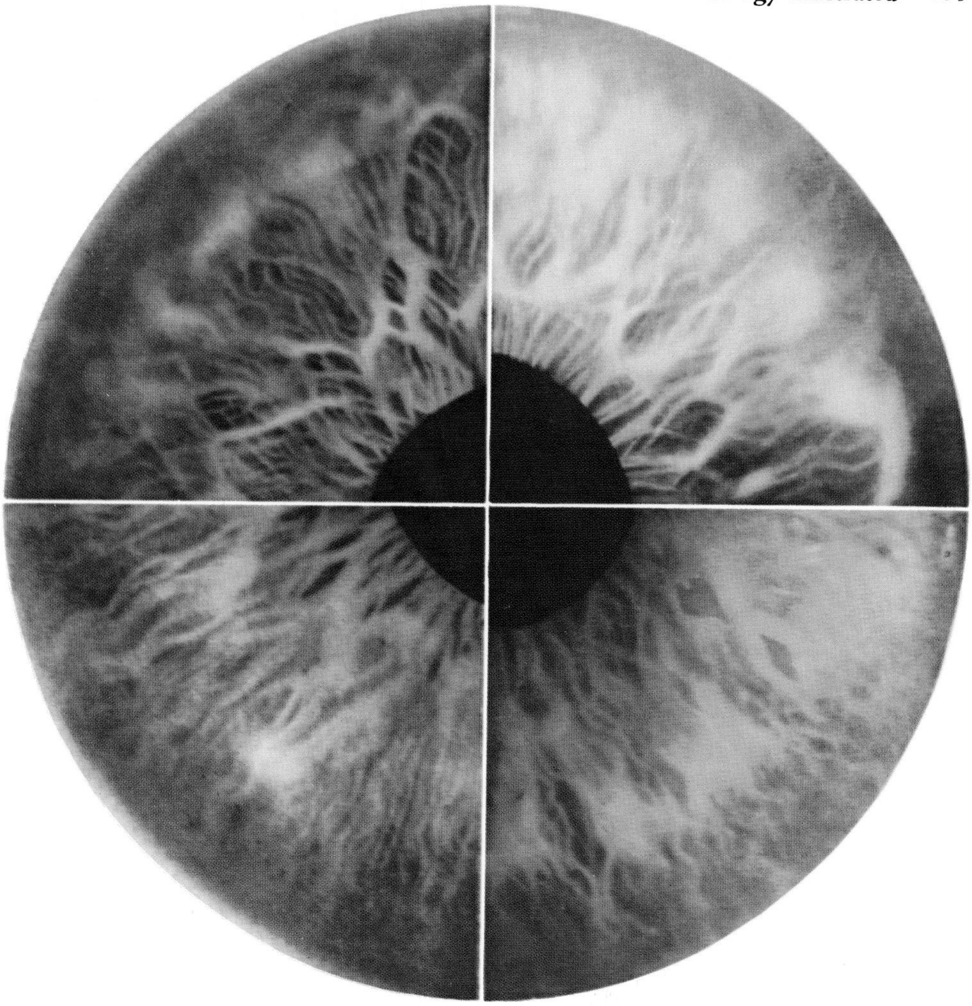

Color Plate No. 8

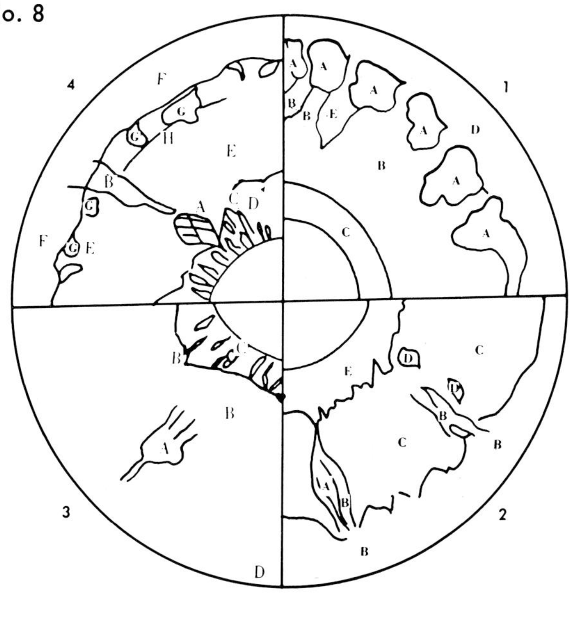

Color Plate No. 9

Section 1—Left iris; blue. Density 3½. Acute ovaritis.

    A. Acute ovarian inflammation.

    B. Bowel pocket.

    C. Acute inflammation, autonomic nervous system.

    D. Deposits of sulphur, iron and iodine in colon.

    E. Drug deposits in lymphatic rosary.

    F. Scurf rim.

    G. Large pocket opposite breast area; breast congestion.

Section 2—Right iris; blue. Density 3. Foul odor of both breath and skin.

    A. Very toxic bowel.

    B. Chronic acid stomach.

    C. Scurf rim.

    D. Heavy acidity and catarrh.

Section 3—Right iris; blue. Density 3. Fatigue. Mental lethargy.

    A. Lesion in animation and life center.

    B. Brain anemia.

    C. Scurf rim.

    D. Toxic absorption from transverse colon.

    E. Nerve acids settled throughout brain area.

Section 4—Left iris; blue. Density 2½. Prolapsus. Rectal disorder. Menstrual cramps.

    A. Two pockets, upper descending colon.

    B. Dropped transverse colon.

    C. Chronic acid stomach.

    D. Scurf rim.

    E. Acidity and catarrh.

    F. Acute shoulder pains.

    G. Torticollis, left side.

    H. Deafness, left ear.

Section 5—Righ iris; blue. Density 2½. Varicose veins. Bruises very easily. Rectal disorder.

    A. Liver congestion.

    B. Lymphatic rosary.

    C. Very toxic bowel.

    D. Chronic acid stomach.

    E. Scurf rim.

In this Color Plate compare the sub-acute sign in the stomach area in Section 2 with the chronic state in Sections 4 and 5. Note the chronic condition plus drug settlement in Sections 1 and 3. Section 3 shows absorption of drugs from intestinal tract directly into the fibres of a particular organ. Iris fibres actually take on drug colors.

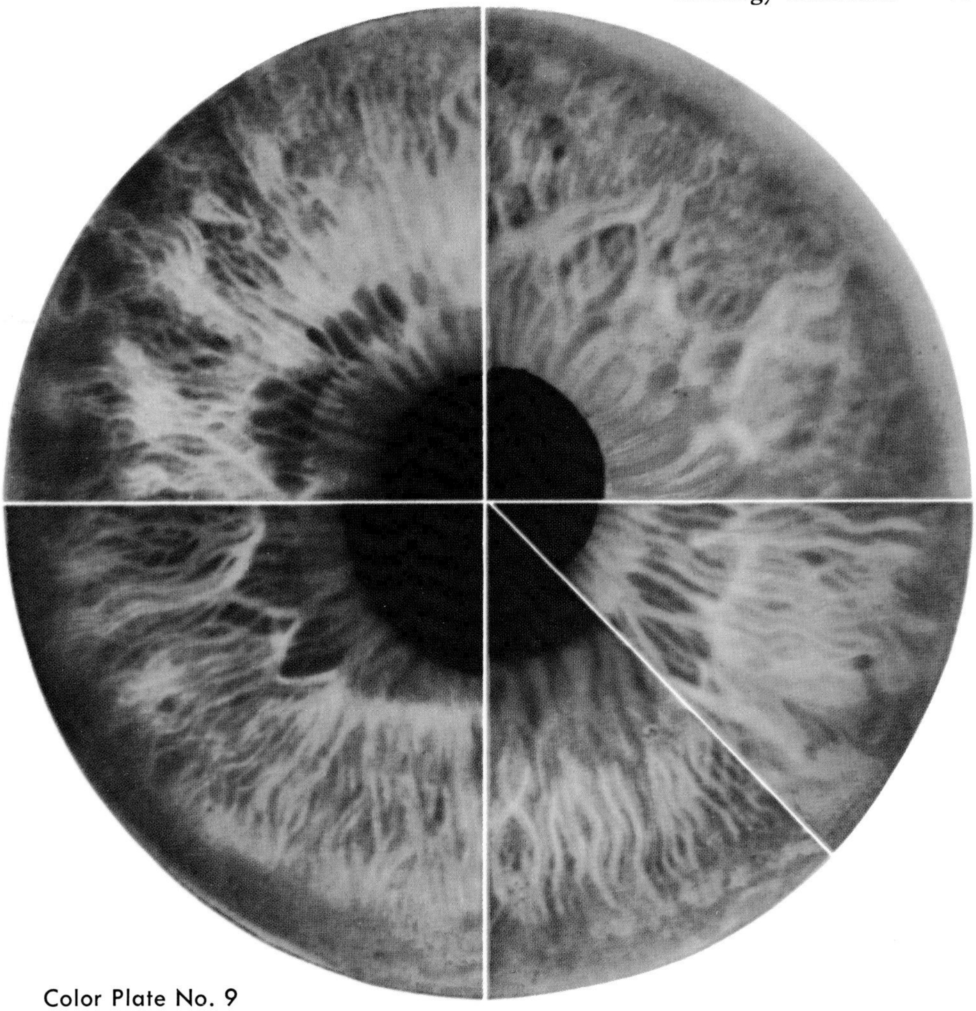

Color Plate No. 9

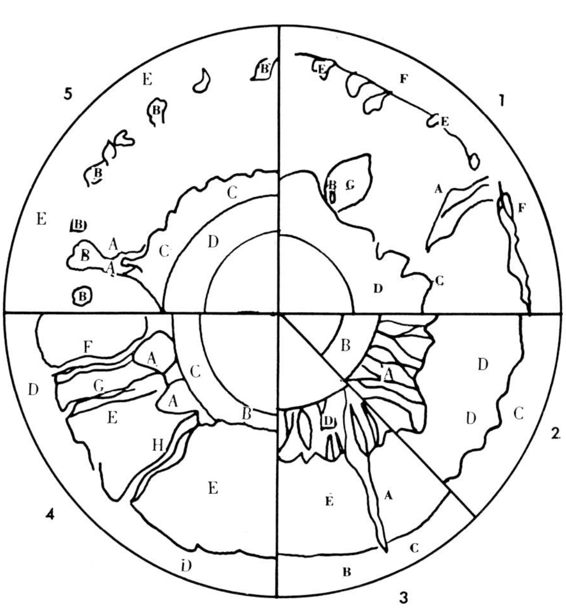

Color Plate No. 10

Section 1—Left iris; blue. Density 2½. Constipation. Lower bowel gas. History of taking iron tonics for anemia. Muscular hypotonicity. Inferiority complex. Lacks courage.

    A. Anemia in extremities.

    B. Iron settled in bowel area.

    C. Dropped transverse colon.

    D. Scurf rim.

    E. Over-activity of autonomic nervous system.

Section 2—Right iris; blue. Density 3½. Pain in right hip from injection.

    A. Drug deposit after injection in right hip.

    B. Toxic bowel.

Section 3—Right iris; blue. Density 3. Deafness. Poor circulation. No taste. Memory failing. Right shoulder pains. Gastric ulcer for years. Consistently used bicarbonate of soda.

    A. Iron and sulphur spot in duodenum.

    B. Chronic gall-bladder.

    C. Pancreatic weakness.

    D. Large pocket, upper ascending colon opposite shoulder area.

    E. Anemia, extremities.

    F. Sodium ring.

In Section 1, nerve rings are fairly distinct. They are present in all heavily encumbered irises although they may not be seen. One factor which makes them less obvious in photographs is that light is used directly in front of the eyes. The illumination should be far to one side in order for the depth of nerve rings to be visible. Since these are indistinct for the most part in the above color plates, we include here a black and white photograph which shows nerve rings clearly. Note that in places three and four rings are visible.

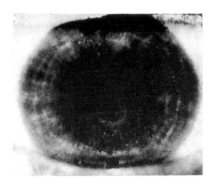

In Section 3, notice that the sodium ring narrows down toward the center of the body, showing the heaviest settlement in the upper extremities, brain, and lower extremities.

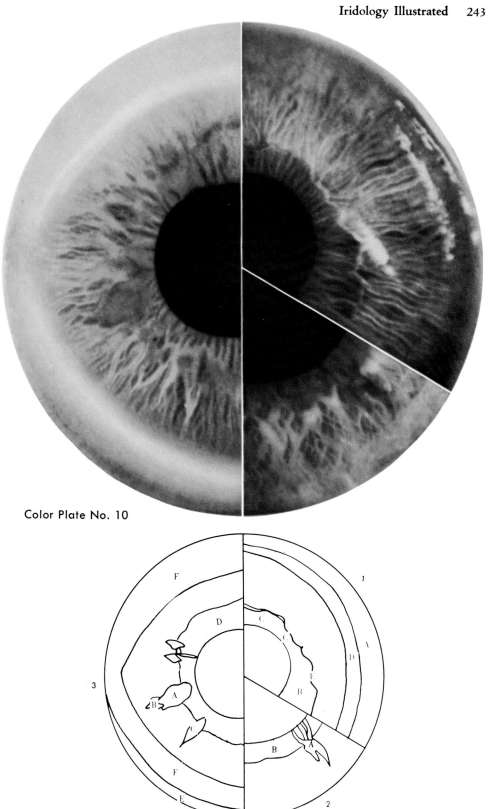

Color Plate No. 10

Concluding Remarks

There are many preconceived ideas regarding the science of iridology and perhaps as many doubters concerning it as there have been of all discoveries before they were proved to everyone's satisfaction. Before provable facts have been established, we must work with theories. Before William Harvey (1578-1657) discovered the circulation of the blood, he had to work with theories and ideas; he had to make his own observations and experiment upon himself to see nature at work.

In the study of the iris I have made my own observations, starting from "scratch," uninfluenced by previous investigators, and what I have proved in this treatise is based on direct inspection of some 300,000 eyes. I realize that this work is in its infancy and that what I have presented is preliminary to what future developments will bring, especially after scientific equipment has been perfected which will prove that the applications of this work are practical and far-reaching. Many of Harvey's claims regarding the circulation of the blood were proved after the invention of the microscope, for then the precise path could be traced. Improvements in this instrument enabled Malpighi in 1660 and Leeuwenhoek in 1688 to see the hair-like vessels between the arteries and the veins, called capillaries. Any student with a modern microscope can see this circulation in the web of a frog's foot.

Galileo saw some 3,000 stars; now we see 3,000,000 and there are more to come. It takes more than a Galileo to make this possible; it takes a Galileo plus a telescope.

Many doctors who examine the iris never see how it is actually constructed. I believe that powerful cameras and improved lighting equipment eventually will prove what I have tried to demonstrate in this volume. I believe that the laws governing reflex symptomatology will be discovered just as diagnostic equipment has been developed. I am convinced that with adequate equipment we will be able to determine nerve blocks, irritations, sedative and stimulative effects, etc., causing symptoms in remote parts of the body.

The laws of nature always are in operation whether man is aware of them or not. The iris did not suddenly come into existence at the time when von Peczely and Liljequist discovered its diagnostic significance. Goethe once remarked to a friend, "Nature knows no trifling; she is always sincere, always serious, always stern; she is always in the right, and the errors and mistakes are invariably ours."

It is not what college a person attended or what degrees he holds that are important; it is insight and the capacity correctly to interpret the natural laws in operation around him that makes him an instrument for bringing natural law into expression in our world in the form of various "inventions." Through scientific method we make use of nature's laws as brought into form by such observers. Many men had studied electrical activity, but it took George Simon Ohm, after whom the unit of electrical resistance is named, to demonstrate the law for determining the intensity of an electrical current passing through a wire.

Recall the doubt expressed during the attempts of the Wright brothers to fly a heavier-than-air machine in 1908. Scientific improvement has developed the unbelievable aircraft which we have today. Marconi, inventor of a wireless telegraphy system, was not only doubted but was accused of being insane when he declared that messages could be transmitted through the air. After it already had been accomplished the doubters were willing to say, "We knew you could do it."

This presentation of iridology may be new to some readers and by some of them may be misunderstood and laid aside. Those who give it only a few moments' attention cannot see what possible good it can be. Such individuals also asked, "What good is the wireless?" We of course know the answer to this even had it never been developed beyond the stage it was at the time it saved the lives of the 900 passengers who were crowded into life boats from the sinking Titanic. Those 900 persons owed their lives to the "crazy Marconi" who invented the fantastic wireless telegraph, for it was by this means that rescue ships were informed of the disaster.

My studies in iridology have been developed and recorded in this book solely for the purpose of extending knowledge and helping human beings to a better way of living.

We have no complete inventory of the universe, but as scientific development is applied to each discovery brought through human channels from the invisible into the visible world, we see revealed before us worlds within worlds and beyond the worlds of our imagination. When we penetrate into the depths of anything, we discover worlds heretofore unknown to us. The truth of what lies recorded in the iris exists whether we are aware of it or not. Whether it is the depths of the iris that we probe or something else, when its inner nature is revealed, it is another occasion for uttering, reverently, "Marvelous are Thy works."

Part V

CASE HISTORIES

19

CASE HISTORIES ACCORDING TO IRIDOLOGY

Any theory, hypothesis, sect, philosophy, creed or institution,
that fears investigation, openly manifests its own error.

—*Andrew Jackson Davis*

Case histories are presented here not to show what I can do, but rather what irid-ology and natural healing methods can do. I consider this work to .be greater than any practitioner. It succeeds if we have the cooperation of the patient. No matter how good the doctor is, if the patient's living habits are such that they undo the benefits gained through the doctor, the results will not be complete and satisfactory.

This work is worthy of deeper study and greater development. It is not a fast healing method; it is a natural process of growth and repair, and one that requires time. The results are positive and proven.

In these case histories I give the di-agnosis of the patient, illustrations and photographs, and our method of correction. Many of these cases are on the unusual side, and were selected for the purpose of showing that difficult cases can be handled in a drugless manner. Not because I wish to demonstrate than I can do it, I bring out the fact that if the work is performed properly the patient will respond. I am trying to bring out also that healing is ac-complished not with just fasting or with any one type or system of treatment. While I have appreciated the value of chiropractic

in many cases, for example, I realized it was not a panacea. While corrective diet made many fundamental changes in cell structure, in many cases changing the thought patterns was just as important.

In the cases presented I probably had the opportunity of doing more than the doctor in ordinary office practice could do, because of our sanitarium, where we could take the really serious and severe cases. I do not want these case presentations to be considered as testimonials. I want them to demonstrate how the body responds to its environment, how it adapts itself to pat-terns of living. While some of the cases with which I succeeded had been failures under other systems of treatment, I do not wish to criticize those other methods, for there were times when I failed also. I repeat that what I am trying to emphasize here is the fact that in the treatment of disease we need to include fasting, dieting, and a complete right-living program. This therapy works. I want to emphasize that there is a system for building good health, and that ailing persons should follow a health program rather than look for a cure in a doctor's office.

Everyone has an obligation to his body

as far as health is concerned. Without a method of keeping himself well, a patient cannot expect to regain and maintain his health through any doctor. It is imperative to correct living habits. A healthful-way-of-living program includes proper diet, ex-ercise, and natural therapy. This is what I teach.

As examples of how this type of therapy really works, I include here a few case history accounts and letters of appreciation, with my comments:

Case of Arthritis—(Enervation, Malnutrition [calcium depletion])

Los Angeles, Calif.
May 26, 1938

"These experiences I am about to relate are true facts, occurring over a period of 28 years.

In my babyhood and early childhood days, I was considered a prob-lem child. The doctor who was responsible for my entrance into this world, informed my parents that I might survive, and might not; to keep me in air and sunshine and ask nothing from me in the way of work. This program was carried out and apparently for a few years I outgrew the ill health that I was started out with. The first 10 years I caught all the diseases that catch nine out of ten children—measles, mumps, chicken-pox and whooping cough, etc. From these I emerged seemingly none the worse. Most of my baby teeth were decayed before my permanent ones were ready to come in. Cavities followed one by one in my permanent ones. Before I had reached the age of twenty, extractions had made bridges and fillings necessary.

During high school years a siege of canker sores took me out of school for a period of a month. Being unable to eat or talk, school was out of the question. The family medical doctor prescribed a mouth-wash to use just before meals. After using this wash, to eat immediately was imperative, or not at all. No other medicine was given and no diet prescribed, so merrily I continued to eat meat, eggs and fried potatoes galore.

Entering Business College after high school, a cough and sore throat took me to the hospital for a tonsil operation. Fatigue was always pres-ent after my day's work, and to get enough sleep seemed to be my goal. Entering Nurse's training I went down with 'flu twice in one winter and colds were always present. Foot trouble took possession of me with endless expense in shoe fittings and doctor bills. Two trips to the hospital for major operations didn't encourage me to a more pleasant frame of mind. My fingers would become numb and stay that way for weeks at a time, making work a nightmare. At one time it was a task to comb my hair due to numbness in my right hand. From there it went into one corner of my mouth, making smiling a one-sided process.

A few months later I lost the sight of my right eye. Doctors' efforts were of no avail, and at the end of approximately two months vision returned. Chiropractic treatments were an endless expense as the ver-

tebrae in my neck and back would not stay in place. The left knee developed a strange numbness which traveled into both hips. To arise and prepare for a day's work was worse than the actual work. To drive a car was an impossibility, as I was unable to feel either brake or gas feed with the right foot.

From doctor to doctor I went with this, none of them diagnosing the case to be the same. The diagnoses varied all the way from nervous breakdown to tuberculosis of the bone. After visiting with these good doctors, who eventually numbered ten, and extended over a period of two years, I was sent to a chiropractor and M.D. combined. His diagnosis was arthritis, catarrh, etc. Immediately I was put on a strict diet, exercise, sunshine, fresh air. Under his care I have made rapid progress, and at the finish of another year I expect to take an active place in the world once more, and in health such as it has never been my privilege to know or enjoy.

In closing, I can only say, if all other, than doctors employing natural methods were banished from the doctor profession, this would be a much healthier and happier world. The average person attempting to work, through trying health conditions such as these (and there are many), is handicapped beyond anyone's wildest imagination. So cheers to those doctors who have braved obstacles put in their way, by doctors who do not understand or believe in mother nature's ability, and may they carry on to higher and higher fields.

I was twice in the hospital and when I came to Doctor Jensen's, just finished eight tuberculin shots in the hip. I walked into Doctor Jensen's office a skeptic and the most doubtful person on earth that there was a doctor left who could help me. However, I decided to start treatments because I had nothing to lose and was more or less like a drowning man reaching for a straw.

After following Doctor Jensen's advice for three months, I dropped my crutches which I had to use to first see him, and was roller skating on the sidewalks of Santa Monica. I am grateful and cannot express in words but would like others to know what Doctor Jensen's Nature Cure regime will do for those who are really sick enough to get well.

(Signed) J. S."

Discussion

Here is a typical case of malnutrition; a person who had a poor start right from the beginning of life; whose parents did not know a right living program. The eye showed a typical "white iris"—demonstrating a lack of calcium and sodium. The thyroid gland was broken down so that the calcium in the body was not controlled. It is a wonderful thing to see how a person placed under the right living program responds. It is done without drugs, surgery or medicine. It is a good example to bring out the fact that we owe our body a good living.

FIG. 134

This drawing of the patient's right iris shows the causes of her symptoms. The main iris signs in this cause were nerve rings, chronic acid stomach (sodium reserve exhausted), bowel pockets, leg inflammation, right ovarian weakness, chronic gall bladder and liver congestion, inherently weak lung structure, toxic thyroid gland, impaired intestinal absorption, chronic settlement in Peyer's patches (suppressed fever in childhood), poor skin elimination (heaviest scurf rim opposite thyroid and back areas), impaired tactile sense.

Arthritis

Long Beach, Calif.
May 21, 1951

"I came to Doctor Jensen's office in April 1940. I was drooped over to the right, head down considerably below my shoulder level. No one could touch me or I would scream with pain. I had gone to chiropractors but received no help. I had gone to many different kinds of doctors but no one seemed to help me. I went to an orthopedic surgeon. He said I would never get well. He told me that the spine had many arthritic spurs on it and that bone surgery was the only thing to help it. He said he could probably straighten out the spine but could not guarantee that I would not be stiff the rest of my life. Another doctor said I would be bed-ridden the rest of my life and to just make up my mind to accept it.

After going from doctor to doctor, I seemed to be at the end of my rope and with no help in sight. I did not know what to do. Then I heard of Doctor Jensen. When I first saw him, I asked if he could do anything for me and he said he did not know what he could do. He gave me an iris analysis and then started me on an eliminative program with diet and detoxifying treatments. I saw him every day for thirty-seven days and then every other day for a short time after. He did not start adjusting my spine until after the fourth month. It was about the sixth month that the spine began to straighten out and after eight months under Dr. Jensen's care my spine straightened and I was discharged from any further treatment. I was forty-one years of age at the time

*I went to his office and now, eleven years later, I have absolutely no re-
currence of my pains, no recurrence of any of my spinal troubles. I
can work hard and I am as straight as I ever was before my arthritis.*

*I remember what Doctor Jensen said at one time when I was taking
his treatments, that sickness is a blessing to some of us. It has been to
me. I have learned a way to live; I have been able to keep in good
health. I take care of my father and even after he was seventy-eight
years of age we got rid of his rheumatism that he had for years. The
successful overcoming of this problem I owe to Doctor Jensen.*

E. N."

Discussion

In commenting upon this case I might say that not all cases of arthritis are so easy
to handle. Although I have had few cases that were as serious as this one, there were
few cases in which I had such wonderful response. It is said that the calcium deposits
on the joints, called arthritic spurs, cannot be dissolved. In most cases, this kind of arthritis is for life, and produces immobilization. In this case, though, by a heavy program of
elimination and specifice diet using a lot of sodium foods, the chemistry of the body was
normalized and the calcium deposits in the joints were dissolved..

FIG. 135

This patient's right iris shows an inherent weakness in the
back area; inherent weakness in the leg area; pancreatic
weakness, disturbing the function of the right ovary; inflammation in cecum; chronic acid stomach (showing depletion of sodium); poor skin elimination; heavy toxic
pocket in upper ascending colon (bowel distention); heavy
toxicity in liver.

FIG. 136

The left iris shows considerable disturbance of chemistry in back area; slow elimination in descending and sigmoid colon.

Arthritis

Winthrop, Wash.
October 30, 1949

"Dear Sir:

Your advice in regard to sodium foods for arthritis has helped me and I thank you.

Respectfully,

(Signed) Mrs. J. R."

Discussion

For discussion of sodium foods in arthritis, refer to the chapter called The Sodium Story. The person who has calcium deposits in the joints has unbalanced chemistry. Sodium is the element to keep us young, active and limber. When the joints become stiff and deformed, it is a sign that we need a lot of this "limbering up" element. Not all cases of arthritis respond easily. To correctly treat any disorder, we must treat the patient and not the disease. In arthritis, therefore, we do not treat the joints, we do not treat the effect; we normalize the digestive, the glandular, and the nervous systems, and then the effects leave.

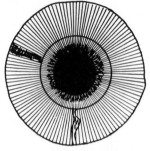

FIG. 137

This left iris indicates poor calcium-holding ability in skeletal structure, poor metabolism (defective thyroid function), and chronic acid stomach (showing lack of sodium).

Asthma

Oakland, California
January 26, 1934

"Dear Doctor Jensen:

In reference to our 7 year old son who has been under your care, thought you would be interested in a summary of ailment that brought on case as you found it, and to express our gratitude for the way you have helped him.

In 1927 when he was 11 months old he contracted pneumonia, which developed into asthma by 1929. From that time until we brought him to you on November 12, 1933, he suffered many attacks, and none of the medical men were able to help him.

You were recommended to us, and as a last resort we brought him to you for an examination. Your diagnosis convinced us that you were familiar with his ailment, so when you recommended a 21 day water fast we agreed.

He weighed 53 lbs. when he started on the fast and lost weight to 44 lbs. in the 21 days. In five weeks he has returned to 60 lbs. He has not had an attack since you have had his case, and you will never realize how much we appreciate what you have done for him.

Yours very thankfully,

(Signed) Mr. & Mrs. K. D."

Discussion

Although asthma usually is very difficult to correct, I have had very good results. Asthma is a chronic disease which develops after years of malnutrition and poor elemination, and there is nearly always a history of drug suppression.

There are many ways in which we can treat asthma to get the desired results. Among the dietetic measures are cutting out dairy products, adding more of the stimulating, electro-positive, protein, foods. Asthma patients usually are on a diet of some kind; they cannot eat this or that food, they are allergic to this and that, and some of them finally get to a place where all they eat is "peanuts and rootbeer," as one patient said.

The thing which I think has been most neglected in the healing arts is a good health standard, a right-living program. The hardest thing in all asthma cases is correcting the effects of the suppressive treating methods that have been used. For getting rid of these symptoms, we guided the patient through the reversal process of the disease; and in the retracing process we had to handle the elimination of drugs that many times had been used for the 'flu, the bronchitis, or the hay fever they had before the asthma.

FIG. 138

There are many combinations in asthma cases—some involving mostly the glandular structures, others the bronchial tubes and lung structure, and still others the bowel. In this case the left iris showed heavy bowel encumbrance throwing toxic material into the left bronchial tubes and lung. Extreme amount of congestion in sigmoid colon and rectum. Clogged skin, which prevents toxic material from being eliminated through it. When a scurf rim develops, as in this case, allergies are easily developed.

Asthma

Oakland, California
April 9, 1934

"*I am a man 86 years old and have been afflicted with asthma off and on for over 50 years. For the past two and a half years I have had asthma steady which would not allow me to move much, keeping me in a chair most of the time. Before taking Doctor Jensen's asthma cure I was taking three to four injections a day. Now after going through with the treatments I am free from asthma and some arthritis I had. My father and my daughter had asthma.*

Over one hundred physicians attended me with no results and some saying I would never be cured, others saying I had the worst kind of asthma to cure. I feel like working again and my neighbors are all surprised to see me getting outside and walking, and even without a cane.

(Signed) Dr. M. D."

Discussion

This doctor was in a position to get the best that medical science has to offer since he was a medical practitioner, but it had not solved his problem. In spite of his age he responded well to the right-living program. It is a shame that the methods we often advocate are not used until near the end of life or after many years of suffering.

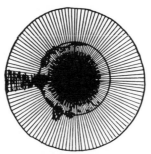

FIG. 139

In this asthma case there was considerable disturbance of the lung, with the cause of the trouble originating in the colon. Due to extreme breakdown of the pancreas he was unable to handle starches and sugars. Chronic acid stomach, and considerable prolapsus of the trasverse colon.

Asthma—(Bronchitis, Arthritis, High Blood Pressure)

Phoenix, Arizona
July 29, 1951

"In 1948 my condition was asthma, bronchitis, arthritis, and high blood pressure. Today, after following your program, blood pressure is normal, no asthma, sinus condition still improving. Feel much better physically and mentally. Could not work before I started, but in past month sold five cars and feel full of pep.

Sincerely yours,

(Signed) Mr. B. M."

Discussion

This patient was heavily laden with catarrh. After his elimination was improved and his diet changed, his body automatically repaired itself. The effects and symptoms always leave when we build our health.

In most cases of asthma we find the intestinal tract area in the iris very black, denoting a very underactive and toxic condition of the bowel. This we clear up first, and the effects, such as have been decribed in the patients mentioned, automatically leave.

Here we illustrate how the left iris of one asthma patient, Mrs. F. E. N., looked before treatment, and how it looked after a few months of corrective therapy.

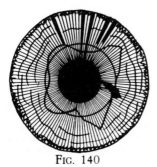

FIG. 140

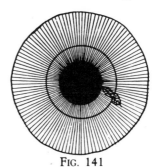

FIG. 141

Back Disorder

Phoenix, Arizona

July 28, 1951

"*Regarding Doctor Jensen, I think the following will show what he has done for me.*

I have always admired my husband's ability to accomplish things and his capacity for enjoying life. One day a few months after my following Doctor Jensen's program I began to wonder what had caused my husband to change so. He seemed to have slowed down and lost a lot of his zest and vitality for life in general. I asked him how come the change. He answered, 'Well, I haven't changed a bit, you're the one who has—you've not only caught up with me but passed me.'

After quite a lengthy discussion on the subject he wound up by saying 'I wouldn't take a fortune for what you have learned from Doctor Jensen.' Well, I wouldn't either and I shall always owe him a debt of gratitude!

It is wonderful to be rid of constant pain in my back after 18 years. These past few weeks I have been driving tractor, raking weeds, sawing logs, painting, etc., and I might add enjoying life. Six months ago if anyone had told me I would be doing these things I would have said it was impossible. I still have a long way to go but I know the right way makes all the difference.

Sincerely,

(Signed)   Mrs. D. H."

Discussion

Many cases of back pain result from abnormal position of the abdominal organs and from calcium deficiency. Gas pressure in the bowel also can cause back aches. If we mention only these three causes, we can see that our right-living program would diminish the back ache of a lot of people. I feel this program should not be used for just home treatments, but should be the method used by the doctor in supervising his patient's recovery.

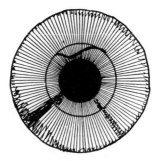

FIG. 142

This left iris shows chronic inflammation of the spine. The
scurf rim has widened in the spinal area, showing the greatest toxic settlement there. The prolapsus probably has had
something to do with the constant back ache because of
pressure symptoms developed. The pelvic and inominate
areas also show some acute inflammation, demonstrating lack
of calcium in the skeletal structure.

Cancer

Salt Lake City, Utah
February 20, 1950

"Dear Doctor Jensen:

While visiting you at Nature's Retreat I said I would write you.

*When I left Los Angeles in the fall of 1942 after much sickness, etc.,
the doctors there said I had about six months to live. (Cancer and heart
conditions).*

*I loved life very dearly as I had a wonderful husband and three small
sons. As soon as we arrived here in Salt Lake City I went from doctor
to doctor getting all the care they could give. (Two operations, trans-
fusions, X-ray therapy, liver and iron shots by the dozens, it seemed
like every kind of pill and medicine on the market). I was still in such
terrible pain, hemorrhaging and growing weaker every day.*

*I was told about fasting; also about the grape diet for cancer and
that you recommended it; and a lot about your method on the 'correct
way of living.' The book was loaned to me and after reading it I threw
out thirty bottles containing pills and medicines. I went on the grape
diet 100 per cent. At first I felt worse, by the end of three weeks my
pain was less and my color better; by the end of six weeks I was completely out of pain for the first time in four years. I was able to be up
and around. After two months people were amazed at the change in
me especially people who thought I was out of my mind to even think
of food doing what the medical men with all their knowledge couldn't
do for me.*

I have gone to all your lectures and have taken your classes since I was first told about your 'right way of living.' I have encouraged many people; seven members of my family, also one chiropractor to go to your classes and lectures. They all have greatly benefitted by doing so.

I sincerely appreciate all you have done for me and my family. I can say at this time as far as I know I am in perfect health, or I should say out of pain and can enjoy life as I should.

Sincerely yours,
(Signed)   Mrs. M. S. F."

Discussion

It is difficult to believe that cancer often responds to a health way of life. Many patients have been surprised at the results they had by simply living correctly. No matter what the condition is, as far as any sickness is concerned, we should learn to live correctly. That is the secret of getting well and keeping well. Cancer is considered to be very difficult to handle. We consider it an extreme chronic disease, and realize that after a person has a cancer it is very difficult to correct it. A wonder thing to know, however, is that the most necrotic tissue found in cancer responds to a change in diet and other living habits.

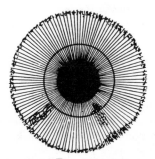

Fig. 143

In this case there was considerable inflammation in the uterus and right ovary, and an extreme amount of toxic settlement in bowel area opposite the uterus. The greatest toxic absorption is coming from this part of the bowel. The widened scurf rim at this area shows that this organ was more heavily laden with toxic material than any organ in the body. There was also a drug base at the site of inflammation in the uterus, indicating suppression and poor tissue repairing ability.

Cancer—(Of the Breast)

Nature's Retreat
October 7, 1947

"As I sit here thinking that in a few short hours I will be home again, my thoughts turn back twenty-three years ago when the word 'Cancer' of Breasts was pronounced to me at a time when another needed my help badly, so all thought of myself was cast aside for three years. That word is met with fear and trembling. But it need not be so. I was a veritable will-of-the-wisp going from clinic to clinic, medical doctors, chiropractors, osteopaths, masseurs, healers, etc. and received benefit from them all, so I could carry on my profession from two years to eight years but never found the cause of the trouble. Two years ago I came to the end of the trail, and like the one hoss shay collapsed, was content to step out of the picture as gracefully as I could when a friend told me of Doctor Jensen, so decided to try again. I was a sorry specimen of humanity with many involvements when I had my first iridiagnosis. With the Divine Power guiding and my faith in Doctor Jensen I went through 24 days on a water fast. Now after five months with Doctor's plan of living (Nature's way) I at the age of 65 years hope to carry on many years longer in this beautiful world of ours. The battle I had to fight through this period of time has been alleviated by the kindness exuded by those around me. With sincere thanks to Doctor Jensen, Mrs. Jensen, Professor, who have made my stay so pleasant, I wish the best of health and happiness for each of you.

Not goodbye, as I hope to visit this mountain top again sometime. Just so long.

P.S. Dr. Jensen found the 'cause' thus solving the enigma.

(Signed)   C. H. N."

Discussion

Finding the cause is all-important. Isn't it interesting that in this breast cancer case the cause was in the colon? This was discovered through iris analysis, as the accompanying illustration shows. Her breast tissue was inherently weak, and since her breast was her weakest organ, this is where the cancer took root. Her iris chart showed a line extending from the pupil to the autonomic nerve wreath at a point opposite this inherent weakness in the breast area.

Examination by nervometer also indicated that the point of greatest inflammation was the colon. No one had done anything to normalize the colon: no one knew its true condition. Iris analysis revealed it.

When I took the case, the breast had been draining for three months under self-care. After a fast of 25 days, the growth came to a head, broke, and drainage reduced it from the size of a grapefruit to that of a walnut. She was given carrot juice and vitamin A; had a great deal of rest and very little exercise. After she began to eat vegetables and fruits, she continued to average four glasses of carrot juice daily. (There is a photograph of this case in the chapter on Reflex Areas).

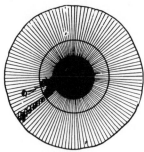

FIG. 144

This patient's right iris showed that the liver and gall bladder were quite inactive, and that liver detoxification was incomplete. Bowel inflammation was extreme, and considerable absorption from the bowel settled in the right breast area.

Cancer—(Of the Nose)

Mrs. T. had cancer of the nose. She went 55 days on grapes and carrot juice. I sent her to the Cancer Institute at Savannah, Missouri, and the report came back that she was free of cancer of the nose structure. I sent her to have plastic surgery, but they claimed she was too old (she was close to 75). If she could go on grapes and carrot juice at the age of 75 for 55 days, some of us kids should not kick. We are never too old to make ourselves beautiful; this lady had a becoming plastic nose made. That was six years ago and she is still good and strong.

There are many different kinds of diets that I use. Personally I think there is no food that has a specific effect on a person to cure any disease. I believe that the mono-diet or a juice diet gives the body enough rest so that it can recuperate and repair itself, for I have had equally good results in using many different types of eliminative diets.

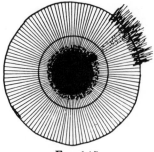

FIG. 145

This right iris shows a heavy scurf rim and anemia sign in the nose area, and a chronic lesion in the small intestine.

Cancer—(Of the Skin)

Los Angeles, Calif.
November 29, 1946

"I had a skin cancer on my left temple above the eye that was the size of your small fingernail with a hole leading right into the bony structure. This doctor I went to started me out on a proper dietetic procedure. He used physical methods for getting my abdominal tract in perfect order, used the slanting board and skin culture methods, and used a blue glass with sunshine directly over the sore. He believes in the grape cure and in my case I have flooded myself with a lot of grape juice.

Today, after working this doctor's procedure for three months, which included the proper mental attitude, I am now free of any trouble on the temple. And, incidentally, through these methods, I am feeling better than I have in years.

If more people could only know the value of this system of what nature could do for you, I am sure they could be made just as happy as I.

(Signed)   Mrs. L. J. M."

Discussion

In commenting on this condition we might say that the right living program not only treats the effects from which one is suffering, but that the whole body is benefitted. No one can follow a right living program without benefitting the whole body. To say that this method will cure every disease would be foolish, but it is one that should be used when we are trying to replace old tissue with new. To treat any effect without building the whole body would not result in a lasting change for the better.

Cancer—(Of the Throat)

Mr. G. J. of Atwater, Calif., was sent to me by a Mr. Huffman, president of a Western branch of a stainless steel company. This man had been diagnosed by medical doctors as having cancer of the throat, and had been given only a few days to live. He had lost some sixty pounds in weight and was unable to walk. He was sent to our sanitarium by airplane ambulance (on Sept. 12, 1949).

There was inflammation in the neck, lymph glands, chest, arms, liver. He was unable to talk, had lost his voice, was unable to eat. I had carrot juice and raw goat milk fed to Mr. J. by teaspoon. On the fifth day he was able to walk around and sit on the veranda. Through specialized dieting, he constantly gained weight and improved in health. In about six months' time he regained his voice and went back to work.

This is another example which shows there are values in drugless methods which merit investigation and study. If it does not in every case "cure," it can prolong life and make us happy while we are living. We all deserve the knowledge of how to live correctly, so that we may get as much out of this life as possible, and set good examples for the coming generation. It is hard to do that when we are sick.

In this case there was some drug suppression from years past, but in the reversal process the body was cleansed, new blood surged through the tissues, and repair was the result. For us to prove how much was accomplished, or to say the condition is cured forever and will never return, is an impossibility. Many people know of this case, and especially Mr. Huffman, President of the Huffman Corporation of California, by whom he had been employed and who suggested his coming to me.

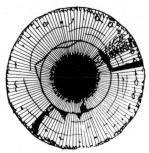

FIG. 146

This iris shows considerable congestion in all body structures. Drug deposits and toxic materials settled mostly in
lymph gland structure in neck area. Thyroid was affected.
Eliminative processes very poor. Chronic acid stomach.
Liver and gall bladder congestion. Pancreatic weakness.

Cancer—(Of the Chest)

Many persons are skeptical as to what can be done in detecting many of our ail-
ments through the iris of the eye. One skeptic, a drugless doctor himself, said that if we could arrange to have autopsies on some of the conditions diagnosed, we probably could prove the value of iridology. Here is a case for the skeptic:

Mr. A. developed chest pains, and my analysis of the case was that he had cancer of the chest. Iridology showed that he had a drug base settled in the bronchial tubes, which usually is indicative of cancerous tissue. Since this man was a close friend of the family, I preferred that he seek treatment elsewhere. Photographs were made by Doc-
tor P. of Monrovia, California, showing no pathology in the lungs or bronchial tubes, but X-rays do not reveal conditions in so incipient a stage. He was sent to Doctor M. of Pasadena, California, who could not find any pathology in the lung tissues through X-ray or laboratory tests. Doctor M. called me and wanted to know what I had found. When I told him cancer of the chest, he said they could not find it. It was hard to believe it was there! Three and a half months later, however, this gentleman died. Report was given by Doctor M. that he died of lympho-sarcoma—cancer of the chest. This is one case in which autopsy proved what iridology revealed long before the ordinary testing methods could have enabled the doctors to detect what was wrong. This we have done many time. And for the skeptic we might say that, through the proper investigation, he would come to these conclusions also.

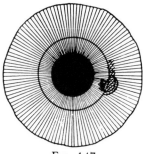

<small>FIG. 147</small>

This iris showed heavy drug deposits of iron, sulphur, and
iodine in the bronchial tube and chest areas, and evidence
of considerable toxic absorption from the bowel.

Cancer—(Of the Breast)

Another cancer case was that of a Mrs. B., who was sent to me by Reverend L. of
Pasadena, California. According to her medical doctor's report, she had only a few
weeks to live. She had a cancer of the left breast, could not walk, talk, or move her
body. Although her normal weight was 125 pounds, she now weighed less than 80
pounds. With feeding of small amounts of juices and natural foods, this patient recovered to the extent that in three months' time she was driving her car. A visit back to
her doctor brought the remark that a "miracle" had taken place; and truly it had. He
said that there was no longer any cancer of the breast, although he had diagnosed it as
cancer before. Three years after this, Reverend L. received a letter from Mrs. B. stating
that she had been out mowing the lawn. She had gained back her weight and was
feeling fine again.

Cataract

> "After 20 days on a water fast and five days on whey made from
> goat milk, I gained light perception in my left eye where no light had
> shown through for over three years. My right eye also improved as a
> result of this fast, and I consider these improvements worth much more
> than the 75 meals I missed.

> *(Signed)*   C. H.B."

Discussion

Cataracts are very difficult to handle, and I have seen but very few cases cleared up
entirely, through right living methods or any other method. I have seen definite improvement, however, when they started living healthfully.

If improvement can be brought about after a condition has developed, what a wonderful blessing we should consider knowledge of this way of living to be, so that we can
prevent the diseases we have today. Cases with catarrhal troubles respond very nicely to
the drugless eliminative routine. Through making sure that toxic wastes are thoroughly
eliminated, the body is cleansed and made ready to handle the proper foods.

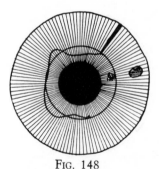

FIG. 148

Thyroid gland dysfunction was the most outstanding lesion
noted in this iris (patient had been operated upon years
ago). Therefore the calcium metabolism was disturbed.
The cataract weakness was found in the eye area of the
right iris.

Catarrh—(Chronic Coughing, Sneezing)

Los Angeles, California
November 22, 1946

"Dear Doctor Jensen:

*I don't know whether or not you ever have occasion to use a testi-
monial letter, however, if you do, please feel free to use this entire letter
or any part thereof. We are so grateful for what you have done for
our son, Ronnie, that we feel this is the least we can do to show our
appreciation.*

*For the past three or four years of his eight years of life he awoke
every morning and went through fifteen minutes of continuous sneezing
and clearing of his throat. In the beginning it would only occur during
the winter months, but later on it continued into the warm weather.
Every time we would consult a doctor he would go through the same
routine of asking whether or not there was asthma in the family and
when they were informed that one member of the family had had it,
they would shake their heads wisely as though that was the answer,
and then tell me there was nothing they could do about it. One doctor
even told me to go home and forget about it, as if one can forget anything as loud as coughing and sneezing. However, they never failed to
send their bills for anywhere from seven to ten dollars. Why didn't
they forget the bills if they couldn't relieve the condition?*

*Now, after about a month and a half of following your advice, Ron-
nie awakens every morning with not a trace of a single cough or sneeze.
Both my husband and I listen carefully every morning to make sure*

that we're just not dreaming. I waited for two hours in your office to see you and it was the best investment of time I ever made.

Again please accept our heartfelt thanks.

Sincerely yours,

(Signed) Mrs. S. S.

P.S. *Several of the doctors prescribed a drug which they told me was not a cure but would offer some relief."*

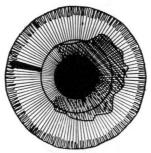

Fig. 149

This left iris shows a toxic and distended bowel, very heavy scurf rim, and poor skin elimination.

Catarrh—(Smell, lost sense of, Sinusitis)

Nature's Retreat
Altadena, Calif.
April 26, 1947

"Dear Doctor Jensen:

Knowing you were so busy I did not want to interrupt you further before you left, but I knew you would be interested in my experience.

Seven years ago I was thrown from a horse and suffered a fractured skull and I lost my sense of smell . . . On April 11, 1947 I came here to Nature's Retreat, to fast under your care. I have felt better than I ever have before . . . I have never been so happy, never had such peace of mind, and I have found something here that I have been searching for. Now on the 12th day of my fast I awakened to discover that my sense of smell has returned. I could smell the Eucalyptus, the orange blossoms, the good fresh air and all the earthy smells around my cabin . . .

Sincerely yours,

(Signed)   B. F."

Discussion

The average person is very grateful when all the little symptoms begin to leave after this big problem of catarrh has been solved.

A lady came to me from **Long Beach** who had bronchiectasis and had been told she was incurable. It took nearly a year on a good living program to clear up the condition. Her husband, following the diet program, found that his stomach condition, which was claimed to be ulcerous, improved..

Our sense of smell and taste are improved when catarrhal conditions are eliminated from the body; unpleasant body odors disappear; the sinuses drain less. When the body becomes clean enough that catarrh is not formed, discharges automatically stop. There is no need of stopping discharges from the outside, for we know that a clean body will not have abnormal discharges.

Deafness

San Diego, California
July 7, 1949

"Dr. Bernard Jensen

My dear friend: . . . My ears are better . . . Wishing you the best of everything.

(Signed)   L. B."

Eye Ulcers

Lomita, California
January 22, 1947

"Dear Dr. B. Jensen:

Thank you for the help you have given me. With your diet and treatment, I have not had a single eye ulcer. Before, I had several ulcers and one being very serious. Also the use of the slanting board has been very fine to keep the eyes in good condition.

Most sincerely,

(Signed) L. H. D."

Discussion

Eye ulcers can be treated a good deal like any other ulcer of the body, by changing the chemistry so there is sufficient calcium and other elements for the proper nerve supply and to quicken tissue responses. Developing a good circulation of blood which carries the right food is the key to healing ulcers.

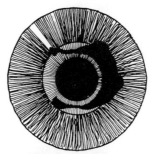

FIG. 150

These iris markings show considerable neck tension and nerve irritation, considerable toxic absorption from the bowel, prolapsus, and digestive disorders.

Eyesight Restored (Heart Trouble)

San Leandro, California
March 1, 1943

"*What Dr. Jensen has done for my father:*

Four years ago my father was taken to the hospital with an unusual type of heart trouble. During his stay in the hospital he was under the care of nine medical physicians and heart specialists. They told my mother and I that he would not live.

Father remained in the hospital for nine weeks. Seeing that there was no improvement in his health we decided to take him home. Shortly after we brought him home he had a spell so mother called another medical physician. His suggestion was to operate, but we thought with such a weak heart as he had, an operation would be impossible. It was then that his eyesight began to fail. We took him to an eye specialist. He wanted to operate on his eyes. This would have cost us $500 without guarantee of his getting back his eyesight. The specialist also told us if the operation was not performed soon he would go blind.

It was at this time that Dr. Jensen, Naturopathic Doctor, was recommended to us. This we consider a godsend. Words can never express our appreciation for what he has done for my father. Since my father has been under Dr. Jensen's care, which has been since last May, he has improved his health and most important of all he has again restored his eyesight without medicine or operation.

Very sincerely yours,

(Signed)   G. L."

Discussion

In this case the reversal process was quite severe. During the crisis, heart conditions of the past were re-experienced, but the patient was in fairly good health.

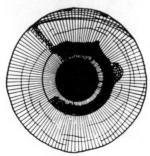

FIG. 151

In this case, heart pressure developed because of bowel distention. The entire digestive system was under-active; there were insufficient digestive fluids, and extreme gas.

Facial Neuralgia (Tic Douloureux), Neuritis

Long Beach, California
June 29, 1949

"Dear Dr. Jensen:

I wanted to give you a little resume of what I have gone through during the past few years regarding the pain in my face, which has been diagnosed as tic douloureux.

In February 1939 the first shocking pain started in the right side of my face. I was in the bathtub taking a bath and put the wash cloth to my face and then was when I felt the first pain—it felt as though I had gotten an electric shock. I cried out and my husband came to see what the trouble was. Following that I visited Dr. G. F. W., dentist in Long Beach and Dr. H. B. A., dentist, of Hollywood, thinking it was coming from my teeth. An X-ray showed a couple of old roots which had been there for twelve years. These were removed.

The pains continued periodically from that time on. I visited twelve doctors or institutions for treatment of the trouble since 1943, Mayo Brothers Clinic being one of them, where there were eight doctors who looked over the case; they were all nerve specialists. It was called neuralgia of the nerves. The doctors I visited were: . . .

The pain continued and was quite severe until I came to you, Dr. Jensen, and continued while under your care until I went under a water fast of seventeen days. On the third or fourth day of the fast I got relief from this pain. There has been no recurrence from that time.

*I can hardly tell you what this means to both me and my husband;
we are so grateful to you, to know you and your work. My friends
can hardly believe it when they see me now—my whole general health
is so much better. It just seems wonderful.*

Sincerely yours,

(Signed)   Mrs. J. S."

Discussion

Neuritis is a very painful condition. I have known of cases where the most extreme
measures were being resorted to through drugs and surgery to control the pain. The
right way to live can change all this. I have seen the drugless way bring relief.

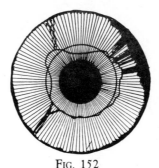

FIG. 152

This iris demonstrates considerable toxic settlement throughout the facial areas. Some head injury in the past indicated.
Toxic liver and gall bladder.

Glaucoma

Hollywood, California
January 18, 1950

"*To Whom It May Concern:*

*Some time ago I was having trouble with my eyes—my vision began
to leave me—I couldn't read, crochet, etc. . . . I decided to go to an
occulist or doctor of the eyes. . . . He said I had glaucoma and that
there was no cure for glaucoma. . . .*

*When I live as Doctor Jensen has taught me to, I have no trouble
with my eyes and use no drops or any prescriptions. I am free mentally,
free of any thoughts regarding an operation and not only thankful for
what has been done for my eyes but my whole outlook on life has com-*

pletely changed. If Doctor Jensen only knew, when I talked to him on the phone for the first time, I couldn't even see the figures to dial; all I could tell with my eyes was whether it was day or night.

This Christmas I could see everything on the tree. Last year a ball of fire.

(Signed)   Mrs. L. M. K."

Discussion

Glaucoma is an arthritic or hardened condition of the eyeball. It is one result of unbalanced chemistry. In this case there was an extreme emotional problem to handle. After the tension of mental anxiety was relieved, we saw the results above described.

Goiter—(Poor Eyesight)

Altadena, California
July 13, 1948

"After 30 days on a water fast and 30 days on raw food and goat milk diet, I am in perfect health and feel wonderful. I am leaving my goiter and glasses here as I no longer need them. I will always be indebted to Doctor Jensen. May God bless him.

(Signed)   J. R."

Discussion

I do not like to be an extremist in my work, but in some cases it takes extreme measures to overcome chronic diseases. While I am a great believer in fasting, I do not fast all cases. There are many things to consider in the handling of patients. Some of them need to change their mental attitude before fasting or other natural healing procedures are begun.

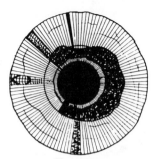

FIG. 153

This iris shows an extreme overload of toxic material settled in the thyroid gland. The blackened colon area indicates toxemia and inactivity of the bowel. This iris also shows an acid stomach and overworked kidney.

High Blood Pressure

San Francisco, California
November 25, 1947

"Dear Doctor Jensen:

    . . . Father had his blood pressure taken about a week ago and it had come down from 222 to 180, which we were pleased to hear. He is very happy to see Mom and I getting along so well and is grateful to you. . . .

(Signed)   E. H."

Discussion

Abnormal blood pressure is a symptom or an effect which changes as soon as the bodily conditions that are found to be the causes have been corrected. I have very good results in high blood pressure cases, bringing most of them down within a very short time, at least to a point that is not dangerous. Our office records indicate that in most cases there is a drop from ten to thirty points in a matter of one to two weeks, and invariably there is a slow drop after that, according to the way the patient lives. Many times we cannot normalize it with diet alone. Sometimes we have to relieve emotional strain that may be at the bottom of most of the trouble.

We usually start in with an eliminative diet of some kind, and when the person follows the right-living program taught him, the blood pressure usually becomes normalized. There is no treatment for the blood pressure itself, so we usually take care of the intestinal tract or glandular imbalance which may be the cause. We find that by using the "left side diet" or the starch diet we get a wonderful response in blood pressure cases, and especially so when there is any heart trouble involved. Any doctor using this regime will find the results so gratifying that he will make it a part of his practice thereafter. In this particular case the intestinal tract was the cause behind the symptom of high blood pressure, as demonstrated here in the iris illustration.

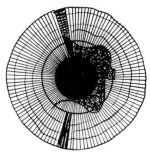

Fig. 154

This iris shows that the blood pressure center is involved,
being reflected from the transverse colon. Secondary kidney
inflammation. Heart pressure, bowel distention, and gas.

Intestinal Disorder (Constipation 27 Years)

Salt Lake City, Utah
July 3, 1950

"Dear Doctor Jensen:

We want to take this opportunity while you are in Salt Lake City to let you know how we appreciate the help you have given us in diet, advice and treaments.

Mrs. B. has been troubled all her life with chronic constipation. She applied your health program and after two months of following it there is no necessity of any laxatives. . . .

From the bottom of our hearts we do appreciate what you have done for us. Thank you so much.

Very respectfully,

(Signed)   T. N. B.
(Signed)   Mrs. T. N. B."

Discussion

Constipation is one of the most common conditions requiring correction. In handling any disorder, I work on the bowel first because I realize that if the bowel is not functioning normally no other organ can work right either. It is through the intestinal tract that we get our nourishment and eliminate wastes. Unless it is healthy and has the power to get rid of wastes and assimilate food properly, we cannot repair, rebuild and rejuvenate tissues that may be broken down in various parts of the body.

After changing to natural diet and natural living habits, we invariably hear from the patient, "My bowels are better." That is the first thing that tells us we are getting results in whatever condition we are correcting. Many times symptoms that may be causing trouble in remote parts of the body will not respond until after the intestinal tract is working well. It is a wise doctor who first takes care of the intestinal tract of a patient and outlines a proper diet program. He will see little white healing lines appear throughout the intestinal area of the iris of the eye. We should also remember that exercise is necessary for normal tone. In many cases it takes two or three months or longer before these white lines fill in completely the intestinal tract area. These white lines signify that the condition of the intestinal tract has improved and that the intestinal flora has been changed.

It is hard to believe that we can do such a wonderful job just through correct diet. It is also wonderful in this work to see what happens to patients who have had the laxative habit. For a while they may insist that laxatives are necessary to them, but a day comes when they begin to have natural bowel movements. We disapprove of taking laxatives and feel they are unnecessary if a person does the right thing in keeping his body in good order. The establishment of normal bowel function has been experienced by employees at the sanitarium who ate the foods served there. There was no menu, and everyone had to eat the natural foods. No devitalized foods were served. Although the employees were not under my care, many of them reported that whereas they used to be constipated, they were now experiencing excellent bowel elimination. In one instance a man and woman with two children who were working there refused to take their check at the end of the month because they were having natural movements. The woman, who had suffered from sinus trouble and sinus pains every night, no longer had them. One of the children who had had a running ear, no longer had any discharge from the ear. Now that is without any doctor's care but the result of being on a natural diet as was given at the sanitarium. Imagine then what can be done under specific care and guidance.

Fig. 155

These iris markings show heavy toxic settlement in bowel areas, with bowel distention and gas. Black coloration indicates inactivity, poor motility, and poor contractility. Scurf rim and skin areas are also black.

Intestinal Disorder—(Colitis, Intestinal Inflammation with Fermentation and Putrefaction, Gas)

Glendora, California

"Dear Doctor Jensen:

Progressing wonderfully, but slowly. Your unorthodox methods sure get durable results—Wow! but I'm happy. . . . Your methods are slow, but so very thorough.

I'm sure not trying to hurry this up. I'm really enjoying living and now that I've formed the habit I'm going to keep on for quite some time. Thanks to you, Doctor.

Just me—

(Signed)   D. W."

Discussion

In this case the principal abnormality was inflammation of the bowel wall. This patient was a nervous wreck, had abdominal pains, gas, and bleeding from the rectum. His iris showed black specks throughout intestinal tract area; a heavy catarrhal condition, scurf rim; bowel pockets. Under specialized diet of juices, taro root, and banana powder, this man passed off many feet of intestinal lining, some ten feet passing off all at once. The specimen was presumed to be cancerous in nature when reviewed in a laboratory. This man passed mucus from time to time for a period of a year. This was so extreme at times that I wondered whether there was some actual disease settled in the intestinal wall. The fermentation and putrefaction that developed in his bowel were so pronounced that there were times when the mucus was black, and odorous material was passed that I felt had been there for a long time. He spent over five years to get himself in shape so that he could work again. In the beginning he was in a serious condition, both mentally and physically, and to get it all straightened out meant a lot of hard work. Although he must follow a special diet, he is a living example of a very extreme case, which was believed to be cancer of the bowel.

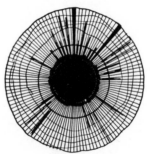

Fig. 156

The numerous "spokes" in this iris denote an extremely toxic condition in the intestinal tract; entire mucous lining involved. The narrow black margin around the pupil indicates extreme nervous irritability of bowel.

Intestinal Disorder

Tucson, Arizona
August 5, 1949

"Dear Doctor: . . . I think it is wonderful what you are able to see through the eye, and I know that it is accurate: I have sore spots right where you have indicated, and have had for many years.

Yours most sincerely,

(Signed)   C. C. A."

Discussion

1 find iris analysis to be quite accurate and that those places in the bowel area which indicate abnormality usually correspond to where the patient complains of having the gas disturbance and pressure symptoms. It is wonderful to see these symptoms leave under the proper dietetic routine. Many of the other symptoms this woman had were developed from the sore spots that she was complaining about in the bowel.

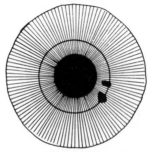

Fig. 157

Two bowel pockets in left iris, showing source of infection and point of inflammation.

Intestinal Disorder

Altadena, California
June 1947

"*Just went through an 18 day water fast. I broke my fast with a glass of orange juice, diluted, and nothing in the world ever tasted better to me than this first glass of juice. My present condition is excellent, I feel much more energetic, and don't seem to have the need and urge for lengthy afternoon siestas. Fasting for a while seems to be the easiest way to take care of all kinds of body disorders and to improve health. My best wishes to the continued success of Dr. B. Jensen.*

(Signed)   E. N."

Discussion

While I do not fast every case, I have found that an eliminative diet or a brief fast, preceding our right living program, usually sets the patient up with the proper mental attitude and the feeling that everything is all right. And, usually very quickly, the body showed the person how it could feel when it was properly cared for. Some people are not satisfied with a slow process of healing, but our work is comparatively fast because at times we use radical measures to bring it to normal. It is my job to see not only that the intestinal tract is taken care of through diet, but that there is adjustment of the mental attiude, for I realize that this may be a major part of the problem which has to do with improper bowel function. I have said many times that you cannot be well unless you are happy and you cannot be happy unless you are well. And I feel that it is not enough only to see that a person gets well, but also to teach him how to keep well.

Leg Ulcers

Oakland, California
October 19, 1939

"*Dear Doctor Jensen:*

. . . I've really been as fit as a fiddle these last four years—I've even put on a few pounds—weight 124 now. Never had any recurrence of my leg trouble but I still have a scar which I don't mind at all. You worked so hard to heal it—that's the important part. . . .

Very sincerely,

(Signed)   I. B."

Discussion

This lady, age 30, had thirteen leg ulcers, the size of a dollar and larger, running yellowish green pus. For years she traveled throughout the country trying to find the "cure." Through natural treatments—using specific diet measures,—foods high in calcium, plenty of greens and tops of vegetables,—we finally accomplished a healing. She was able to wear stockings for the first time in three years. This was accomplished in a few weeks' time after changing entirely to natural methods.

Leg Ulcers

Before

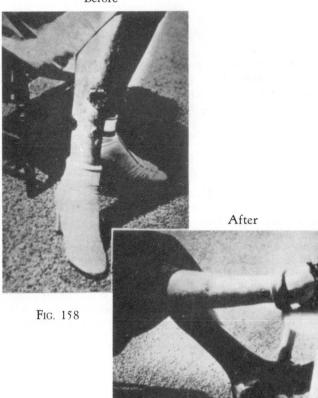

Fig. 158

After

Fig. 159

Fig. 160

Both of this patient's irises indicated very poor circulation in the extremities. The right iris showed signs of poor calcium-holding ability in the leg area. Thyroid was affected. Bronchial tubes heavily laden with catarrh. Considerable toxic material within the bowel.

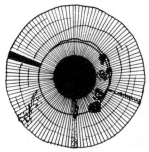

FIG. 161

The left iris showed imbalance of calcium in the back areas;
this produced an excessive curve. This iris also indicated
thyroid dysfunction, which would affect the control of
calcium.

I have found that leg ulcers heal nicely during a fast. If they are not completely
cleared up during the fast, a right-living program usually brings about correction in the
month to follow. In the chapter on Fasting and Eliminative Diets we discuss a man's case
and include photographs showing the changes that fasting and right living can bring about
in just ten days. It is wonderful how the body can repair and rebuild, especially when
we start out right. And if we can possibly restore the mineral balance in the body, that
patient not only can continue to make improvements, but can keep well.

Malnutrition—(Psoriasis, Dental Caries, Hemorrhoids, Sinusitis, Stomach Distress, Constipation, Nervousness, Insomnia, Exhaustion)

Los Angeles, Calif.
November 5, 1937

"Dear Doctor Jensen:

*I will endeavor to outline my experiences with sickness, hoping that
no other human has to ever go through what I did.*

*My age at present is forty-four, a Swede by nationality; they say
Swedes are noted for their dumbness, and the writer is no exception to
the rule. Up to and including the age of twenty-one, we had served
in our home, meat, potatoes and gravy three times a day. Rarely were
vegetables prepared and if they were I would promptly refuse to eat
them. This eating program caused me to break out with psoriasis; a
skin eruption with which I've been afflicted ever since.*

*Considerable money was spent on the skin ailment until I was forced
to give it up as a bad job. Sun-lamps, special concocted salves, certain
injections to compensate for inactive glands were all tried, when finally
one kindly doctor told me to stop spending money on a cure that was
hopeless. I followed his advice.*

I took out health insurance when I was eighteen years old with the Preferred of New York. When nineteen years of age I had a rheumatic attack and was forced to lie in bed for nearly eighteen months. My carcass was used for experimental purposes. The attack came while I was living in my home town, Des Moines, Iowa, but later I was taken to Hot Springs, Arkansas. Some doctors thought that my sickness was caused by the psoriasis; they didn't really know. After returning home in no better condition than when I left and feeling like a paralytic, at Rochester it was discovered that I had a cavity in my tooth and an operation for hemorrhoids was performed. Six weeks later I was able to work and felt fine once more though the experience cost better than $1800.

War broke out; I enlisted and entered an officers training-camp which was really a school of aviation. I was discharged because my equilibrium was all haywire. Still intent upon being a soldier, I joined the slackers detail, the quartermaster purchasing group. Starting from a job as private, I later was made sergeant of the senior grade. This activity did my health no good. I worked two hours a day, ate the very richest and finest foods and played the remainder of the time. The reason I didn't eat everything made was because I never thought of it; the Congress Hotel in Chicago served no better.

At the age of twenty-six years, I was married and my wife forced me to eat vegetables. In a couple of years I could eat and enjoy any vegetable going and I relished raw salads.

War time being over, I associated myself with Montgomery Ward Company in the Chicago main office, buying fabric goods for the automotive department. After three years I resigned—no future for me. I connected with U. S. Rubber as salesman. A year later my position was raised to assistant zone manager; then sickness hit me—hard this time. I resigned; it seemed I could not keep up with the parade. This session was a panic—plenty of blind man's bluff, guess who's got the button: First, all my upper teeth; second; I had my antrums pumped forty-two times; third, every other day injections shot in my hip to stimulate circulation, pep and what have you.

That was seige—I don't want to mention any doctors' names. This fellow only treats big people; I don't mean elephants (that should be his speed). You certainly had to be put in on the ground floor by some influential individuals before he treated you. People came to him from all over the world; he being a big specialist. He charged me in line with my income—I could not be held down so I got well.

When I arrived in California, I connected with General Motors because I wanted to coast awhile but within three years my position was area superintendent, causing plenty of headaches. I was with this group for thirteen years before I resigned on account of sickness. The parade had gone past and had run me down completely. My diet was orange juice for the next two months and most of my time was spent in the mountains. After this rest I felt lots better and began to want to buck-in-and-work once more.

I decided to enter into my own business, because my poor health would hinder me oftentimes, became so detrimental and made me less dependable. It was a good buisenss and I was proud of it. The Pacific Sign Company, specializing in outdoor advertising, was an old estab-lished company in the city of Los Angeles. At times the breaking out was very bad, other times my body and face showed no signs of red blotches or any ailment. Stomach attacks came often, later the trouble was constant. It hurt me to drink water even and plus all this I had a great deal of constipation; enemas wouldn't move my bowels, so I sent back east for a J.B.L. Cascade—"boy that works!" I always felt draggy, pepless and wanted to sleep all the time. This stayed with me for seven and one-half years and each time I tried something new it meant more money going out. I'll now tell you what I did from that time to this.

First, I went to a special osteopath with the cabinet and colonics for a year, located in Santa Monica, about six months twice a week and later six months once a week. The benefits derived lasted only for a short time. Next I spent nine months another place seeing if the Morris wave, colonics and adjustments would help. While enumerating all these things I can also honestly say that I had 150 extra high colonics and 100 adjustments sandwiched in here and there. One noted medical doctor chief of staff in one of our leading hospitals said to me one day, "Boy, you've got something there!"

I took enough medicine to float a battleship and have plenty left that I would like to sell, cheap. Then I even studied medicine, made and mixed my own, all the time experimenting on myself for I was nearly dead anyway so it didn't make a great deal of difference. Follow-ing kindly suggestions got me no place either. One of my last tryouts was to drink good, high-grade whisky before the evening meal. Since I am not a drinking man, the psoriasis came out plenty. The more lax-atives I took, the worse I felt and always I would have to change brands because one would work only for a short time. After all this, I took a complete course from one of our leading health and diet lecturers. He really was splendid as far as he went but I found that his work did not follow through.

A friend of mine insisted that I come to you for treatments and kept after me for one month, until finally I came more to please him than anything, because I felt that all trials were more or less useless. I came to you and talked things over. You offered encouragement and I felt willing to try again. At this time my legs were numb, also my arms; I couldn't eat, sleep or do anything properly. My nervous system was shot; I could hardly write my name. In three weeks I could work like nobody's business, and now, today, I am feeling fine. The psoriasis has disappeared, my legs and arms feel human instead of like wood and my nerves are at last steadied. All this has been done under your guidance, Doctor Jensen; the diet which I follow religiously and the exercises which I do, plus the valuable lectures I attend without fail. I had to get well somehow; I was gradually losing my business that I now have regained. Health is vital when we have it, and miracles can *be accomplished if only it is regarded as a precious possession never to be abused or taken for granted. . . . Words would fail utterly to express my deep and sincere appreciation for all the instruction regarding health you have so graciously given me.*

Always your friend,

(Signed)   E. M. W."

Discussion

Very seldom do we use specific treatment for any one disorder, and we present this case to show that in spite of numerous troubles, the body responds to right living. We aim toward normalizing the entire organism rather than treating the disease itself. No matter where the trouble exists—whether it be nervousness, dental caries, skin disorders, bowel disorders,—through right living processes you will see a change for the better. Every part of the body will improve in health because we are working on the principle that good blood, circulated where it is needed, will repair the tissues if repair is at all possible.

FIG. 162

The black scurf rim in this iris denotes poor elimination through the skin areas. The blackness in the bowel area indicates a high degree of toxic settlement there. Very chronic acid stomach, accompanied by very heavy nerve rings.

Malnutrition (Iodine and Calcium Deficiency)

Seattle, Washington (1948)

"*Dear Doctor:*

We are so very grateful for the health that has come to our baby that I must tell you about it. You may remember a year ago in November I brought S. C. to you from Tacoma, Wash. She was two years old and had never walked and could not turn herself over in bed or feed herself. The doctors who had seen her did not agree but she was thought to be partially paralyzed and didn't do anything to help her. In five weeks after I brought her to you she was able to turn over in bed and a week later she was strong enough to bring herself to a sitting position. In seven weeks she began to walk and is now twelve pounds. Her trouble was caused by a pre-natal deficiency of iodine and the cure was brought about by supplying natural food elements and natural living entirely as no drugs were used. It is a joy to see her well and strong. A very happy little girl.

Most gratefully yours,

(Signed)   Mrs. L. P."

Discussion

This is a typical case of malnutrition. Sometimes when there is inherent weakness, as in the thyroid gland, the power to control the calcium in the body is lacking. In spite of the fact that this child was very young, she was lacking iodine for the control of calcium in the body. Children respond especially well and very quickly to natural healing methods because they have the power and energy to work with. Since the strength is there to respond, all they need is to be supplied with the proper building materials.

We have seen this child many times since her recovery. A right-living program has been continued, there has been no recurrence of her difficulties, and she is enjoying good health.

FIG. 163

This photograph shows the well-nourished appearance of the little girl after recovery.

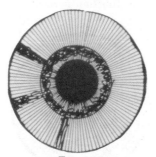

FIG. 164

The iris signs illustrated here show that thyroid, kidney and back disturbances were the principal conditions to consider. This iris also indicated that there was a deficiency of calcium and iodine.

Mental Disorders (Nervous Breakdown; Mental Disorientation)

Oakland, California
November 25, 1946

"Dear Doctor:

. . . We all send our best regards, and again may I thank you from the bottom of my heart for all you did for me. You made me see the light. You helped me to think straight and reason things out for myself. I had to learn that I could not harbor a hatred in my heart toward my mother and have a well body or a happy mind. I was so set and stubborn I could not and would not see the Truth. For this and many other things you taught me I am indeed grateful. . . .

Sincerely,

(Signed)   Mrs. H. F."

Discussion

In cases where there is extreme mental difficulty, I find that it can best be handled if the physical problems are dealt with first. In this case especially, the effect of the emotional strain was too great a load for the physical structure. Through straightening this out first, the patient attained greater emotional balance, she could reason better, and correction could take place. We have taken care of many cases of mental disturbance. I have had the best results by taking care of the physical body first.

One such case was a girl who had been kept under the influence of dope and had been shedding tears for so long that it was difficult to determine what her problem was. But I was able to take her out of an institution, and, through fasting and learning a proper living routine, she was enabled to return to her home and take up her duties with her family again, normally.

Another case that comes to mind where there was quite a mental breakdown was that of a young lady who had not had a bowel movement in eighteen days. Now how can any mind work clearly without that proper functioning of the intestinal tract? The toxic condition that had developed from this poor physical elimination would cause any nerve tissue to become underactive and unable to function normally.

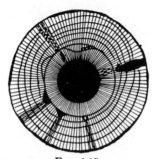

FIG. 165

The numerous nerve rings in this iris show that the patient had extreme nerve tension throughout the body. Three nerve rings indicate a serious condition, but when there are four and five, the person is at a stage where a nervous breakdown could develop. The thyroid was thrown out of balance, which affected the metabolism. Other glands severely affected were the ovaries and adrenals. The mental area was affected, and an extremely toxic condition existed in the bowel and liver.

Parkinson's Disease

Honolulu, Hawaii
August 26, 1947

"Our dear Doctor Jensen:

It is now more than a month since we wrote you and time to make a further report.

We are sure you will be glad to know that Mr. D. continues to show improvement. His arm and leg movements are better co-ordinated; his throat condition is greatly improved; the salivary glands are under better control; he does not tire nearly as easily; . . . Besides all this his courage has risen and his outlook is more cheerful. . . .

Of course we do the skin brushing and the slanting board exercises, and the Spiritual exercises of faith with the joyful expectancy that the next thing to happen to us is the best thing. . . .

We are so grateful to you and always will be.

Your grateful friends,

(Signed)   E. and A. D."

Discussion

In Parkinson's disease the brain and nervous system are involved, and it is very difficult to handle. Most doctors consider it an incurable condition. In this particular case, good results were obtained from the natural methods used. In a period of a year the control of speech came back and re-establishment of brain and muscle coordination developed beautifully. While there was not a complete cure, the last time I saw these people, it was gratifying to see what this type of work would do when other methods of healing had failed.

FIG. 166

This iris shows disturbance in the center of locomotion and
in the fatigue center in the brain, and depletion in the animation and life centers. The thyroid was affected. A very
bad rectal condition also existed. Prolapsus and an extreme
amount of toxic absorption from the transverse colon were
causing considerable irritation to the brain areas.

Rheumatic Fever

One rheumatic fever case was that of a girl fifteen years of age, whose parents had
traveled from place to place in a trailer, seeking the proper climate, etc. for her health.
She had a bad heart condition which did not permit much exercise, and had been unable
to attend school for several years.

After living for a time in accordance with the health regime at the sanitarium, where
she had the advantage of having raw goat milk, she overcame the problem. She returned to school and finished with other children her age, was able to enjoy horseback
riding, etc.

FIG. 167

This iris demonstrates a pocket half way down the descending colon, causing a reflex condition in the heart. The kidney area and lower back area were affected. Nervousness,
indicated by the numerous nerve rings, was at the base of
this case.

Another case of rheumatic fever was that of Mrs. Y. of Oakland, California. Doctors had pronounced her condition incurable, and an insurance company was paying for her illness. After she had been under our care for some time, she recovered her health. The insurance company then said there must have been a mistake in diagnosis to begin with, so they made a diagnosis and said they could not believe that rheumatic fever had been cleared up in this young lady.

Skin Disorders—(Eczema)

Long Beach, Calif.
July 30, 1941

"Dear Doctor:

I wish to take this opportunity to thank you for curing our M. of eczema. We took him to different doctors and tried many remedies for his eczema before taking him to you.

We are indeed grateful to you.

Most sincerely,

(Signed)   Mr. and Mrs. C. B."

Discussion

It is difficult to say just how long it will take to get rid of skin troubles, but children respond very rapidly. While in this particular case we put the child on a fast, we do not like to do this because of the attitude of most parents. They are more difficult to handle than the child in fasting. After a ten-day fast this child's skin cleared up and there has been no return. Eczema, again, is an effect, usually due to toxemia that is working out through the skin. As we clean up the body, make it toxin-free, with normal elimination, and then feed vital foods containing the proper chemical elements, the body heals itself.

Skin Disorders—(Psoriasis)

Santa Monica, Calif.
January 2, 1941

"Picture if you can, a man thirty years of age, with a swell wife and a fine baby, domestically happy, wondering whether or not life was worth living. At times it seemed as though it would be an act of kindness towards wife and family to end it all. Such was the condition of the writer a year ago.

The best medical doctors in the country told me that my case of psoriasis was incurable, and that everything known to medicine had been tried and there was nothing more that could be done. At the time their decision seemed logical. I had been troubled with eczema all my life. My parents had done everything in their power to relieve the condition. Thy took me to one doctor after another. It would be impossible to remember all the various remedies in the form of salves, lotions, and tonics that were recommended by well meaning friends, and hopefully tried on me. Every so often we would hear of some new doctor who was supposed to be 'good on skin conditions,' and away we would go to another disappointment.

As I grew older, and earned money of my own, I began consulting specialists, at times traveling many miles regularly, to see them. One tried X-ray, one baths, another ultra violet rays, then injections, allergy tests, diet, serums, vitamin pills, and finally sedatives. All this time I grew steadily worse and more and more of my body became affected. It itched constantly, kept me from sleeping, hampered my work, and just about drove me insane with worry and fear of what I could see would be the final outcome—helplessness. In a desperate effort to get sleep and relief I took more and more sedatives; as the doctor told me that they would not hurt me. I ended up in the hospital drunk on dope. We then decided to move west as the sun seemed to be the only thing that would help. A friend advised that I try a fast. Although I knew nothing about fasting I went without food for six days, and because the bowels were not kept open during this time, I became worse. I was then about decided that my case was hopeless.

Shortly after that fast a friend gave me Dr. Arnold Ehret's book on Natural Methods of Healing. As soon as I started reading it I became enthused. Many questions that had bothered me for years were answered; for the first time the mystery of disease was discarded, and in its place was substituted logic and good common sense. Through the publishers of the book I came to know Dr. Bernard Jensen. Hope and confidence took the place of despair, and a new life opened up for me. Eventually through Doctor Jensen's boundless generosity and humanitarianism, a plan was worked out whereby I could go to the doctor's Mountain Retreat and really go to work at the task of correcting previous wrongs and of getting well. In order to quickly clean the body of the toxic material responsible for my skin trouble I went on a fifty day fast, putting nothing but water into the body. Gradually the hard, tough, dry skin peeled off and the skin became soft and clear. Surprising as it might be I was still able to chop wood and do various odd jobs on the thirtieth day of the fast. Of course I lost weight, but what of it? I was getting well! For the first time in my life I knew the answer!

After the fast, I followed Doctor Jensen's daily health regime. Each day I learned more and more how to get well and how to stay well. The best part about it, is that it is not hard to do! Natural foods are more enjoyable than any other kind; and what a relief it is not to be spending money on drugs; not to be worrying about catching cold, or the 'flu epidemic.

As I think back now, I realize that had anybody told me of a similar experience several years ago, I would not have believed them. Nature cure seems so simple and so easy, that many people find it hard to accept it; I was the same way, and it was only after the medics gave me up as incurable that I was open-minded enough to listen and to learn.

Now with my skin worries at an end, I'm looking forward to getting a job and going back to work; to think that as little as a year ago it seemed that I would never again be able to hold down a job, seems incredible. If by means of this article, some of those who are now stumbling along in poor health, will be benefitted by my experience, then that experience will not have been in vain. No words can express my gratitude to those who finally put me on the right road—the road to health.

(Signed)   H. G. M.

P.S. I might add that my brother suffering from the same condition came West from Wisconsin, and underwent the same treatment, going on a 17-day fast followed by a six-day fast; he returned East greatly improved, his skin in better condition than it had been during the last ten years."

Discussion

The account of this case really speaks for itself. Psoriasis is considered to be incurable, and the dermatologists are having a difficult time trying to find what causes it. Most patients suffering with this disorder go from doctor to doctor getting allergy tests and many other kinds of tests. This man spent considerable time getting allergy tests, trying to find out what was causing his trouble, and finally he was in a position where practically every food except watermelon was prohibited. But after fasting and living on a health-building program, tests showed he could tolerate almost any kind of food. I believe that allergies which have developed in a body that is not well, will disappear when the body has been cleansed and remineralized. To treat the condition from the outside, to treat the skin condition without working from inside out, is only working on one part of the body. In this case I did not treat the skin at all, but found that a wonderful result was obtained through use of the fast and right living methods. The fact that this man's brother was similarly afflicted would indicate a family weakness for that condition. His psoriasis also cleared up after a fast at the sanitarium.

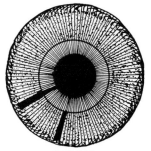

Fig. 168

This shows the appearance of the iris when there is an excessive amount of drug settlement throughout the body. In this case the settlements were particularly high in sulphur and iron. Most of the drug settlement was migrating to the skin areas. Poor kidney elimination. Considerable bowel disturbance.

Skin Disorders—(Psoriasis)

Altadena, California
November 27, 1948

"It is very gratifying to be able to say that in five weeks here at the Retreat I have accomplished what I set out to do. Under the expert guidance and wise counsel of Doctor Jensen, and with the competent help of Mrs. Jolly and her way with Nature's foods, the Prof's experience to give one added confidence, the goal was changed to reality.

I came here with a vicious 'crop' of psoriasis spots and chronic stomach and intestinal difficulties. After fasting thirteen days on distilled water, eight days on carrot and celery juices, and vegetable broth, two days on prune and pineapple juices, I felt completely rejuvenated and ready to begin the building program. Sun bathing, skin brushing, slanting board exercises and all the other items on Doctor Jensen's complete health program contributed to the final goal. My skin is more clear than it has been in twenty years, and the diet the doctor has arranged for me, I relish and enjoy (as I have never been able to enjoy food in the past). These five weeks have given me a new start in life—the future looks wonderful now that I have the pep and the zest for it. Thanks from the bottom of my heart to the man who has made this possible and to his wonderful staff for their help in carrying out the program.

"I feel Wonderful."

(Signed)   A. E. E.

P.S.   I pray that others who are in ill health and have lost their zest for living may find their way to this glorious place and a new life.

Most thankfully attested by J. O. E., husband."

Discussion

The wonderful results obtained in cases of psoriasis through fasting seem indeed miraculous. I have seen many cases who returned to their old habits of living and had their psoriasis return. This happened to one patient who returned to beer drinking.

Itching disorders can be classed with eczema. As part of the body processes we get rid of quantities of waste acids through the skin. Itching that accompanies the elimination of these acids through the skin can be relieved tremendously by changing the body chemistry.

Skin Disorders—(Pruritus, symptomatic. Severe Chronic Itching of Anus and Rectum)

Palm Springs, Calif.
August 5, 1945

"*The quiet and meditative state of mind that comes as a logical ef-fect from fasting, and complete bodily rest—brought me at least one great truth: That the universe is one tremendous, orderly plan. Every-thing in the great universal organization is in order. There is only one element in this magnificent organization that is disorderly. The culprit is man. And man only realizes that he has been disorderly after he has gone through the experience of the meditative transition from disorder into order—or right living. By some it has been called the 'Metanoia' or 'safe return.'*

My best wishes will always be with the chap who has been in-spired to devote his life to directing this transition into 'right living' for struggling mankind—my dear friend, Bernard Jensen.

(Signed)   G. C. D."

Discussion

This patient, thirty-five years of age, spent considerable time in a hopsital with ex-cessive itching of the rectum and lower intestine, developed while in Service in the South Seas. He had been given all types of treatment over a period of two years without ob-taining relief. He spent a month and a half in our sanitarium, and after a twenty-eight day fast was completely healed and restored to health.

Spastic Paralysis

Mesa, Arizona
May 19, 1949

"*Dear Doctor:*

. . . *L. is improving. She weighs over 20 pounds now, and looks good. Everyone is surprised that she looks so well and we are truly grateful. Her spastic motions are calmer now. Again thanking you,*

Your sincere friends,

(Signed)   E. and V. L."

Discussion

It is not an easy thing to tawe care of spastic children through drugless methods, but I have seen some good results obtained, and I believe that certain branche of the drugless art, specializing on spastic children, are doing some wonderful work. I have handled very few spastic paralysis cases, and extreme cases I could not correct, but through improving the functioning of the intestinal tract so they could assimilate their food properly and have better eliminiation, most of their health problems were solved even though the paral-ysis was not corrected. I do not believe there is any condition, no matter what it is, in which the doctor shouldn't consider taking care of the fundamental health problem first. If surgery or any other form of treatment is indicated, the best end-results will be ob-tained if we start out with a fundamental right-living program.

Toxemia—(Ulcers, Malnutrition)

Richmond, Calif.
December 15, 1933

"I am writing these experiences I have had with doctors, and my struggle, or their struggles in my case, and I hope others may benefit by them.

The first sign I noticed of anything being wrong, was when a skin irritation appeared between my toes and on the bottom of my foot. I showed my sister and not wanting to take any chances, we went to the doctor right away. The doctor examined me and told me that I had 'Athlete's Foot.' He put my foot under an ultra-violet ray, then he made out a prescription to put on the infected places. I carried out his instructions, but my foot continued to get worse. We went back a few more times after that, and then he said it was beyond him and told us that we should go right away to see two skin specialists in Oakland. We went to them- the same day, and they said they wouldn't take the case unless I went to a hospital.

I went to the hospital and the swelling went down, but in the meantime two open sores, or ulcers, had formed on two toes and two on the arch of the foot. After ten days, they sent me home with a pair of crutches and with instructions to come back twice a week. The ulcers would close for three or four weeks, and would then open again for three or four months.

That went on for eight months, and I went to school on crutches. I then developed severe pains in my left side. We called the doctor and he diagnosed it as pleurisy, and then taped my side. I lay on my back for two months, my sister having to feed me. In the meantime, my foot had closed. I kept losing weight until I was only 103 pounds, even though I was eating three big meals a day. The doctor took X-rays, and saw a spot that was apparently on the lung. They then decided that I had tuberculosis, and said that I should go to a tuberculosis sanitarium.

I went to a sanitarium in Redwood City, and stayed there for three months. They then decided I was not reacting the way a tuberculosis patient should, so they took me to San Francisco and had another type of X-ray taken. It showed the spot to be on the rib instead of the lung. The doctor suggested taking my rib out, but after consulting with two other doctors he decided to try X-ray treatments on it. They let me go home, and I went back and forth from Richmond to San Francisco for the treatments. My foot had opened again.

After taking about twenty-four treatments on my side, a drainage from my third rib opened in the middle of my chest. It began by draining about three-fourths of a cup of matter a day. My foot started to drain again, and the both of them drained for about six months. Then they closed for three months, but both reopened again within a few weeks of each other. They kept this up until it was about two and a half years since the time my foot had first opened.

After all this doctoring without any results, and our finances coming to an end, we went over to the University of California Hospital. They had me stay there for six days while they took tests of all kinds, from blood tests to guinea pig tests.

About fifteen doctors, specialist included, came to the conclusion that I should have my rib out as soon as we could arrange for it. Later, they said that if the foot didn't heal, and they didn't give us much hope that it would, they thought that it would be best to have the foot taken off at the ankle.

Well, that was a pretty big mouthful to swallow, but the way they explained things and the length of time that it had already dragged along, it seemed to be about the only thing left to do. We were just waiting the coming week to go and make the necessary arrangements.

A friend of ours who knew of our plans, came to see us about then. This friend explained Doctor Jensen's methods, and told us of the wonderful results his own wife was obtaining from the treatments. We considered all this and it sounded logical enough, but we wanted to see it applied because we had never heard of this kind of treatment before.

We went to Doctor Jensen's Rest Home, and talked with some of his patients. They told us about the other doctors they had gone to see, and how, in most cases, the doctors had wanted to operate. They said that since they were under the care of Dr. Jensen they had felt better than they had felt in years. We were convinced and arrangements were made for my going there.

I probably will never fully realize the importance of that decision. Miracles seemed to be happening when, after one week there, my foot and chest had stopped draining. I put my crutches away and I have not used them since. What made it seem more miraculous, was the fact that no medicine was used.

I was told that nature would take its course and it certainly picked a wonderful one for me. It has been just four months since I first met Doctor Jensen and started on the road to health under his supervision. I am home now, feeling fine, exercising three times a day, and being able to run for the first time in over two and one-half years.

(Signed)   D. E. D."

Discussion

In dealing with toxemia, the intestinal tract is always the first thing to start normalizing. In all cases of toxemia there is need for mineral balance, and it is well to consider a complete right-living program. Even the worst cases respond beautifully. Although this patient had been traveling around from doctor to doctor for years, a program of right living helped him to progress from the very poorest of health to good health. This was accomplished not so much through treatments as through his own efforts. It is important for us to see that a health education is necessary for the average patient. In fact, everyone should be taught a right-living program; it should be part of every college curriculum.

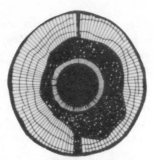

Fig. 169

In this case toxic material from the bowel (indicated by the blackened area) was being thrown into all parts of the body, the greatest amount being settled in the leg area. There was inherent weakness in the leg area. Toxic material held in the body due to heavy scurf rim.

Tumor

San Diego 3, California
May 19, 1949

"Dear Dr. Jensen:

I received such wonderful help that I did not have to have the operation that the medical doctor prescribed. Thanking you for all past favors and help, I am

Sincerely,

(Signed)   B. M. P."

Fig. 170

This right iris contains an acute closed lesion in the uterine area, and shows considerable toxic settlement in the uterine and vaginal areas. This patient had a very toxic liver, and an extreme degree of toxicity in the bowel.

Tumor of Breast—(Constipation)

Oakland, California
April 2, 1934

"Until 1928 I had never had occasion to visit a doctor. When I was eighteen years of age I had typhoid fever and was ill for one month in a hospital in British Columbia, Canada. From then until my fast, I had very bad headaches and a constipated condition, and then from a run down condition while in Seattle, Washington, I got this growth on my breast, little bigger than an egg.

I went to one doctor there who wanted to operate on me and have my breast completely removed and that it should be done at once as he said sooner or later it would develop into cancer.

I couldn't make up my mind to have it done, so I went to another doctor who said it was nothing but a little growth, and he could cure it in a few weeks by X-ray treatment. I took them for two weeks and three treatments a week. It seemed to help me just a little.

Then I left for Oakland, and went to Doctor Jensen as I had heard of him before. He told me he could help me by putting me on a fast in his sanitarium. On November 28, 1933 I went to his sanitarium in San Leandro. I felt very hungry and had a headache the first and second day. The third day wasn't quite so bad and the fourth day hunger left me entirely, every day I got up and dressed, I was getting weak, but went for walks and sat around every day.

I was not sick any time during my fast, my head felt clear. I weighed 114 pounds when I went in, and lost a pound a day for the first week, on my nineteenth day I began to feel very hungry.

I was quite weak by then, and on my 20th day Doctor Jensen came and told me I would break fast, he ordered the nurse to give me a glass of orange juice at 5:00 p.m. that evening. I thought that time would never come, my first sip I will never forget. It was delicious and sweet, it took one hour and a half to drink it down. I weighed that day and weighed exactly 98 pounds. From then on I started to gain in weight and strength.

During my fast, day by day that growth on my breast kept getting smaller and smaller until the day I broke my fast there was only a small lump there and Doctor Jensen said that it was just a scar tissue and will be there always.

I am certainly glad I was not operated on. Besides being cured my whole body has been cleaned and now my bowels move three and four times a day. That alone is worth quite a bit to me. I am home now and feel a hundred per cent. I have gained quite a bit and my strength, and vitality is great.

Many many thanks to Doctor Jensen.

(Signed)   Mrs. E. W."

Tumor

Hollywood, California
November 23, 1951

"Dear Dr. Jensen:

Just recently I gave your address to a lady who was very interested when I told her about my tumor that had disappeared two months after following your diet and I think she will come in to see you about her own condition. It is now just about one year and nine months that you put me on your health diet and I am very glad to tell you that my tumor, which was the size of an orange at that time, hasn't returned.

I want to express my gratitude for having helped me so wonderfully.

Sincerely yours,

(Signed)   N. H. V."

Tumor

Fresno, California
June 15, 1947

"Two months have passed since my 28 day water fast. The realized results can hardly be expressed in words. The possibility of a cancer-ous breast and three or more uterine tumors were all taken care of— things of the past now. The secret of fasting is to really carry through strictly obedience to instructions. I am so thankful to count Dr. Jensen as such a helpful friend.

(Signed)   Mrs. L. W. B."

Discussion

Tumors are very difficult to get rid of, but I find that a very strict diet to reduce them is worth the try, for we may be able to prevent that operation. We find that lumps on the body—as in the breast, lymph glands, etc., will respond to proper dietetic care. The mammary glands are part of the lymphatic system, which should be kept toxin-free. I believe that all tumors are developed out of an unclean body, no matter how many bumps or bruises we get. I think the bumps and bruises are secondary, though they can develop trouble if the body is not clean and in good functioning order.

Uterine Disorder—(Emotional Problems, Constipation, Nervousness, Low Vitality, Poor Complexion)

Oakland, California
January 19th, 1934

"My experience of my fast as I remember it:

My most important reason for fasting was a condition of the uterus; others were constipation, nervousness, lack of vitality and poor complex-ion.

I am 23 years of age, 5-feet 4-inches tall, and weight before the fast 123½ lbs.

1st day: I experienced slight headache and persistent craving for food.

2nd day: less headache and craving for food; beginning to notice strong body odor.

3rd day: headache relieved, feel normal; no thought for food at all; body odor strong, tongue coated.

The next three days remain about the same, very strong body odor, tongue very coated and unpleasant taste in mouth.

7th day: slight pain through sciatic nerve system.

8th day: pain more severe through lower back.

9th day: pain very severe, being relieved by menstruation; this was not a normal period, as my normal menstruation had just cleared three days before I began my fast. The discharge expelled was almost black and very thick, odor very bad. This was the most important reaction of my fast, as I had carried this poison in my uterus for nearly two years, being left there after the birth of a stillborn child.

10th day: strong body odor, tongue very thick, strong breath. (this was up to the fifteenth day.)

15th day to 26th day: same, except for rolling settling movements in abdomen.

27th day: getting very hungry, mouth very moist.

28th day: extremely hungry, broke fast. Weight 105 lbs., losing 23½ lbs. in all.

At the time I write this I am still under Dr. Jensen's care, but the results of my fast, up to this time have been wonderful. The poisons in my uterus have been expelled, giving it a chance to become normal again.

My constipation has been fully relieved, and for this alone I consider my fast has been well-worth-while.

My complexion has not completely cleared, but the skin is of much finer texture and color.

My vitality and nervousness is improving as time goes on, because my system is clean, and has a chance to become normal again, in every way.

I fully believe in fasting and would not exchange a day of my fast for any amount of money.

(Signed)   Mrs. A. M."

Discussion

In correction of uterine and other disorders, we must have a clean body and clean blood stream, in order to have better tissue. Many acids and toxins are produced by wrong living habits and thinking processes; it is necessary to realize that a right-living program includes the three phases: mental-physical-spiritual, for balance.

Varicose Veins

Wilmington, California.
November 5, 1951.

Dear Dr. Jensen:

"... I have been doing that slant position exercise regularly, then by sticking my leg straight up, and massaging the blood downwards, I got those ugly varicose veins to go down. Entirely well in three weeks' time. I had them 30 years and they had got so I was bed-fast 10 weeks.

Sincerely yours,

(Signed)   J.A.R."

Discussion

Varicose veins are very difficult to correct, especially because stagnant blood (for many years in some cases), has enlarged the vein structures to such an extent that they cannot shrink and contract properly. I have had cases where it was accomplished, however, and include a case here to show that most diseases respond to right living. Since some of the worst conditions do respond it is easy to see what could be accomplished with minor ones if patients stuck to some kind of a program. This case demonstrates that by using only physical means, there was definite improvement. What a wonderful thing it would be if the average person realized the value of having the proper diet, a clean liver, and adequate exercise and activity.

Weight Loss—(Bowel Condition)

Long Beach, California
September 29, 1945

"Just ended 28 days on water. Had no main object for doing so other than I'm sold on fasting for any and all purposes. I lost 32 pounds and feel like sixteen. My tastes are so different as I now relish the simplest kind of food; vegtable broth and goat whey being my speciality. I'm homeward bound today and glad as I am to be back with my family after five weeks away; I know I'll miss the family here I learned to love. We shared with each other everything. I don't expect this to be my last visit here, so until then . . .

Sincerely,

(Signed)   M. L. R. S."

Weight Loss

South Pasadena, Calif.
July 7, 1945

"My fast lasted 20 days—the sole purpose was to lose weight. I lost 25 pounds and feel 100 per cent better.

(Signed)   E. S.'

Discussion

The average person may not have considered that an important factor in normalizing body weight is proper thinking habits. A person must have the right desires; such a strong desire to do the right thing that no craving can disturb him. Through mental, emotional, and physical adjustments we can normalize weight. I do not have a definite reducing program because I feel that if we build good health, the body will normalize itself. Nature is always interested in beautiful curves, and if you are overweight, by living correctly She will bring you down; if you have no curves, She will build you up and develop them through a right-living program.

The following is a statement given by Dr. Darwin L. Alsop of Salt Lake City:

"I have known Dr. Bernard Jensen some two years and have observed his work very closely during this time. Let me tell you of just a few cases, during a day's period, which came to my office to see Dr. Jensen:

Case No. 1—Mrs. B.

She has had multiple sclerosis some eighteen months. Her irises indicate definite spinal degeneration. Under Dr. Jensen's recommendations she is now regaining her health. She has gained some twenty-five pounds, is now able to walk, where previously she was given no chance to live; in fact they only gave her three weeks to live when she turned to the natural healing art that Dr. Jensen prescribes.

Case No. 2—Mrs. L., a Swedish immigrant.

She had to talk to Dr. Jensen through an interpreter. Dr. Jensen had never seen her before. He spent ten minutes examining her irises. When he had finished, Mrs. L. asked how he could know so much about her when she had told him nothing. She is subsequently on the road to complete recovery.

Case No. 3—Mrs. J.

Has had a lump the size of a lemon growing on the right side of her face for many years. Under Dr. Jensen's care this lump was reduced in size more than half during a three month period.

Case No. 4—Nine year old K. L.

Had been completely stiff from muscular dystrophy for some six years. His mother, acting upon Dr. Jensen's advice through another party, had given the boy ten cups of oat straw tea daily for three days. On the fourth day she noticed that he was becoming supple and the hardness was leaving his body. Doctors had said this boy would never recover. The boy was then brought to Dr. Jensen who gave them further advice, and he is now beginning to stand, never having walked for more than a few months as a small boy.

Case No. 5—Mrs. W. and her son.

Both of them had been in ill health for several years with kidney infections. After only one month under Dr. Jensen's regime they returned to him for a recheck virtually free of any pain or illness. Mrs. W. said she felt simply wonderful.

Case No. 6—Mr. B.

Had continuously, time after time, been refused life insurance. He was seeking an answer to this problem. Dr. Jensen, through iris diagnosis, told him of an old kidney weakness, and predicted that if this was taken care of he could get the desired insurance. He now has the insurance after only two months on Dr. Jensen's program.

Case No. 7—Mrs. C.

Mrs. C. was left blind in her right eye after childbirth. She was given one of Dr. Jensen's books. Dr. Jensen gave her an iris examination and told her she would see again. After only one month, due to following some of the suggestions in his book, she began to see again. Mrs. C. exclaimed that she would just like to devour Dr. Jensen's book, it was so wonderful. She said she had been everywhere looking for help with no results.

Case No. 8—Mrs. J.

Had a blood pressure reading for three years as high as 280 m.m. After six weeks under Dr. Jensen's care her blood pressure reading dropped to below 200 m.m.

Case No. 9—Mr. M.

This man was seventy-nine years old. Had heart trouble and an extremely painful case of arthritis for nearly seven years. During this seven years he had to strap oxygen to his back to breathe, if he ever left his home. He was carried into my office. In thirty days he was walking and at the end of sixty days was looking for work. He says he cannot thank Dr. Jensen enough.

Case No. 10—Mr. A.

Had eczema which bled lymph continually over a large part of his body. In a period of only two months the eczema had stopped bleeding, had virtually cleared up and new skin was filling in those places where this terrible disorder had been.

The aforementioned cases are only a few of the many that have come to my office to see Dr. Jensen in their quest for complete health when all other means have failed to give them that health.

Dr. Jensen has found in iris diagnosis an almost infallible means of answering the problems of those who are hopelessly ill. There will come a day when this man will be widely acclaimed for the wonderful work he has done and is doing.

Those who are narrow cease to live for lack of breadth; those who are shallow perish for lack of depth. Only those survive who are in all things moderate, in all things consistent, in all things natural; for they live on because they partake of the qualities of continuance which can be found in all of the teachings of Dr. Bernard Jensen."

Comments on Dr. Alsop's Letter

We can say very little here except that we have been teaching our work to doctors throughout the country, and know that they get the same results as decribed above. It is not a matter of the individual applying it, for this work is greater than any doctor using it. It can stand up under any type of investigation. A doctor who has schooled himself so that he can teach the patient to do the right thing at home, is stopping troubles where they first start. If a person is producing his troubles at home and brings the effects and consequences into an office, the doctor must realize that the greatest results can come from having the patient stop the processes of breaking down his health. He can then get good results with his office procedures. Most doctors, however, are trained in a system of treatment, and have their money invested in treatment equipment, hospital equipment, sanitarium equipment, etc. While it is difficult for them to give up that which has afforded them a good living, practitioners of the healing arts will have to add to their curricula, training in teaching people how to guard their health, and offering proper guidance in how it can be regained when lost.

While some of the foregoing history material we have presented may make it seem like we are advocating a cure, this is not the case. We feel that the person who has built new, perfectly functioning tissue in place of the old which was not working properly, is as close to correction or a cure as can possibly come about. We are interested in correction. We are interested in putting new, better tissue in place of the old; tissue that functions at a high health level. And we find that that person usually is satisfied with his body because it is free of aches, pains, acids, growths; free of all the symptomatic effects that we call disease today.

This was demonstrated well in a little lady who came to me at one time with fingernails that were practically black. I told her that when those fingernails came out pink she would have a better body. It was six to eight months before we could see patches of pink taking the place of the black fingernails. As she improved in health through being fed properly and living correctly, you could see the new tissue replacing the old. It seems to me that this is what we should be trying to achieve —whether it be in the stomach, the kidneys, the bowel, or any part of the body.

I saw this work demonstrated beautifully in the case of a young man by the name of Dave Powers who was in the Veteran's Hospital for a long time, where he was told he had tuberculosis and many other complications. He took his problem into his own hands, and through right living processes has regained his health to such an extent that he has received honors for his health activities. To see how he raised his health from a very low grade to one of excellence, puts most of us to shame with our many little ailments for which we are constantly seeking a cure.

Those people who are interested in working with the better things in life realize that natural methods are right and that they work. We have found that the principles of success can be applied also to the human body. For instance, we are told in Napoleon Hill's writings that to be successful we must have a good healthy body to carry through a program of success. If we have the right mental attitude and the right goal, but do not have the physical health to carry through, we may fall short of the ultimate in success. There are many capable people today who are unable to do the things they could if their bodies were in good health. Napoleon Hill, author of "Think and Grow Rich," has recognized the value of natural methods for years. He has seen many cases respond under our care, and realizes that if you want to have complete success you must have good health. There are men throughout the country who realize that they must have good health in order to be successful.

We have had patients from all walks of life and all parts of the country who are more than grateful for what has been done for them. We have had people with the financial means for obtaining the best, yet they could not buy this health. They had to earn it, and it takes hard work. For instance, the president of an insurance company in the middle west who brought his wife to us, found that through the right living processes she was enabled to control her arthritis and get rid of the pains and aches that she had had for years. They had had the best physicians and insurance doctors to take care of her, yet she had to go through these processes for release.

With improvement in health through natural living, we have seen all kinds of conditions diminish or disappear: cold sores, easy bruising, frequent nose bleeding, etc. Through proper nutrition and the restoration of chemical balance, we have seen bleeding gums corrected, loose teeth tightened, dry hair regain its proper lustre, and have seen pinhole dental cavities fill in, showing that all parts of the body respond.

While we recognize that this is not a panacea or a cure for every ailment, we definitely believe that a longer, happier, and healthier life is possible for everyone who will take care of his body through the right living processes that we teach.

It is my wish that the foregoing case histories demonstrate the importance of removing the *causes* of dis-ease rather than suppressing symptoms and reaping a harvest of chronic illnesses later. I feel I cannot repeat too often the importance of teaching and establishing living habits which build new tissues in place of old and therefore produce permanent correction, and enable patients to find out what it is to feel really well and to enjoy life as they were meant to enjoy it.

In the above review of cases that have received results through application of the laws of health taught in the right-living method, they were not presented with the idea of claiming that this or any system is a cure-all. We should like to see it applied mainly from the standpoint of prevention. If such positive results can be accomplished *after* a person has become sick, consider the great value of teaching these people to live healthfully and *prevent* degeneration.

If the various disorders which are manifested in the cases herein described could be eradicated without specific treatment but in most cases by a right-living program,—there is every reason to believe that those diseases we have not mentioned and those which are yet likely to develop because of our living habits, can likewise be corrected.

The success of this work has been due in great measure to the adjunct of iris analysis. Both diagnosis and treatment today have too many faults and failures because they deal with symptoms or effects rather than causes. Also, the average diagnosis does not reveal what is wrong with a person until in many instances it is too late for correction. It deals too much with individual organs instead of with the whole body. Then treatments *follow* the diagnoses, so it is no wonder there are so many treatment failures today. To see necrotic tissue disappear in the worst cases of cancer under proper nutritional guidance and other natural means is the most wonderful thing any doctor could experience. But in many of these cases a cure is impossible because the patient's trouble was diagnosed too late and treatments were instituted only *after* a diagnosis was made. No wonder nearly every chronic disease is on the increase and our asylums, doctors' offices, hospitals, jails, are filled to capacity.

Iridology does not wait for a manifestation of disease; the patient may not even be aware of its incipient activity. The iris of the eye can manifest the beginning stages of the effects of poisons, irritants, toxins, by shadings, which are not in the painful stage as yet. Iridology belongs to the doctor who wants to normalize all the organs in the body, raise his patients' health standards, and show them how to keep well. He will know through tissue reaction and through color changes in the iris what is normal and what is abnormal.

Iridology tells the condition of the patient NOW, without waiting for the patient to become so sick that a diagnosis can be established. If a cause of disease,—if a cause of cancer, if a cause of arthritis, etc.—is developing, iridology will reveal it long before effects have become manifest and the patient goes to the doctor for diagnosis. We need diagnostic methods that will enable us to *prevent* disease and keep people well. Instead of being engrossed in diagnosing pathology, we should learn all we possibly can about health. This would automatically eradicate most of our diseases.

Part VI

ADVANCED RESEARCH

in IRIDOLOGY

20

REFLEX AREAS and REMOTE SYMPTOMS

*Problems in human engineering will receive
during the coming years the same genius and
attention which the nineteenth century gave
to the more material forms of engineering.*
—*Thomas A. Edison*

Doctors who have studied and worked with reflex actions in the body will need nothing to whet their interest in this subject. They know that the seat of a patient's complaint may be at some point removed from the site of manifestation. Doctors who base their diagnosis upon symptoms only, are at a disadvantage. Institutions, clinics, hospitals, etc., are filled with patients whose symptoms have reached a point of intolerance. The tendency in therapy is to apply the remedy which will most quickly quell the discomfort and to "never mind" the cause. Many volumes have been written upon how to diagnose diseases from symptoms but little upon getting down to rock-bottom causes.

One of the most important considerations in diagnosis and treatment should be first causes. The desire to find the causes behind symptoms has inspired some doctors to persist in iris observations in the belief that therein lay a means of developing a technique for determining these fundamental causes. Since my findings have been verified over and over, I am convinced that certain relationships in the body exist and that these relationships can be determined from the iris of the eye.

When you are able to see this proof, you will realize that the chart of the iris is constructed, not by choosing arbitrarily to place one organ area here and another there, but because they can be nowhere else. Thus do the areas of the intestinal tract and the autonomic nerve wreath form the hub, the wreath lying between the intestinal tract area and the remaining organ areas of the body.

As stated previously, through iridology first causes can be detected in their incipiency long before symptoms have developed. We might make a comparison with the seven notes of the musical scale which can be composed into unnumerable complexities and variations of arrangement. Likewise, the first evidences of disorder in the body may develop into intricate chains of symptoms. When patients come with numerous complaints, it is difficult for the doctor to determine what dysfunction, what organ, or what incoordination among organs, is responsible for them. That is when he wishes he had a method of getting back to the basic cause from which these various symptoms were elaborated. I have found this evidence in its simplest form in the iris of the eye.

When definite disorder has developed in some part of the body, certain other parts are going to be affected, reflexly. The disturbance of which the patient is conscious may be at some distance from the seat of the difficulty, where there may be under-activity, irritation, toxic settlement, etc. The most demonstrable source of such conditions is the intestinal tract, and from the iris we can show that there is such a thing as toxic stasis in the colon and resulting irritations in remote parts of the body. One of the first cases that brought this to my attention was a man with a large swelling on one side of his neck.

Upon examining the iris of this man I found that opposite the location of the swelling was indication of toxic stasis in the colon area just medial to the hepatic flexure. I noticed, however, that there were healing signs in this part of the colon area, which indicated it was trying to force toxic material out of some part of the body. I was seeking the cause of the condition in the neck, but I wondered about these healing signs in the iris area of the colon opposite it. Reasoning that he must have been doing something out of the ordinary, I enquired whether he had been on any special kind of diet during the past

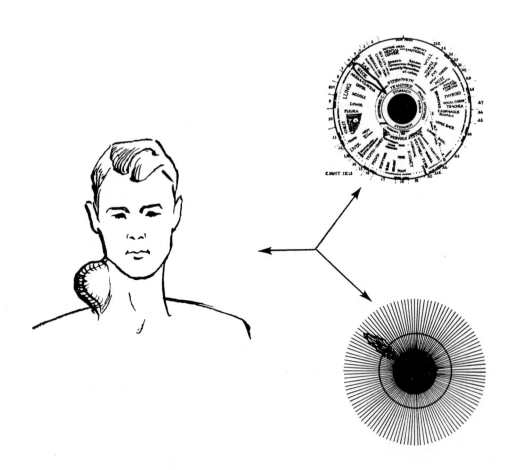

FIG. 171. This drawing indicates the location of the cyst which developed on the side of the man's neck, and the iris chart shows the neck area involvement.

few weeks to produce the healing signs. He related that a truckload of oranges had been upset on the highway three weeks before and that he had picked up enough for himself, to go an an orange juice diet. He had eaten nothing else for three or four weeks. The eliminative process which was in evidence I attributed to this. Had he consulted a doctor who did not understand that this was an eliminative process, the condition would have been treated as a disease and suppressed.

Later I had a similar case in a lady patient with torticollis or wry neck. For five days she had been treated mechanically by osteopathy, chiropractic, and physiotherapy, with no relief whatever. When I was first called on the case I also thought it should be handled from the mechanical standpoint, by manipulation of the muscular and bony structures of the neck, but my iris analysis revealed a focus of infection a little below the splenic flexure, which I judged to be quite putrefactive and gas-forming. When I asked the patient whether she had any difficulty in that part of her body, I pointed and started to touch the area, but she warned, "Oh, don't touch me there. That has been sore for months!" When I enquired whether she had received treatment for it, she replied that no one had suggested anything.

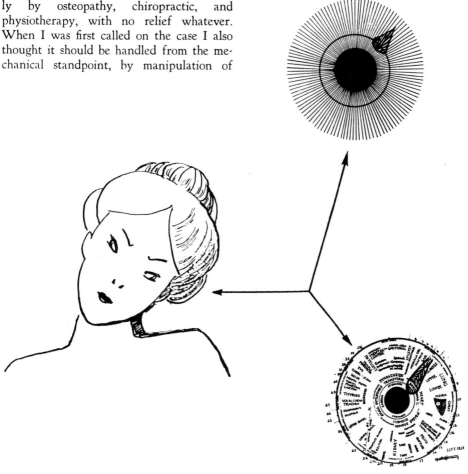

FIG. 172. These drawings indicate the reflex relationship between a condition in the intestinal tract and the neck symptoms for which this woman sought relief.

Upon further questioning I learned that she had had no bowel movements for seven days. With this information, a different plan of therapy was begun immediately. In a series of enemas, a great deal of extremely putrefactive material was eliminated, and within three hours she had almost complete relief from all neck symptoms.

Following the observations in these two cases, I went into a thorough study of reflex areas as brought out by the iris of the eye and the causes behind many of the symptoms manifested in the body. Photographs and charts presented later in this chapter illustrate the various types of cases handled.

Two cases which I wish to mention particularly, to begin with, were both men with throat cancer. One was Mr. George Johnson from Atwater, California, who was brought to the sanitarium by an airplane ambulance in a prostrate condition. As he was unable to swallow, he had not eaten for some time and had lost around sixty pounds of weight. He had not been able to use his voice for nine months, and was unable to walk. The verdict of his medical doctor was that he had but three or four days to live when he came to me.

The iris showed an especially chronic condition in the bowel area opposite the throat area. In the handling of this patient I began immediately with the intestinal tract—clearing the way for better liver and kidney function, and opening all channels of elimination. I did not touch the throat.

Within a week's time this man was able to get out of bed and sit up, and it was apparent that his vitality was increasing and he was gaining strength. Within three months, after special dieting, etc., he was eating well and digesting his food well. In five months he was able to return to his work. He had gained between forty and forty-five pounds, and had regained his voice.

The other man with throat cancer has a different story. His throat was operated upon, after which he was able to breathe better. But the cause of his malady was not removed and he was not instructed in healthful living, so he continued his smoking and other bad living habits. In two months he was back in the hospital with abdominal dropsy, enlarged liver, gas, bowel distention, and was still constipated. Nothing had been treated except the local condition. Within two months the man's body could no longer survive these conditions and he died. In his case, also, the iris showed a relationship between the cancerous throat condition and a toxic bowel.

One of the things we can prove is that toxic stasis of the intestinal tract is demonstrable in the iris, and that wherever toxins settle they give rise to specific symptoms in specific parts of the body. This refutes the belief that toxic substances cannot be absorbed from the colon and that regular, natural bowel movements are not essential to well-being. Reflex symptoms also can result from mechanical irritation, such as distention, especially if this occurs at a site of toxic settlement. The irritation will be conveyed through the autonomic nervous system.

Whether the irritation is from toxins or trauma, there will be reflex reactions in various parts of the body. I am convinced that most symptoms are a reflex manifestation of disorder in some vital organ, most likely the colon. In some instances the intestine is the recipient of influences, both mental and physical. *Iris analysis bears out the belief that toxemia and enervation are basic causes in most diseases.*

The Colon

The importance of the intestinal tract may be judged from certain interesting facts concerning it. In the first place, its area occupies practically one-third of the iris, and therefore also takes up about one-third of the iris chart. Incidentally, in abnormal conditions I have seen the intestinal area occupy as much as half of the iris, which represents a considerable enlargement compared to the space it normally occupies. In

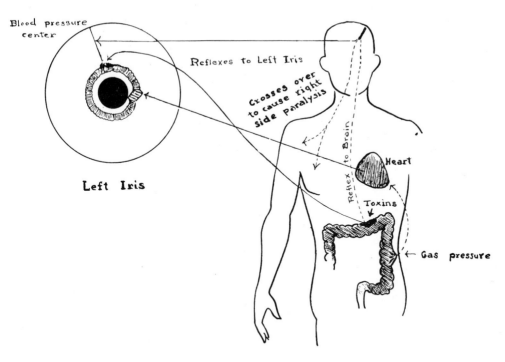

FIG. 173. This diagram illustrates the reflex relation between lesions in the iris and corresponding parts of the body. Arrows denote the relation to a toxic settle-ment in the transverse colon, the blood pressure center in the brain, and the heart. Note the indication that a gas pocket in the descending colon is causing reflex symptoms in the heart.

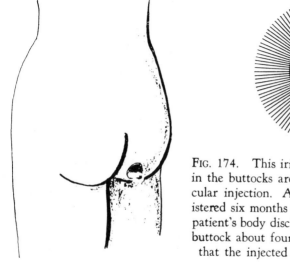

FIG. 174. This iris lesion represents a drug base in the buttocks area resulting from an intramus-cular injection. Although this had been admin-istered six months previously, examination of the patient's body disclosed a brown spot on the right buttock about four inches in diameter, indicating that the injected drug had not been absorbed.

the second place, all other organ areas are connected with the intestinal tract area. In the third place, it is located at the center, the hub. This is significant for it represents a center of important activities. It is in the intestinal tract that absorption of both nutrient and toxic materials takes place.

Those who doubt the direct relation between the colon and the functioning ability of various organs in the body should consider the daring work of Sir William Arbuthnot Lane, M. D., in England. He proved. the relationship because when he removed the lower bowel from certain patients, their sysmptoms of arthritis, rheumatism, etc., disappeared within weeks. Thyroid enlargements responded immediately; tuberculosis was relieved; amputations were prevented. Even in cases of Raynaud's disease where there was gangrene of the fingers, the hands were restored to perfect condition a short time after removal of that cesspool of infection, a toxin-laden lower bowel.

Professor Illya Metchnikoff, director of the Pasteur Institute of Paris, made the statement that if the large colon could be eliminated from the body, much disease could be overcome. His assistant, Doctor Distaso, proved through his experiments that the bowel is the ideal breeding ground for disease germs, and made the statement that almost every chronic disease can be traced back to their harmful action.

It would not be practicable to analyze by any gross tests the bowel contents or the bowel wall covering them. Iris analysis, however, will reveal in what portions of the bowel wall there are toxic settlements, etc.; the iris recording will indicate the acute, subacute, or chronic stage of inflammation of any segment of the bowel. Any activity or condition in any part of the intestinal wall will be reflected in the iris. Over a period of time various conditions may develop, such as spasticity, ballooning, atony, diverticuli from gas pressure, etc. I believe all these conditions develop in accordance with the inherent weakness of the bowel wall. Various diet-

ary habits produce various types of waste in the colon, with various kinds of germ life, which in turn produces various types of end-products, toxins, and pathological changes. All of these conditions will reflexly affect the bowel wall.

Of the ways in which the large intestine differs from the small intestine, the fact that it is sacculated is of the most importance to this discussion. Drawings are presented here to aid the reader in visualizing the conditions in individual segments and those conditions in relation to the autonomic nerve wreath and the various organs.

The first drawing (Fig. 175a) represents a normal colon. The row of X's along the midline of the longitudinal axis and the lines extending transversely from that, represent nerve distribution; and these show how conditions in any part of the colon can be transmitted reflexly to any other part of the body. To the right is a schematic representation of this nerve structure without the bowel structure.

In the next drawing (Fig. 176a), the portion of the colon marked "A" indicates distention or ballooning and just beneath that is a portion which is spastic. The bacteria in the ballooned area will be entirely different from those in the spastic area. The portion marked "B" indicates a diverticulum developed through pressure from gas or from bacterial invasion. It indicates inherent weakness of the bowel wall. The diagram to the right represents the nerve structure of that abnormal bowel.

The next drawing (Fig. 177) illustrates, in the left iris, the markings of an abnormal bowel condition in the iris of the eye. We see that the condition indicated by the blackened portion of the bowel area extends toward and affects the neck area. The neck area is as black as the bowel area opposite it. Whenever there is a local condition, such as this one indicated in the neck, invariably it is reflexly related to a condition in the colon. This is proved by the fact that when a bowel area which has been chronically abnormal (as indicated by

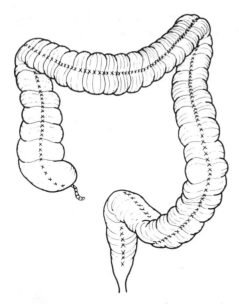

FIG. 175 (a). Drawing of a normal colon. The X's represent nerve distribution.

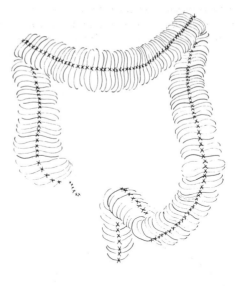

FIG. 175 (b). Schematic representation of nerve structure of intestine.

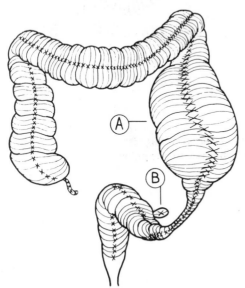

FIG. 176 (a). In the above drawing the portion of the colon marked "A" indicates ballooning, and beneath that is a spastic area. The portion marked "B" indicates a diverticulum.

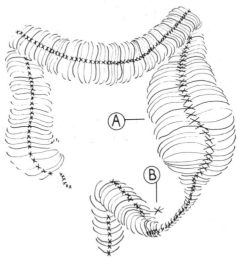

FIG. 176 (b). This diagram represents the nerve structure of the abnormal colon pictured at the left.

A and B in the drawing) becomes normalized, the chronic condition in the corresponding organ disappears. The darkness in these areas of the colon and the iris disappears only through right living habits.

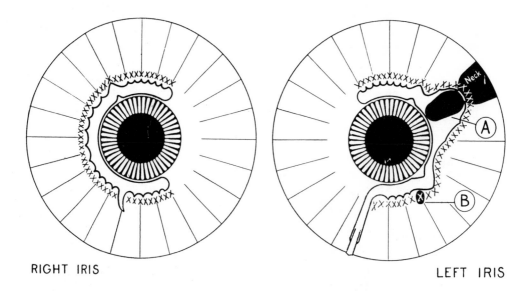

RIGHT IRIS   LEFT IRIS

FIG. 177. This drawing illustrates the relation between symptoms in the neck and a condition in the colon.

The next drawing (Fig. 178a) of a section of the colon shows nerves, blood vessels, haustrations, musculature, and the outline of a normal bowel. Lifted from this is the drawing at the right represent- ing again the nerve structure so that it will be understood that this is the starting point of reflex irritations transmitted by the nervous system to various organs of the body.

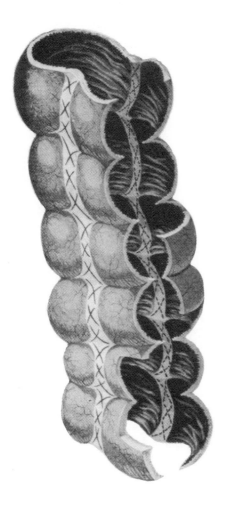

FIG. 178 (a). The above is a drawing of a section of normal bowel, show- ing nerves, musculature, haustrations, etc.

FIG. 178 (b). The above drawing represents the nerve structure of the section of colon pictured on the left, in order to emphasize that it is in these structures that irritations are re- flexly transmitted by the nerves to various organs of the body.

The next drawing (Fig. 179a) of a section of the colon illustrates an abnormal
condition. The diverticulum or ensaccula-
tion, marked "B" as previously, will send
vibratory impulses to the iris of the eye.

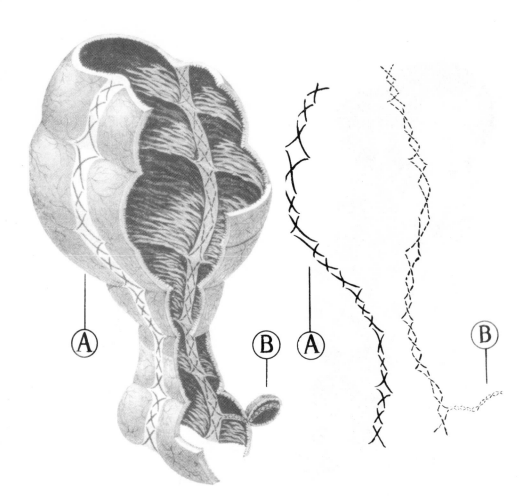

FIG. 179 (a). In this drawing the
portion marked "B" represents a diverticulum, which will send vibratory
impulses to the iris of the eye.

FIG. 179 (b). Schematic representation of nerve structure.

In the next drawing (Fig. 180) this diverticulum is enlarged. We would expect to find certain bacteria in it, busy at their work of devouring waste matter. Consequently there would be certain bacterial poisons that would have a certain specific reaction on the nerve fibres and the organs to which the nerves transferred them, and in these organ receiving stations certain symptoms would appear.

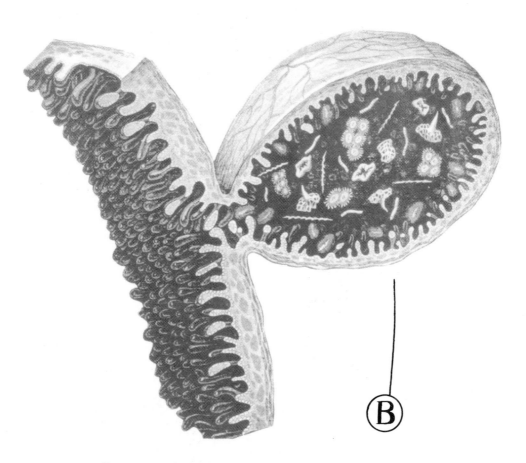

FIG. 180. This drawing illustrates an enlargement of the diverticulum, indicating the presence of bacteria, whose toxic effects, carried by the nerves, can cause symptoms in the organs to which they are carried.

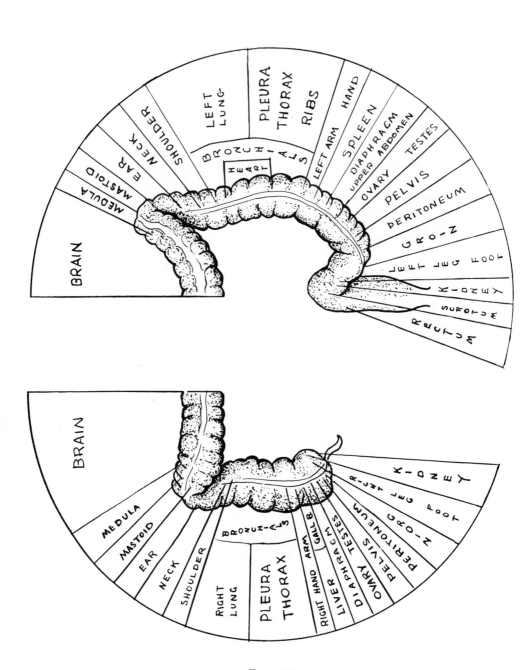

FIG. 181

We might compare the vibratory nature of reflex transmission in the body to the mechanism of television. If the color red or black or if the material steel or iron is used to send a vibratory message from a sending station, it would be quite impossible for the receiving station to register the color green or blue or the effect of copper or aluminum.

Whatever condition of color, acid-alkaline relationship, bacterial poison, etc., reacts upon the wall of the diverticulum and the nerves in it, will produce a characteristic condition in whatever organ is reflexly affected. The degree to which the organ is affected can be determined from the iris, the shadings ranging from white through gray and dark gray to black. In accordance with the type of germ life, the chemistry, etc. in this diverticulum, will a vibratory effect be established which will be reflected as a symptom, in some organ. If there is an acute irritation in the bowel wall, the vibratory effect will be acute irritation in an organ. In the iris this will be manifested by extreme whiteness of the fibres in the areas involved. If the condition in the bowel wall is chronic, there will be corresponding symptoms in the organ to which it is reflected, and the iris sign will be black. Referring again to our television comparison, if vibratory effects emanate from a colon condition degenerative enough to be represented by black in the iris area, then the reflected symptom in the receiving organ must also be represented by black in that organ area in the iris.

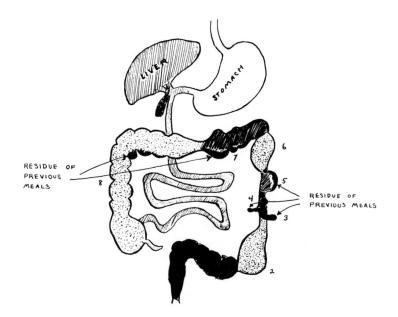

FIG. 182. A toxic sign in any organ area of the iris is a reflex indication of disorder in the intestinal tract. For example, toxic residue that has not moved along properly (as illustrated by numbers 3, 4 and 5 above), will cause definite deleterious effects in the organs opposite it in the iris chart. The nerve wreath affects and is affected by the colon; you will note it outlines the intestinal tract area. If a particular part of the nervous wreath is affected, the colon opposite that particular part will also be affected—giving rise to our somatic conditions.

There is a direct relationship between every part of the colon and the various organs of the body. Most symptoms in any part of the body can be traced to toxicity in the colon. And the conditions at both the sending and the receiving stations can be seen in the iris.

Follow the patients' stories shown here in picture form, and you will become convinced of the relationships described above. In the cases pictured I asked each patient to stand up and point to the part of the body which had troubled him all his life. Study of these pictures shows where the disorder is, where it should be seen in the iris according to our chart, and the part of the colon from which it is reflected. In each case the patient points to the spot in the colon which corresponds to the iris findings. This does not happen in only a few cases; you will find that it occurs in every case. It is proved even from one generation to the next, as demonstrated in the cases of the mother and daughter who had cancer of the forehead.

If we were trying to describe Broadway in New York City to a stranger, we would have to characterize the section say at 42nd and Broadway in comparison to the section at 89th Street, etc. So it is in the segments of the intestine. If we examine one segment, for example, we might find that it has inherent weakness in the wall. It may be considerably different from sections above or below it. The one above may be encumbered with toxic settlement. The one below may have lost tone. Etc.

Remember now that we are talking about the tissues of the bowel wall, not the bowel contents. It is the tissues of the wall that become irritated, encumbered, atonic, spastic, etc. Each sacculation, however, may be subject to different pathological conditions, depending upon the material in the bowel. In the iris, therefore, the reflex indications or markings in the autonomic nerve wreath and the organ areas opposite one portion of the intestine may be different from those in another portion. It is almost as though *each sacculation* were *an individual organ within the bowel*. When we see that one section of bowel wall can so differ from adjoining ones, it is easy to understand why combinations of ballooning and spasticity are seen in so many colon X-ray pictures. Each of such segments can act and react in an individual manner, and cause a variety of reflex symptoms.

The varied functioning of these areas you can determine from the iris. I have verified these findings over and over by other diagnostic methods; by palpation, percussion, nervometer, history of complaint in the particular area year after year, etc. The photographs which accompany this chapter demonstrate the relation between these sacculations and a patient's symptoms. I have yet to see a case in which this relation did not exist.

While the chief function of the large intestine seems to be the condensing and disposing of waste, yet some absorption of nutrient material can take place, especially in the churning processes in the ascending colon while the mass is still semi-liquid. As the mass passes along through the transverse and descending portions of the colon, more and more moisture is absorbed from it. Certainly it is very possible that toxic materials (such as those formed when fermentation and putrefaction result from the intake of improper foods over a period of years and those eliminated by bacteria), which are in solution, also will be absorbed into the blood and cause reflex symptoms.

It has been my observation that bowel functioning is damaged in patients after they have been given drug "shots" and injections of various kinds. This indicates to me that these substances are enervating. This enervation inhibits eliminative processes, which in turn results in encumbrances in the body which favor the development of chronic disorders.

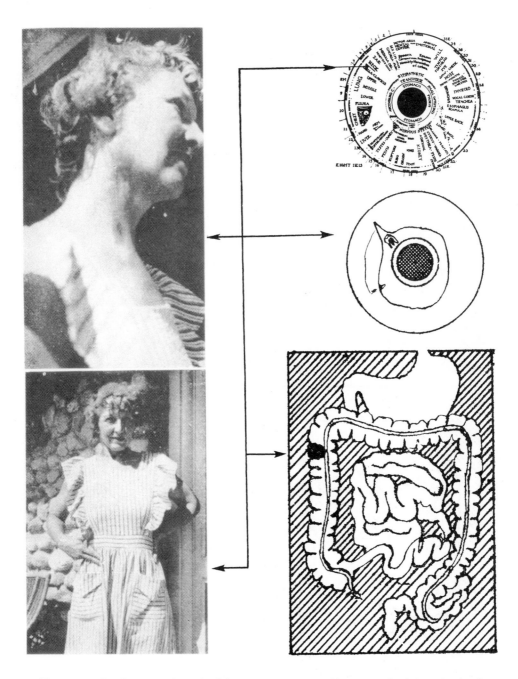

FIG. 183.   In this case there had been an operation for removal of lymph gland cysts, yet when asked to point to that part of her body which had given her the most trouble, she pointed to the right side of the colon. The portion of the colon involved (as illustrated in the colon drawing) corresponded to the neck area in the iris. The iris drawing indicates how the condition appeared in the iris.

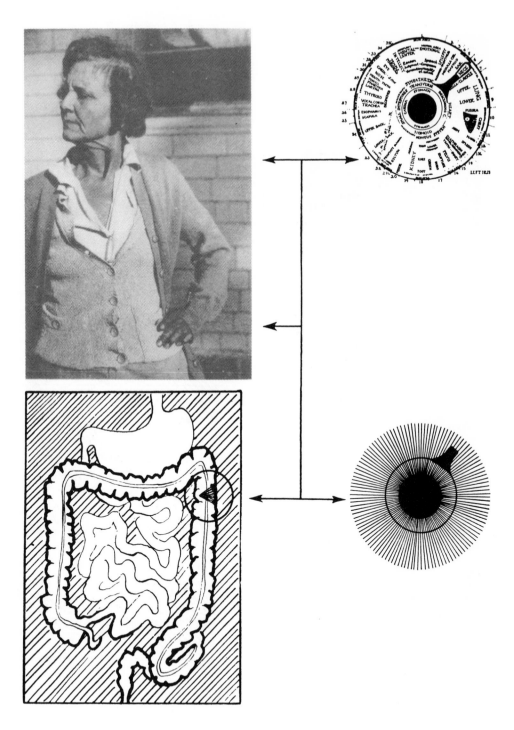

FIG. 184. This case also had neck trouble, which was reflected from the colon, as indicated in the photograph, the iris chart, and the drawing of the colon (the sequence is indicated by the arrows).

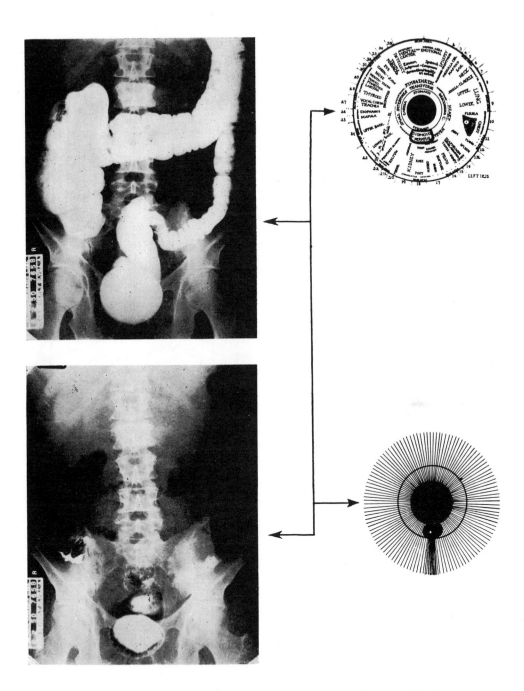

FIG. 185. This case demonstrates a condition in the sigmoid colon, whose iris area is opposite that of the left leg—as indicated on the iris chart. This man constantly held his left leg close to his abdomen because of the pain in it. The X-ray photographs verify the abnormal condition of the sigmoid colon. The drawing of the iris shows the iris appearance of the sigmoid colon and leg involvement.

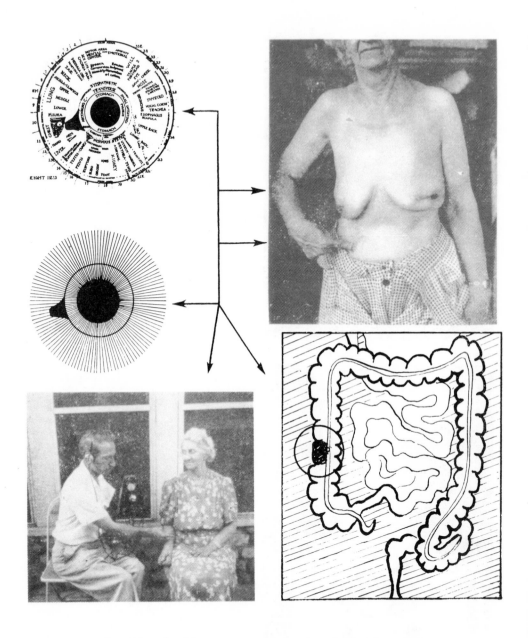

FIG. 186.   In this case a nervometer, as pictured here, was
used to locate the point of difficulty, which was found to
be in the ascending colon. This patient had been suffering
for many years, and when asked to point to the place which
had bothered her, she pointed to the area of the ascending
colon, as indicated in her photograph. This was taken after
the cancer had been reduced from the size of a grapefruit.
The right breast area is indicated also in the accompanying
iris chart and iris drawing.

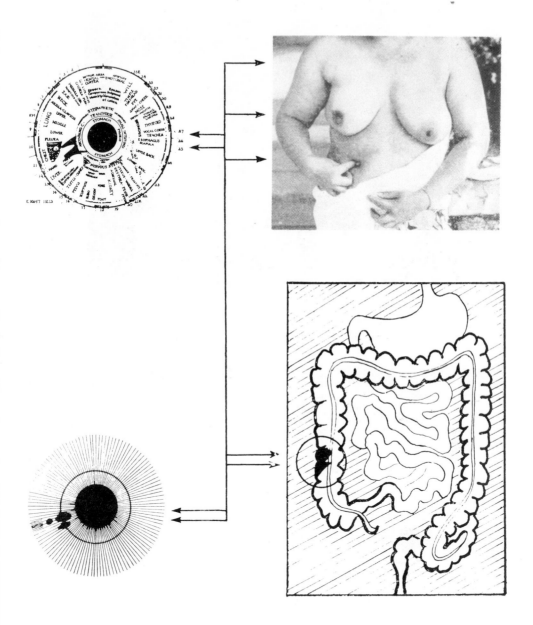

Fig. 187. The photograph of this patient shows lymphatic
enlargement under the right arm, cancer of the right breast,
and shows her pointing to the area which had been painful
most of her life. Following the arrows, note the areas marked
in the iris chart, in the iris drawing, and in the drawing of
intestinal tract. All of these verifications were in agreement
with the case history.

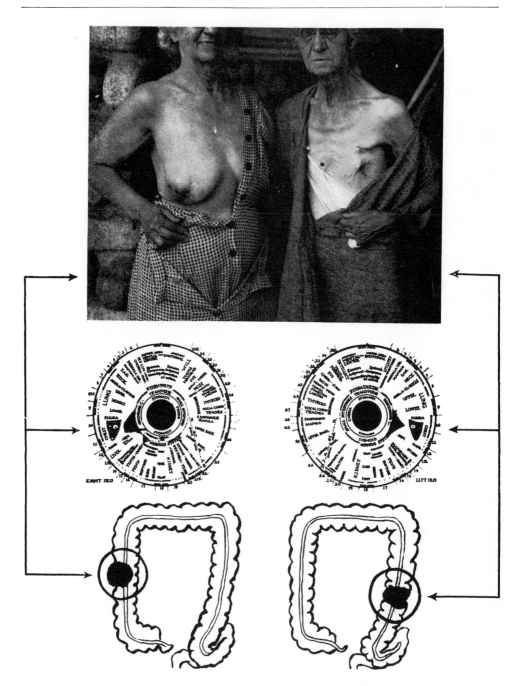

Fig. 188. The first woman in the photograph points to the right side of her colon, which corresponds to the findings there, in the iris, and in her history. She had cancer of the right breast. The second woman is pointing to the left side of her colon, where she had trouble most of her life, and her symptomatic manifestation was cancer of the left breast.

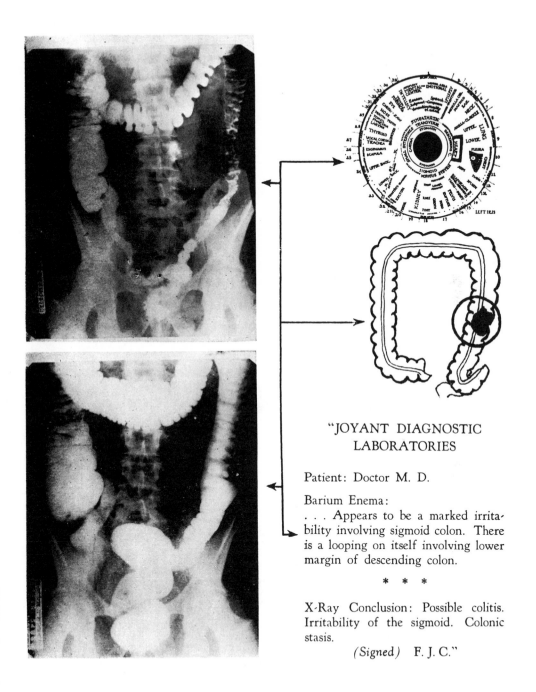

"JOYANT DIAGNOSTIC
LABORATORIES

Patient: Doctor M. D.

Barium Enema:
. . . Appears to be a marked irritability involving sigmoid colon. There
is a looping on itself involving lower
margin of descending colon.

*   *   *

X-Ray Conclusion: Possible colitis.
Irritability of the sigmoid. Colonic
stasis.
            (Signed)   F. J. C."

FIG. 189. This is a case of a doctor who had complained
of heart trouble for many years. The drawing of the colon
indicates where an abnormal condition might be expected,
and the X-ray photographs and copy of laboratory report
verify this location, and corroborate my contention that reflex symptoms begin in the colon.

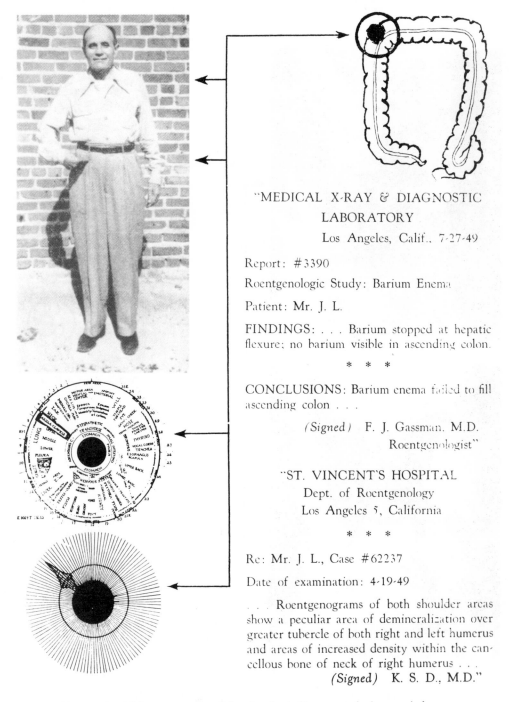

"MEDICAL X-RAY & DIAGNOSTIC
LABORATORY
Los Angeles, Calif., 7-27-49

Report: #3390

Roentgenologic Study: Barium Enema

Patient: Mr. J. L.

FINDINGS: . . . Barium stopped at hepatic
flexure; no barium visible in ascending colon.

* * *

CONCLUSIONS: Barium enema failed to fill
ascending colon . . .

(Signed) F. J. Gassman, M.D.
Roentgenologist"

"ST. VINCENT'S HOSPITAL
Dept. of Roentgenology
Los Angeles 5, California

* * *

Re: Mr. J. L., Case #62237

Date of examination: 4-19-49

. . . Roentgenograms of both shoulder areas
show a peculiar area of demineralization over
greater tubercle of both right and left humerus
and areas of increased density within the can-
cellous bone of neck of right humerus . . .
(Signed) K. S. D., M.D."

FIG. 190. This man reported having had distress and abnormal functioning of the colon the greater part of his life, which was verified
by an X-ray laboratory report. The reflex manifestation was cancer of
the shoulder. Note that his iris chart shows shoulder involvement opposite the area of the colon to which he points.

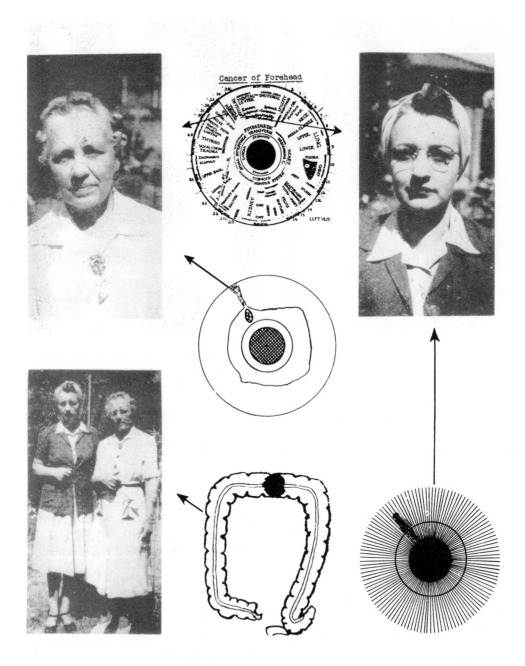

Cancer of Forehead

FIG. 191.   These are photographs of mother and daughter, the daughter having inherited the mother's weakness. Both pointed to the same area of the intestinal tract as their source of difficulty; both had cancer of the forehead.

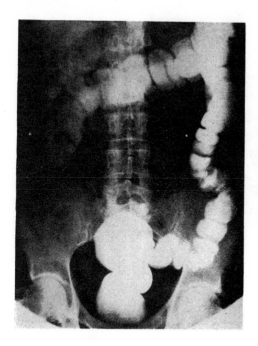

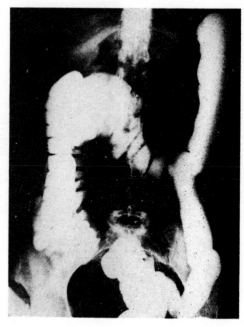

FIG. 192 (a). The settlement of barium which can be seen half-way down in the descending colon shows how toxic material can be held in some part of the bowel and cause symptoms in remote parts of the body.

FIG. 192 (b). X-ray picture showing considerable irritability in mid-section of transverse colon. Patient also was having considerable heart disturbance. X-ray reveals little except the V-shaped formation half-way down the descending colon, which is the area opposite the heart area in the iris of the eye. The irritability in the mid-section of the colon has caused considerable mental disturbance and extreme emotional strain involving both the thyroid and the heart. In this case, both mental and physical regeneration are indicated.

I recommend learning how to normalize the colon. It behooves us to find a way to revitalize these tissues so that as soon as all nutrient materials have been absorbed, they will be capable of eliminating waste residue promptly. We need to develop tissue tone and freedom from toxic settlements, diverticuli, etc.

In this chapter we have attempted to present evidence that reflex areas exist. To strengthen this contention I suggest a review of some of the cases which underwent the healing crisis. In describing these cases we showed that if the patient followed a certain program, the conditions indicated in the iris would develop. You may recall the case of the lady whose iris indicated sulphur settlement in the brain areas, which was eliminated through

her hair roots during the crisis. A similar case was that of a man whose iris showed a sulphur settlement mostly in that part of the autonomic nervous system connected with the neck, head, and a portion of the face. During his healing crisis, these areas broke out in extreme rash and boils.

We have tried to show that through iridology causes can be determined, whereas with the average method of diagnosis we do

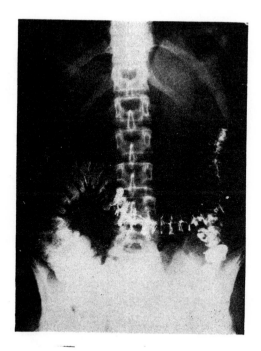

FIG. 192 (c). This irritable bowel is found in a nervous, irritable person. The prolapsus represents a lack of tone and lack of calcium in the body. This reflexly is causing considerable trouble in the brain and mental centers. The prolapsus and irritability were greatest in the sigmoid flexure; patient complained constantly of left leg distress.

not know whether we have discovered the cause or merely a symptom. We have called attention to the fact that a symptom may be a reflex condition with its cause in some remote part of the organism. In all fairness, we have suggested that other diagnostic procedures be used for verification. I know from experience that the iris will reveal to me the existence of conditions which grosser forms of diagnosis might miss. This is especially true in conditions which have not yet become severe or detectable, for with iridology we can pre-determine the development of a condition because in the iris there is already evidence of the incipient state. We therefore sum up by saying we believe it is important to study reflex areas before beginning the diagnosis and treatment of disease symptoms.

21

POLARITY RELATIONS IN THE BODY

THINGS NOT DONE BEFORE

The things that haven't been done before
Those are the things to try.

Columbus dreamed of an unknown shore,
At the rim of the far-flung sky.

And his heart was bold and his faith was strong,
As he ventured in dangers new,

And he paid no heed to the jeering throngs,
Or the fears of the doubting crew.

The things that haven't been done before
Are the tasks worth while today.

Are you one of the flock that follows, or
Are you one of the timid souls that quail
At the jeers of the doubting crew,
Or dare you, whether you win or fail,

Strike out for the goal that's new?

—*Unknown*

Positive and Negative Sides of the Body

I used to try to figure out why the canary stands on one foot at night. Did you ever wonder why he does that? Why is it that I can give two persons the same kind of an orange and in one it will cause gas and other disturbances, while in the other it will not? I have formed some definite conclusions as to the reason, but considerable study, deep thought, and observation of nature and people over a number of years have been required.

In studying the positive and negative polarities of the body, it was very interesting to realize that we are an electrically charged battery and that we carry a life force, energy, spirit, or whatever you wish to call it, that can be measured. This I saw clearly demonstrated in London, where, with Kilner glasses, we compared the aura of a vital healthy person with that of a diseased person, and could see how the aura of the diseased person changed when his health had been restored. It seems phenomenal to see instruments recording and measuring electrical emanations from various tissues in the living body. No reactions are

333

recorded if the instruments are applied to a dead person. In order to understand this we must recognize the positive and negative nature of electricity. In order for tissues to have life and action, there must be polarity, the positive pole working against the negative pole to produce a force which can travel. It may travel over wires as electricity or over the nerves of the body as vibration, thought or spirit.

Let me interpolate here the statement that throughout this chapter, whenever the words positive and negative are used, the terms electro-positive and electro-negative are meant or implied.

The two sides of the body are very different in each person. We inherit these differences from our parents. One side of the body is patterned after the father strain, and the other side after the mother strain. That which we inherit most predominantly will determine our predominant pattern. If we wear out the strength and usefulness of the more dominant side, however, we will then express the less dominant side. That is why the actions of our acquaintances vary at different times when we meet them. We say a person is "in a mood" or has a dual nature.

The first thing I notice when a patient comes to me is the fact that one eyebrow is higher than the other. Observe the nostrils; one is always larger than the other. Notice the corners of the mouth of a person in sorrow, regret and unhappiness. They are always down, while in a happy person they are turned up. Ask any cartoonist and he will tell you that he can make a face look sick by turning down the corners of the mouth, but when he turns these up the face appears happy. A person's mouth may turn up on one side like his mother's, and the other side may turn down like his father's. The one side will appear happy, the other depressed.

The right side of anyone's body, however, is the electro-positive side, the left is electro-negative—whether it be the mother's or the father's strain that is dominant.

When the health of the left side is broken down, the electro-negative influences in life are needed to build it up. For instance, we know that in connection with foods, starches are negative and proteins are positive. If the right side is broken down— which usually is the side affected in 90 per cent of cases because it is the side (especially the liver) that handles the toxic conditions of the body,—the positive things in nature are needed. Such persons need a high altitude, which is positive; proteins, which are positive, and citrus fruits, which combine well with proteins. They should have very few starches, since these are negative, but of course may have all of the non-starchy vegetables, which are neutral.

A person may have one leg shorter than the other. One foot may be larger than the other. It is the predominance of either father or mother principles that determines these differences. Much of the training I have had teaches how to adjust the hips and make the legs the same length. One time I had a patient who had an extreme difference in his leg lengths. His father was extremely tall (over six feet) and his mother was about five feet. One had extremely long and the other extremely short legs. Was it possible, when I looked at the legs, the mouth and nostrils, that I could see one side was like the mother and the other was like the father? Is it possible we are double? Is it possible we have our mother and father make-up both physically and mentally? It is my studied conclusion that we have. One side of the body of the offspring is going to be patterned after the father and the other after the mother. If father has long legs and mother short legs, their child's legs will be of unequal length and cannot work in harmony. Nor would it be of any use to attempt to equalize these lengths, especially if X-ray photographs show one leg to be longer than the other. If one of our parents is a faster thinker than the other, we may have the experience of being able to think faster at one time than at another. You are married in your own body, the right and left sides.

Often we hear the remark, "He looks just like his mother" or "just like his father." We have moods when we behave like our mother and moods when we behave like our father. Sometimes we regret having acted like the one, while at other times we feel joyful and happy when we have been acting like the other. It depends upon what we can do the best and what we like the most. If you have taken after your father, everything that you do as he would will please you most, and if you take after your mother, you will consider as wonderful what you do as she would.

Friction is set up in your body through your moods; the glands are influenced through the nervous system, and the action and reaction of the right and left sides. Do you realize that the right side can be larger than the left, that the glands can be larger on one side than the other? Is it possible to have greater strength of activity on one side than on the other? Do you realize we can have an inherent weakness in the right thyroid gland and a perfectly functioning gland on the left side? It is difficult to believe, but it is so. We inherit weaknesses from our parents, and these we must live with and attempt to control. There are always two sides to everything, from the very good to the very bad. Everything in nature is two-sided—up and down, light and dark, positive and negative, right and left.

If the right side of the cerebellum is the larger, the left mammary gland will also be the larger, and vice versa. Those tissues which are the strongest and the most active, take up the nutrition first. If the right side of the body is the stronger, it will express itself more dominantly because it has the power to absorb nutrition first, the power to eliminate waste materials, and can have better health.

By recognizing that everything in nature is positive and negative, we can use its finer forces for good purposes, especially in the healing art. Applying the positive and negative effects of temperature, for example, nothing more effectively breaks up a fixation

in the body than the increased circulation which can be brought about by alternate heat from the sun and cold from cold water. By using the cosmic vital bath,—submerging the person horizontally in approximately four inches of cold water and exposing the other side of the body for a certain time to the hot sun,—produces, through contraction and relaxation, a rapid flow of blood. By turning the patient over in the cold water every thirty seconds, the vessels relaxed by the sun's warmth will be contracted by the cold and will force blood into the other parts of the body.

The whole body is made up of and is influenced by positive and negative forces, and the day will come when we will recognize that minerals have not completely performed their function in the body unless they are the kind that have an electrical influence. We could tear up a piece of linoleum or a telephone pole and obtain from them all of the calcium that the body needs, so far as would be indicated by any laboratory test, but it has not been organized and electrified through the living plant life provided by God to transform the inorganic elements in the soil to the organic, electro-colloidal form needed by the human body. It is this living substance in the plant that man lives on. It is transference of that energy that makes man a living being. Thus are we united not only to the electro-colloidal forces found in the soil and plant life, but to the entire universe. We make a mistake in trying to force upon the body inorganic minerals and synthetic chemical vitamins, and expect them to contribute to well-being. Mineral elements themselves are eliminated from the body, but what they leave behind in the body is their electrical life force. This will some time be proved scientifically. Mineral elements as compounded by nature cannot be duplicated in a laboratory. We eliminate sodium in our perspiration which cannot be recovered and put back into the body, nor can we get sodium with life-building properties from table salt. We must get the organized sodium from fruits and vegetables.

Certain mineral elements produce an acid reaction in the body while others are alkaline in effect. Sodium and potassium, for instance, are the two greatest alkaline-producing elements. They are especially favored by the sun in growing plants. We have learned that the sun is the source whereby sodium is fixed in our plant life, and fruit that does not get enough sunshine will not be completely matured and will not be alkaline enough to satisfy the needs of the body. One reason why so many persons develop acid conditions in the body is that the immature fruits and vegetables which they buy are low in sodium content.

What we say here regarding the minerals also applies to their close associates, the vitamins. Those vitamins which are so far known have been given alphabetical names, A, B, C, etc. But there would not be enough letters in the alphabet to name all of the vitamins in nature, some of which gradually are being discovered by research workers.

Our seasons and our lives are considerably under the influence of our sun. In the past some races of people were sun worshippers. We should all be sun worshippers because all life comes from the sun and we could not live without it. When we deal with nature's finer forces, we recognize that there is a balance in life, even to the point of producing male or female at will, which we recognize as the positive and negative. A Doctor Jackson has been able to produce male pigeons at will by keeping the father pigeons in darkness. It has been observed that men whose occupation keeps them shut away from light and sunshine, as in the copper mines of Wisconsin, invariably father male children. On the other hand, army officers, mail carriers, and others who are constantly living in the open air and have plenty of light, build a stronger electrical force in their body, and the children born to them are predominantly girls. Nature balances up the positive and negative sides of creation, as we see manifested in the seasons of the year and the provision of suitable fruits and vegetables at certain seasons.

Cosmic Influences

We recognize that the leaf of the plant responds to certain cosmic electrical influences and grows upward, while the root, the coarser part of the plant, responds to the forces of gravity and grows downward into the earth. There must be a cosmic pull upon the earth itself, and I believe that there is something to be gained by man if he uses foods that have been chemicalized and electrified by the sun above the ground. I feel certain that by eating these plants mainly, we would have less gravitational pull on the body in old age when we have less energy and power to resist. I believe that eating foods which are ready to degenerate and go into the soil again, pull the body toward that source more quickly. Such considerations should inspire us to put into our bodies only those foods which are vital and can impart living elements to our tissues in exchange for the energy we expend in digesting, assimilating, and eliminating them.

Speaking of the magnetic currents of the earth, we know that a pull toward the north pole is exerted upon everything that exists above the equator and likewise a pull toward the south pole upon everything below the equator. Climbing plants, such as vines, twist to the right in a clock-wise direction if growing north of the equator, and twist to the left if growing south of the equator. It is claimed that when oil wells are sunk, the oil blows toward the north pole if located above the equator and toward the south pole if below it.

These magnetic currents affect the body, and especially the vital structure called the brain, which needs all the recuperative power possible. Experiments indicate that if we sleep with our heads to the north, we can most quickly recover lost energy. In this position the magnetic pull exerted upon the iron in the blood will be greatest in the brain. It is advisable to sleep without a pillow to avoid pressure against the thyroid gland which would interfere with proper circulation and its opportunity to recuperate during the night. It has been stated that cows stalled in a north-and-south direction give more milk, and that hens roosting in a north-and-south position lay more eggs.

Many influences are involved in the complex processes of photosynthesis. Plants growing above the ground are more positive while those grown below the ground are referred to as negative. Those high in protein draw certain influences from the environment which give them the property of being positive in their electro-biochemical makeup. The influence of the planets, the positive rays of the sun, the electro-magnetic currents of the earth, and water, all have their effects upon plant life. The degree to which they are allowed to act naturally upon our plants determines such conditions as whether fruits are sweet or bitter, whether they have tough skins, etc. It is known now that calcium will not be taken from the soil and fixed in plants unless acted upon by the planet Venus. Unless minerals have been electrically charged by nature through organic growth, our fruits and vegetables are not fit for human consumption.

There are various abnormal ways of growing plants. If we grow tomatoes, for instance, in the air, without any connection with the ground, they will not ripen properly. They must be connected in some way with the earth. Tomatoes *can* be grown in water containing five or six inorganic chemicals, but a diet of those tomatoes causes animals to become bald. Carrot pulp, the fibre which remains after the juice has been extracted, when made into animal food causes the death of these animals as they cannot live on material from which the live elements have been extracted. We are eating "painted" vegetables today and are not getting all of the electrical material we need from these chemicalized plants.

That food which grows above the ground and takes the longest to mature has been subjected the longest to cosmic influences and all of the natural forces, and I believe this is the most natural food for man. Since

all fruits are thus grown, I come to the natural conclusion that fruit is the natural food for man. We must consider, however, that a diet consisting entirely of fruit develops a very psychic and sensitive body, which would not be advisable for coarse, undeveloped, undisciplined individuals. One who has refined his body by living on fruits, must have mental control and stability.

Positive and Negative Foods

No food is completely electro-positive or completely electro-negative, but some foods are predominantly one or the other. Probably the food containing the greatest predominance of positive electricity is meat. In the vegetable kingdom, those grown above the ground are positive while those grown below the ground are negative.

During the early or growing stage of life and the doing and daring stage when there is the urge to actively use the physical body, the starches and other negative foods are needed for building bone and muscle. Proteins are considered to be the brain and nerve builders. In the middle part of life the dietary should be one which balances the positive and negative foods. Towards the end of life, when there is less physical activity and the organism may have become more negative, there is need for the positive foods. A diet which is predominantly positive or predominantly negative may be used at any age, however, when the necessity has arisen for building up one side of the body.

The positive foods are those which are predominantly protein—lean meats, fish, eggs, cheese and nuts. The negative foods are those which are predominantly carbohydrate—the starches, sweets and fats. They include grains, potatoes and other starchy vegetables, legumes and sweet fruits. The neutral foods are non-starchy vegetables and sub-acid fruits (these do not include citrus fruits).

The positive foods need acids to help digest them, while the negative foods need more of an alkaline medium. The left side of the body secretes acid digestive juices, while the right side produces the alkaline digestive juices. Difficulty in digesting proteins may be due to weakness on the left side of the body. When the right side is weak there may not be sufficient alkaline juices for carbohydrate digestion and any disease manifestations which arise will be strictly on the right side of the body. In this acid-alkaline relationship we see another example of the two-way system which lends electrical potential for the handling of foods in the body. Since there are also electrical charges in natural foods, it is through knowledge of how to combine the forces of the body with those of foods that we obtain results.

The right side diet for persons with conditions on the right side of the body and for those past thirty and forty who need to build up a higher rate of activity, is proteins, non-starchy vegetables and acid fruits (citrus fruits and tomatoes). The most electro-positive protein food is meat. It provides the greatest stimulation. Use only lean meats, no fat and no pork. Whenever we eat meat we should have with it stewed tomatoes, canned tomatoes, tomato juice or fresh grapefruit. We may also have any of the non-starchy vegetables with meat.

Meat may be eaten twice a day along with the citrus fruits and vegetables. It may be best to have only citrus fruits for breakfast, and then have the vegetables, citrus fruits and meat for lunch and dinner.

Cases of asthma that have developed from a toxic liver or other conditions on the right side of the body, will respond immediately. The least amount of catarrh is produced when the patient is eating meat, and most catarrhal disorders disappear when one is on the right side diet. If there are no left side symptoms, nerve depletion and glandular imbalance, due to worry and emotional strain or occupational or environmental pressures, can be most effectively remedied through this right side diet. Persons who are studious and have sedentary occupations need the right side diet more than they need the left side diet. This is also the most ideal diet for losing weight.

If a person has aversion or religious beliefs against indulging in meat, he can substitute cheese, eggs, soybeans, soybean milk, and other soybean products. Greater electro-positive activity, however, is found in the meats. Since meat substitutes contain more carbohydrates than meat, they are less effective in building up the right side or the electro-positive force of the body.

Food Classification According to Polarity

Foods that are predominantly electro-positive (Proteins)	Foods that are predominantly electro-negative (Carbohydrates: Starches, Sugars, Fats)	Neutral Foods Non-starchy Vegetables, such as
Lean Meats	*Grain Products*, such as	Artichokes
Fish	Bread	Asparagus
Eggs	Cereals	Beets
Cheese	Pastries	Beet Tops
Wheat Germ	Cookies	Cabbage
Nuts	Crackers	Cauliflower
Milk	Corn Meal, yellow	Celery
Buttermilk	Canned Corn	Chard
Yogurt		Cucumber
	Starchy Vegetables, such as	Dandelion
	Potatoes	Egg Plant
	Sweet Potatoes	Endive
	Parsnips	

Foods that are predominantly electro-negative (Carbohydrates: Starches, Sugars, Fats)	Neutral Foods
	Non-starchy Vegetables, such as

Foods that are predominantly electro-negative (Carbohydrates: Starches, Sugars, Fats)

Winter Squash
Carrots
Pumpkin
Peas

Legumes, such as

Dried Beans
Dried Peas
Lentils
Peanuts
Soybeans

Sweet Fruits, such as

Dates
Figs
Raisins

Other Fruits, such as

Olives
Bananas
Avocados
Grapes
Cantaloupe
Watermelon

Other Sweets, such as

Sugar
Candy
Jams and Jellies
Syrup
Honey
Pastry

Fats

Butter
Oleomargarine
Cream
Oils
Meat Fat

Neutral Foods
Non-starchy Vegetables, such as

Garlic
Green Peppers
Kale
Kohlrabi
Leeks
Mushrooms
Mustard Greens
Okra
Onions
Oyster Plant
Parsley
Radishes
Rutabagas
Spinach
String Beans
Turnip Greens
Watercress
Etc.

Acid Fruits, such as

Grapefruit
Lemons
Limes
Tomatoes (canned)
Strawberries
Raspberries
Blackberries
Blueberries
Currants
Gooseberries
Cranberries

(*Note:* Although these fruits are neutral from the standpoint of polarity, they should be combined only with electro-positive foods or proteins).

The following is an outline of right side diet:

MEAT (tender). No fat, no pork.
FISH (white fish that has fins and scales).
CANNED TOMATOES (pureed).
FRESH GRAPEFRUIT (not canned).
NON-STARCHY VEGETABLES.

Whenever having meat or fish, have grapefruit or tomatoes. Never meat or fish alone.
Any non-starchy vegetables—in any combination.
Tomatoes by themselves or grapefruit by itself.
All meals must contain only the foods listed here.
NOTHING ELSE.

Suggested outline

Breakfast: Canned tomatoes and/or fresh grapefruit.
10 A.M.: Vegetable broth or potato peeling broth (peelings ¼ to ½" thick). Add celery, carrots and parsley to flavor, if desired.
Lunch: Vegetables. Protein. Canned tomatoes or fresh grapefruit.
Supper: Vegetables (as many as desired). Protein. Tomato juice or fresh grapefruit. (Broth or health tea is allowable).

The following is an outline of left side diet·

STARCHES . . . . Choice of:
Starches must always be combined with   Baked Potato
vegetables. Use them for lunch and   Brown Rice
dinner.   Banana
                                         Barley (whole)
                                         Corn Meal, yellow

VEGETABLES . . . .

String Beans	Beets
All Squashes	Beet Greens
Chard	Spinach
Celery	Pureed Peas
Carrots	Endive
Watercress	Parsley
Asparagus	

FRUITS . . . . Stewed fruits or water-pack canned.
Sweet fruits and sweet fruit juices may   Sweet dried fruits. No sugar.
be had for breakfast and in between

Apricots	Figs
Grapes	Pears
Baked Apple	Prunes
Strawberries	Peaches
Cantaloupe	

FRUIT JUICES   Cherry Juice   Fig Juice
No citrus. Use only . . . .   Prune Juice   Grape Juice
                                        Pineapple Juice

Make all meals from above.

Breakfast: Fruit and Starch.
10 A.M.:   Vegetable Broth (carrot, celery, parsley, potato).
Lunch: Two Vegetables and Starch.
Dinner: Two Vegetables and Starch.
               Health drink such as: Oat Straw Tea
                                     Shave Grass Tea
                                     Alfalfa Mint Tea

For the left side diet, the five best starches to consider are bananas, whole barley, brown rice, baked potato, and yellow corn meal. We may also add to this, whole rye and whole oats. I think the average person has had too much wheat in his diet so it would not hurt to change over to another type of starch or grain. Bread is the worst starch of all. I do not approve of bread.

Potatoes should be cooked and eaten with their skins. The little white ring underneath the peeling of a potato is the potassium ring. .This ring contains about 60 per cent of the potato's alkaline salt, and while the potato is an underground, negative vegetable, its potassium content is positive. The center of the potato is the acid-producing or the negative portion. One of the reasons why so many persons today are complaining about acid conditions is that they are using only the inside part of the potato or other negative foods too much. This applies also to eating only the inner portion of grains and not including the outer coverings.

Meals should be balanced by using both positive and negative foods. Most people do not use alkaline and acid foods in proper proportions. In our chapter on Starvation in the Midst of Plenty we discuss potato peeling broth, which is one of the richest sources of potassium and one of the finest broths for overcoming acid conditions in the body. By using the peelings we are using the positive element of the potato. Potassium is one of the highest alkaline salts we can use.

All vegetables may be used in the left side diet except those high in sulphur, such as cabbage, Brussels sprouts, broccoli, cauliflower, kohlrabi and turnips. We advise leaving these out, at least in the beginning of the diet. The fruits to be used are all of the dried and fresh fruits (except the acid fruits). These include figs, raisins, peaches, pears, apricots, and sometimes melons (melons in some instances may cause a disturbance). These foods may be eaten in any combinations desired.

For persons on the left side diet, I advise two meals a day. Vegetables may be eaten at any meal. If fruits alone are desired for breakfast, this is all right—one, two, or even three fruits.

These diets for building up either the right or left side of the body should be considered only for temporary use to help bring about balance. Afterwards, a regular healthful dietary should be followed, including one meal a day that is predominantly protein and one that consists predominantly of starchy and sweet foods. All meals should be balanced with an adequate amount of vegetables, and all should be in compatible combinations. Study the above chart on Food Classification According to Polarity. Only non-starchy vegetables combine well with starches and sweets.

Speaking of combinations, I wish to stress the value of keeping foods that are predominately protein separate from foods that are predominately starch. I state this despite the claims that it makes no difference if they are eaten together—as discussed in the accompanying article from the March 2, 1935 issue of the Pacific Rural Press. There are a number of factors which have not been taken into consideration in this discussion.

Starch and Protein Combination

IN SOME sections of the country there is a belief that it is bad for us to eat starch and protein at the same meal. There is no scientific foundation for this notion. At a recent meeting of the American Dietetic Association one eminent specialist reported the results of over a thousand studies on men and women which he and his associates have conducted in order to find the facts about the digestion of foods in the human stomach.

They have gathered data from the same group of people when they ate meat alone and meat and mashed potato together. Every person in the group digested the meat and potato just as easily and comfortably and almost as quickly as the meat alone. On the average it took them only 4 minutes longer to digest the meat and potato combined. In short, these investigators can find no scientific facts to back up the notion that starch and protein eaten together cause any difficulty in the human stomach.

And as a matter of fact, we do eat protein and carbohydrates together. When we eat beans, for example, or peas, or peanuts, or wheat bread or rye bread. In the wheat grain, nature combined starch and gluten (that is protein) and it's not easy to separate them. As for the hundreds and thousands of made dishes we've grown up on, we need only to compare them with the sandwiches we took to school or now take to business or eat on picnics,—to realize that if all these foods were as dangerous as they been painted, some of us would be in a bad way today.

Fig. 193.   We do not agree with this viewpoint.

With the devitalized foods so widely used today, there is more reason than there would have been for our forefathers, who had whole unrefined foods grown on virgin soils, to find combinations that will be the easiest for the body to handle—especially for persons with weak digestion. Whereas natural foods contain the enzymes, vitamins, and minerals required for their digestion, refined foods do not. Regardless of arguments to the contrary, I have found, as have many others, that there is greater ease of digestion, less gas formation, etc., when heavy proteins are eaten separately from heavy starches. My old friend Doctor Tilden of Denver found that this was very helpful to patients. And hundreds of doctors who have been in my classes are proving also that it works, so this is not a personal opinion. Heavier demands are placed upon the digestive system when a conglomeration of foods are eaten than when foods are plain and compatibly combined.

The person who eats one protein and one starch a day, at different meals, can still have a feast, but he will eat fewer starches and proteins than he did formerly. For example, he will not have toast, biscuits, waffles, hot cakes, etc., for breakfast; sandwiches for lunch; and then potatoes, spaghetti, bread, cake and other starches again at the evening meal. If a person eats all he wants of a good starch at one meal a day, it will mold the body properly. He will eat more vegetables, which is the thing we are trying to accomplish. The person who eats too many starches and proteins crowds out the possibility of obtaining enough vital minerals that the body so needs. The starvation for vital elements that is going on in our midst today can best be made up by adding more of the mineral salts from our vegetable and fruit kingdom. This we accomplish by splitting the starches and proteins and allowing only one at a time.

During each day we should consume a good protein, a good starch, four to six vegetables, and two fruits,—but not all of these should be combined in any one meal or at each meal.

Breathing

In Yogi culture, breathing exercises are taken to balance the electrical influences in the body. Some persons have one nostril more widely open than the other. If you pay attention to a person's moods and mental activity you will notice that he breathes through first one nostril for a time and then the other, according to his activity. A Yogi would tell you that as you turn from one side of the body to the other during sleep, you are alternating the breath and keeping balance between positive and negative forces. The person who is positive in his activities, positive in his expressions, usually has the right nostril open. The negative person who is meek and humble, usually has the left nostril open and the right closed. So we see that an important means of maintaining normal electrical balance in the body is our breathing.

This was exemplified to me by a patient who was expecting to have an operation on the turbinates of his nose to permit better breathing. He was a very negative thinker and lived a very depressed life. His family troubles and financial problems had gotten the best of him, and he was a sick man mentally. It finally developed that one of his nostrils was closed most of the time. A depressed, dejected person does not take a full breath; he breathes in an entirely different manner from the positive person and produces a different electrochemical influence in his body through the way he thinks. While this patient was under the influence of a positive attitude, the right nostril was more open than the left, and when he was in a negative attitude, the left nostril was more open. Through mental channels, with some corrective diet for support in eliminating some of the inflamation, it was possible to change this man's attitude, and then he began to breathe more normally than he ever had before. He breathed more through the right nostril, which is the positive side. This is the side that would have been operated upon had it not been prevented.

This outstanding case, that within half an hour could change the breath from the left to the right nostril by his mental attitude, helped me to realize the importance of the electro-magnetic influence of breathing upon the body. I believe we charge and adjust the finer expressions of the body in large measure through our breathing as well as through the electro-chemical balance of the foods we take into the body.

Right and Left Side Treatments

We can apply the principles pertaining to the positive and negative polarities of the right and left sides of the body in therapy. It has been suggested by two doctors in the East that persons who have heart trouble should use the rice diet. Why should rice be used for heart trouble? They do not give the reason, but later I will tell you. They know only that it has an effect, but we want the answer to this from an electro-chemical standpoint.

All of nature is divided into positive and negative aspects, action and reaction. Electricity is positive and negative. The earth is negative, the sun is positive. Man is positive, woman is negative. The right side of the body is positive, the left side is negative. In some experiments with static electricity carried on at a monastery in England, the work could not be completed because the monks were wearing rubber-soled sandals and this cut off the electrical current between themselves and the earth. This may explain why the canary lifts one leg when he sleeps, to sever the connection between himself and the earth.

In the study of electro-chemistry we find that starches are negative and proteins are positive; that acid fruits are positive and sweet fruits are negative. A high altitude is positive while a low altitude is negative. If you wish to build up the negative side, you should apply all the negative factors together. If the positive side needs to be built up, use the positive factors. For instance, the person who needs more energy, a quickened metabolism, more stimulation, and whose body needs to be made more positive electrically, should go to a higher

altitude, eat foods that are electro-chemically positive, etc. But if there is heart trouble (left side), and if the negative side (left side) of the body has been broken down, the patient should seek a low altitude, electro-negative foods, etc. Do not allow foods that will stimulate the heart, such as meat. A meat meal can stimulate the heart to beat 25 per cent faster, while a meal from the left side diet, will increase the heart's activity only 6 per cent. Conserve the heart's energy by the use of foods that stimulate the heart the least. The person who has trouble on the left side should use starches and sweet fruits in his diet. He should not eat citrus fruits as these will cause a burning in the stomach and belching, and this irritates the heart. The person with high blood pressure should have no citrus fruit and no protein food until balance has been established. I have seen blood pressure drop 20 to 60 points in a week on this electro-negative diet.

In a recent iris diagnosis I found the sodium ring greatly exaggerated on the left side in both irises, showing that the left side of the body had the poorest circulation, the least resistance, the poorest blood reaching each cell of the left side. Upon examination, I found all this patient's trouble on the left side and a blood pressure of 220 systolic. With the administration of a negative diet, this patient will find herself building up the left side and balancing her body; and finally she will be able to carry on with the normal diet, containing some proteins.

A man who came to me from Pasadena had been in a hospital with heart trouble for three years. He was about sixty pounds overweight. In this particular type of case the average advice would be to eliminate starches from the diet because of the overweight. But since this man had a defective heart and most of his weakness and lack of glandular activity were on the left side of the body, we put him on what we call the "negative diet," which is negative in its electrical aspects and activities, and soothing to the left side of the body. This diet gave him starches, vegetables and sweet fruits. The patient lost thirty pounds in about four months, got out of bed, returned to his work, and was in very good health considering his past condition.

Another over-weight patient was a man from Santa Monica who had arthritis and had lost the use of most of the left side of his body. It seemed that the arthritis had settled more on his left side and he had developed an extreme heart condition along with the arthritis. We put him also on the "negative diet," emphasized negative environmental influences, and kept him at the beach. He lost thirty pounds in about five months and was able to get rid of his crutches. After six months on this regime he had a physical examination and nothing was found wrong with his heart.

It is difficult to realize that we can accomplish such outstanding effects from this type of specific dieting, but this is more readily understood when we accept the idea that the two sides of one's body are made up of mother and father, who usually are very different in build and characteristics.

Newspaper articles from time to time have reported the research finding that high blood pressure has been successfully lowered by feeding a diet consisting of cooked rice (without salt), sugar, fruits and fruit juices, supplemented by vitamins

Rice Diet Treatment Described as Aid for High Blood Pressure

CHICAGO, June 12. (P)—A new, entirely drugless treatment for high blood pressure, by a diet of rice and fruit juices, was shown to the American Medical Association today.

It is the result of four years' work at Duke University School of Medicine and the results, in which the majority of cases were helped and many apparently cured, were shown in the scientific exhibit of Dr. Walter Kempner, a refugee physician.

The rice diet treatment is the result of feeding kidney tissues kept alive artificially in glass tubes in the Duke laboratories to test a new theory.

The diet is mostly rice, boiled or steamed, plus ample fruit juices and supplemented by vitamins and iron.

Many Duke patients were very ill. Some were blind and had enlarged hearts. The rice diet enabled most of them to see again, and reduced the enlarged hearts.

Blood pressures of around 200 dropped immediately on starting the rice diet. Thereafter there was usually a long, slow drop until many patients had pressures within normal ranges and well under 150.

FIG. 194.   This is an example of a newspaper article giving diet suggestions for overcoming high blood pressure.

and iron. The article in the accompanying figure is an example. In some instances, wheat is used in place of rice. The patient is allowed no water, no salt, and no fat. The only beverage is fruit juice.

In diagnosing from the iris we recognize that there may be high blood pressure to contend with on both sides of the body. I would say, however, that about 90 per cent of the high blood pressure cases on which I have worked had strokes and were paralyzed on the right side. In these cases the original trouble and the cause were on the left side of the body or from the left side of the brain, which causes paralysis on the right side of the body. Stroke could have been prevented in these cases had they come in time to be put on the left side diet. The toxic material causing the trouble in the left hemisphere of the brain usually lies in the descending colon on the left side. When there is absorption of toxic materials into the body from the colon, more is absorbed from the descending colon than from the ascending colon.

As waste material passes through the bowel, the toxic material absorbed into the body from the left side has a more devastating effect than that absorbed from the right side. This is because more liquids have been absorbed when the fecal material reaches the left side and toxic waste is more concentrated on the left side. As the stool becomes drier, a more putrefactive state will exist. Gas pressure which may develop in the descending colon can cause heart pressure and other disturbances on the left side.

There are cases in which a spot in the descending colon has its reflex activity in the left side of the brain, and may affect the blood pressure center. In these cases we must correct the toxic bowel in order to normalize the blood pressure caused by this toxic condition. Many times an enema or a colonic has reduced blood pressure ten, fifteen and even twenty points by removing the toxic material from the descending colon. We have proven that by using the left side diet, high blood pressure can be brought down from ten to fifty points within a month's time.

It is wonderful to see what can be done as far as altitude is concerned. One patient who had a systolic blood pressure of 180 while staying in Long Beach at the seashore, had his blood pressure raised to 240 when taken up to Big Bear, which is seven thousand feet higher than Long Beach. This is a rise of sixty points in four hours' time, merely by an altitude change of seven thousand feet. This shows the positive and negative aspects of altitude.

In treating cases of abnormal blood pressure, we determine whether there is an extreme manifestation of positive physiological function. In these cases the left side diet and other electro-negative influences are indicated. In those cases where there is a low blood count, lethargy, extreme fatigue, etc., we recognize a negative physiological functioning, and recommend the right side diet and other positive factors.

I do not believe that people who have trouble in the left side of the body should go without proteins the rest of their lives, but only long enough to build up the left side to where it balances the right side of the body so that they can handle a normal amount of protein; then both sides of the body will work in coordination with one another. Although in a sense we have two bodies to take care of, it is seldom that one side must be fed more than the other, except in inherent weaknesses in which one side is extremely different from the other. Under those circumstances when it is necessary, the left and right sides can be balanced through positive and negative influences to the place where eventually the patient can live on a regular healthful diet.

In bringing out the fact that we may inherit greater strength on the left side of the body than on the right, or vice versa, I do not mean that at the time of treatment with diet, altitude, and other means, we have to consider only the inherent condition. A person may have inherently weak organs on the left side and strong organs on the right side of the body, but he may cause these strong organs on the right side to break down (through eating negative foods, etc.) and become weaker than those on the inherently weak side. We can break down a strong positive side of the body by using negative foods and denying it the positive foods to keep it in good condition. Both sides of the body must be developed and maintained.

About 90 per cent of my patients need more right side than left side building. When we have passed the period of our growth, we can take on isolation and the negative influences, but it is in our positive moods that we desire and seek, that we hope and plan, that we accomplish our deeds. We are here to grow and to develop, and I believe that human beings need more of the positive influences than the negative.

Mis-Mating

Many a misfit personality springs from mis-mated parents. The physical, mental, and emotional patterns of the parents inevitably affect the child. Take anyone's photograph and separate the two halves of the face, and you will see that they never are alike. One nostril will be larger than the other, one cheek bone higher, one side of the mouth fuller, etc. I believe that persons whose parents were not well mated have the hardest time in life; they are the most unstable and have the greatest struggle within themselves. There are many different ways of bringing out the fact that we have this dual nature to contend with, but it is difficult to realize that it can ruin our lives without our even knowing the fundamental cause.

Right and left side differences can be seen most readily and in the greatest degree in the pictures of criminals in post offices and police departments. The faces are extremely off center, with one ear always higher and further back than the other, which indicates egocentric qualities. The development and shape of the eyelids differ in many respects on the right and left sides. It is persons like these who are having the greatest struggle between the two sides of their nature. On the other hand, we hear that there is no such thing as a normal person; that normal persons would be out of place in this world. The circumstance of having inherited a dual nature does not mean that inevitably we must develop criminal tendencies. Some of the geniuses who have given to this world some of its greatest talents, had dual natures.

Such mis-mating of parents produces a child with abnormal differences between right and left sides of the body. The victim needs to be taught how to control the strong side and how to develop the weak side of his nature in order to avoid physical limitations and constant mental turmoil and confusion. Many misfits can be helped to find their rightful place when given an opportunity for adjustment and learning to know themselves.

We show on the next page a couple of pictures of a young chap who loved his occupation as long as he was in the mood for that particular work. Though at one time he had loved his engineering profession, the loneliness of the job seemed to be something he could not longer endure. In his second mood he had to have people around him. In his first mood he could not stand these people at all and had to get away from them. To satisfy this patient's two moods we encouraged his having two occupations, or an occupation and a hobby. The point in this example is that everyone has mood swings similar to this young man's since we are different on one side of the body than on the other.

Notice in the photographs that the distance from the ear to the shoulder is entirely different on one side than on the other. The scapula covers the spine on one side of his body, while it is an inch and one-half to two inches away from the spine on the other side. He has thirteen ribs on one side and twelve on the other.

A person whose characteristics are predominantly feminine will hold the palms of

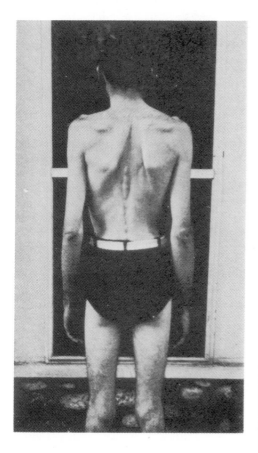

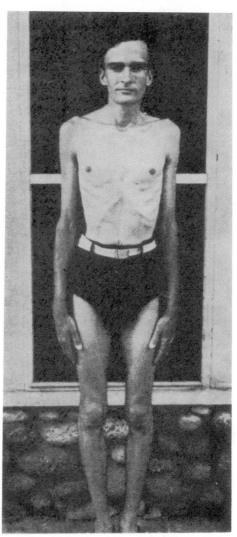

FIG. 195 (a). In this photograph of the young man with various differences between the right and left sides of his body, note the difference in the size of the two elbows, as well as the variation in distance between the two scapulae and the spine and the difference in distance between the two ears and the shoulders.

FIG. 195 (b). In this photograph the most evident differences between the two sides of the body are in the ribs, the inner portions of clavicle (left is lower than the right), and various structures of the face (eyes, nose).

the hands back while one who has mannish characteristics will hold the palms of the hands forward. The palm on one side may be held forward while on the other side it is held backward. Women usually are the ones who are knock-kneed. In knock-kneed persons one leg generally is more knock-kneed than the other. In buying shoes we should have them fitted to the larger foot and should stand while the foot is being measured. Its muscles and bony structure can have an entirely different length, shape and arch formation from the other.

Most individuals are naturally right-handed or naturally left-handed, though some are ambidextrous. If a mother insists that her child learn to use his right hand when he is naturally left-handed and should be using his left hand, she may interfere with his attaining his goal and finding his proper niche in life. Stuttering and stammering could result. We should use the right hand when the right eye is the dominant or inherently stronger eye, for then there is not only better arm and hand coordination, but better coordination in the organs of speech, etc. And effort is spared the brain cells because more activity can become automatic. It is important to remember that we see as we think, and think as we see.

If such knowledge was considered by doctors, and mothers were instructed in a proper training program for the child early in life, I think we could prevent a good deal of the maladjustment we have today. Many children become misfits in life, try to find consolation for their personality, and run wild because they have not found out what they are supposed to do. Statements have been made to the effect that over 30 per cent of the people who have run afoul of the law and entered our courts and jails, were unsuccessful in their past occupations and environment. They did not know where they could be successful or where they were needed.

There is much evidence in the world today that many mis-mated individuals never should have married. The children of these marriages may have great difficulty in adjusting to life's problems, or may not adjust and become delinquent or criminal, especially if the parents have habits of quarreling, drinking, etc. Note the accompanying article which gives accounts of a number of different girls from discordant and broken homes who got involved in such serious difficulties that they were sent to prison.

The day will come when the person who has a stronger development on one side of the body than the other, will be advised by his doctor concerning the most suitable climate in which to live, the best kind of companionship for him, etc. Some companionship is stimulating and some relaxing. The person who needs negative influences should be with someone who has a calming effect, a soothing voice, etc., while the person who has trouble on the right side needs a very active person around for stimulation. He should be told what occupation to follow and what foods to eat for his best development. The person who has a greater brain development on one side than on the other may need to have a second job or a hobby, for this person will be subject to what we call mood swings. At one time he is like the mother and at another time he is like the father. If we know that at times we have a mood during which we like to listen to music, while at other times we can better express ourselves in sewing, woodworking or traveling, we should educate ourselves for a job and a hobby which will satisfy these diversified desires.

It requires self discipline to control our moods and the problems of our two-sided physical characteristics. It is most difficult for the person who has great dissimilarity between the two sides of his body. Though he has the greatest problem, he also has the greatest opportunity to learn and to grow, and in many cases has the greatest possibility of giving this world a great legacy.

Muddled Lives Put Girls Of Tender Ages in Prison

(This is the last of three articles on Illinois' State Reformatory for Women at Dwight, Ill., and its youngest inmates--women under 21.)

By Edan Wright

The younger women at Dwight are no different from their older sisters. Their crimes are the same and they have the same pathetically muddled backgrounds.

There are 16 women under 21 at Dwight, serving sentences for murder, manslaughter, robbery, burglary, forgery and larceny. One of them is 17 years old, three are 18, five are 19 and seven are 20.

The real names of the girls discussed here are not used because of their youth and the fact that they are serving indeterminate sentences with chances for parole.

Marries A Soldier

Katherine, 20, is a manslaughter case. She comes from a small town. She married a soldier and had a baby. When he went overseas, she and her mother, with whom she lived, frequented taverns and picked up men. Katherine discovered she was going to have another child and she gave her mother the explanation that she had a tumor.

Katherine came back from a tavern early one morning and gave birth to her baby by herself. She strangled it with a cord from her dress, wrapped it in the dress and hid it under the bed.

Jane, 17, was born and reared in a big city. She, also, is serving a sentence for manslaughter. Jane never knew her father but she claims she lived happily with her mother and her stepfather until her mother died.

Then she went to live with an aunt and a grown cousin. The cousin spanked her whenever he felt she needed it. Jane violently resented it.

Stabs Her Cousin

When she grew older, the cousin frequently scolded her for staying out late. One evening, after a scolding, he threatened to whip her. He grabbed her and Jane cut him fatally with a razor.

Helen, 18, is serving a sentence for robbery. She grew up in medium sized towns. Helen's parents were separated when she was eight and her father hired a housekeeper to look after her and her brothers.

When she found out that her father was having an affair with the housekeeper, Helen began to run around with boys. Finally, at 14, she went to live with her mother.

She did as she pleased with her mother. She lied about her age and got a job in a factory. Then, since her mother's home was some distance from town, she took a room in a hotel.

Hijacks Autos

She fell in love with a carnival man, 40 years old, who had two wives and a record. With this man and two of his friends, she hijacked two cars from their owners and burglarized a store. It was with a view to vacationing in Florida. But Helen wound up in Dwight.

Nan, 19, was a big city girl. She is serving time for burglary. Her parents were divorced and her mother married twice after that. Nan always felt she was unwanted. She was placed in foster homes and institutions after neighbors complained she was mistreated.

She married a soldier whom she met on a hitch-hiking trip but they didn't get along after the birth of her baby, so she went back to her mother with the child. She had no money.

With a man whom she later married, she began a series of burglaries, principally gas stations, and was caught when police gave chase after a holdup.

FIG. 196. Newspaper account of the fate of several girls from broken homes.

Besides the electro-positive and electro-negative aspects which we have been discussing, there are many two-way aspects in life. And man may choose his direction, which he will follow—right or wrong, love or hate, the light of Truth or the darkness of delusion. But through it all he is ever striving for consciousness of oneness.

To know that we have been given the faculty of "dominion over" is truly a God-send, for in this we can so live above our mental and physical characteristics that whatsoever we do will be good in the sight of God.

A Dual Existence

"I'm a man with a dual existence—I mean in a mental way,
A cloud of magnificent colour, hid behind indefinite grey;
A monster of strange contradiction, a mixture of discord and song,
With feelings that point to the right way, and actions that lead to the wrong.
As hater, none can be more bitter; as lover, none can be more true;
I cling to the old-fashioned methods, yet welcome with gladness the new;
Life's sorrows I swallow in doses, its sweets I consume at a gulp;
Get sometimes the juice of its orange, at others the pips and pulp.
I have pride; 'tis the pride of the poor man—a pitiful pride at best,
And with fears of the future before me, yet I long for the coming rest;
I ache for the hour of midnight, but at midnight I ache for the morn;
Rejoice in the fullness of gladness—yet lament that I ever was born.
I would compass the stars above me, and fathom the depths of space;
Inhabit the planets with fancies, and the astral systems trace.
Pierce deep the arcanum of Being, and its mystical knots untie;
But wonders lying open around me, I pass them unheeded by.
I aim at the Glory of Greatness, but not for the breath of the crowd,
And value not fame and its flourish, because it is blatant and loud;
But the soul that can understand me is the goal I hope to find—
Nor for glory or adulation, but the grasp of a mind to Mind.
As weak as a straw in my own straits, but a towe on which you may lean,
As brave as a lion in danger; but, oh! so afraid of a scene.
In some things as wise as a serpent—in others as dull as an ass,
In some ways by none to be fathom'd—in others transparent as glass.
I'm bad, but I try to be better, and pray hard to be better still,
That my instincts may lead to reason, and my impulse give way to will;
And I manfully plod on skyward, that the heavenly heights may be crowned.
But scarce have I trodden the stairway I tumble pell-mell to the ground.
The warp in the main is a good one, but oh! I'm afraid of the weft;
With head ever turned to the right path, and feet veering round to the left;
I must seem to others a strange man, and even to me it is odd—
Of my whole, part is claimed by the devil—the best of me's owned by God."

22

INTESTINAL DISORDERS

There is but one cause of disease—poison, toxemia, most of which is created in the body by faulty living habits and faulty elimination.
—Major General Sir Arbuthnot Lane, M.D.

In the chapter on Reflex Areas and Remote Symptoms and in other parts of this book, the importance of the intestinal tract has been stressed. There should be no doubt about the relation between health of the intestinal tract and health in the rest of the body. Intestinal management probably is the most important thing a person can learn in a health-building routine. Some of the most important functions of life take place in the intestines. Through it worn out cells are eliminated and new cell structures have their beginning.

For the reason that the colon is supplied with fewer nerves than some other organs, distress signals are not so distinct as they are in most of the other organs of the body. Latent conditions may therefore develop in this area without our awareness of their presence.

We would be very much concerned should any community in modern times revert to some of the unsanitary habits of those times past when the wastes of human and animal life were allowed to accumulate in the streets and elsewhere. Since drinking water was thus usually polluted, destructive epidemic diseases were prevalent and sometimes wiped out entire nations. We have succeeded in improving our external sanitation considerably, with the

result that many of the loathsome diseases of the past have become very rare.

When it comes to human internal sanitation, however, we seem to be less concerned. Persons who are inclined to think it makes little difference how long intestinal waste is retained might give the matter more serious consideration if they realized the actual similarity between the city sewer and the disposal system of the body. Waste material that is not regularly evacuated from the intestines will accumulate and the toxic products of decomposition may be taken up by the blood and lymph and be carried to every cell in the body.

At the Battle Creek Sanitarium I heard Dr. John Harvey Kellog say he knew of many cases in which operations were prevented by cleansing and revitalizing the bowel. He maintained that 90 per cent of the diseases of civilization are due to improper functioning of the colon. Sir Arbuthnot Lane (M. D.) of London has shown the relation between bowel stasis and disease. He left no doubt as to how seriously he regarded the effects of intestinal intoxication when he said, "The lower end of the intestine is of the size that requires emptying every six hours, but by habit we retain its contents twenty-four hours. The result is ulcers and cancer."

351

Besides these world-renowned exponents of intestinal sanitation, other authorities have given recognition to the belief that cleanliness of the colon is necessary to good health. It is believed that disorders such as appendicitis, infected tonsils, liver and gall-bladder infections, dysfunction of the heart and blood vessels, sinusitis, arthritis and rheumatism, etc., no doubt have their origin in a sluggish colon. There is also an increasing number of morbid conditions in the various parts of the colon, involving the flexures, the rectum, and the anus. Consider the amount of surgery and various therapies for hemorrhoids, fistulas, prostate disturbances, and malignancies.

The Principal Causes

A POOR START IN LIFE.—Due to the numerous popular drugs, artificial food products, etc., in use these days, it is difficult for a child to get the proper start in life. The first few days of an infant's life are extremely important; important because it is at this time that the foundation is laid for vitality and health or for low resistance and sickness. How a baby is handled during the first few months may determine whether he will have strong bones, sound teeth, good muscular structure, etc.

In the first place, parents should live natural healthy lives so that they pass on healthy bodies to their children. In the second place, babies should be breast fed, and long enough to give them a good start. Among the reasons for breast feeding is that the infant needs that substance which is present in the mother's milk for three days after childbirth called colostrum. This feeds the acidophilus bacteria in the infant's colon, and this normal flora establishes peristalsis and natural activity throughout the intestinal tract. To feed a baby an artificial formula is to give it an artificial start. Even after birth, the infant is still a part of the mother. There is a direct relation between the chemistry of the mother and the chemistry of her child. Mother's milk cannot be duplicated in a compound formulated in a laboratory. It is a crime beyond all description to cheat the child out of its most important natural right, for mother's milk is a baby's birthright—it gives the baby a normal start during the first few days of life.

We may sometimes wonder why comparatively few mothers today nurse their babies. When there is refusal on the part of a mother animal to nurse her young, we investigate to determine whether there has been a dietary deficiency of manganese. Since restoration of this mineral to the diet stimulates the mother to nurse her young, it has been named "the mother-love element." Whether the human mother refuses to nurse her child because of custom, vanity, or dietary deficiencies, is not easy to say. I am inclined to believe that the advice given mothers in most modern hospitals and "sanitary kitchens" probably is responsible in a large degree. Another factor is excessive tobacco smoking. I know chiropractic obstetricians who refuse to handle an obstetrical case if the mother smokes. Not only is the fetus affected before birth, but after birth the milk will be polluted in about thirty seconds after a cigarette is smoked.

The pattern we start out with we inherit from our parents. It is important to learn how to live correctly, not only to benefit ourselves but the next generation; to benefit not only those for whom we are directly responsible, but those whom we influence in our daily contacts. The mineral elements which the fetus draws from the mother's body must be replaced through proper eating. If the mother is chemically deficient, her child will be born half starved --chemically hungry.

For children who have been improperly fed and do not have a normal intestinal flora, attempt should be made to establish this and to maintain it throughout life. This should be our first duty to such children, for without normal bacterial activity and normal bowel movements, there will be gas formation, diarrhea, dryness of the bowel, and many children's complaints. The flora can be changed by the proper administration of acidophilus culture, which will be discussed later in this chapter. Whey products from goats' or cows' milk, either fresh or powdered, are desirable in the diet because they feed the acidophilus bacteria and sweeten the bowel. If the child cannot take acidophilus culture by mouth, it can be placed in the rectum with a baby enema syringe. For the very young child, a little sugar of milk added to the raw milk in its diet may help to feed acidophilus bacteria that have been implanted in the bowel.

INCORRECT DIET.—Although this subject has been discussed in other parts of this book, we must emphasize again the importance of the optimum nutrition to general health and to normal intestinal function. We have explained the evil effects of denatured foods, so their relation to intestinal disorders should be obvious. We will here add warnings against overeating, hurried eating, eating when not hungry and eating when emotionally disturbed.

FAULTY HABITS.—Needless to say, it is unwise to allow false modesty or any of the conventions imposed by civilization to interfere with bowel evacuation when the signal is received. This signal of nature should be heeded promptly in order to avoid the devlopment of unnatural bowel habits, which will result in destructive consequences.

Many persons deprive the body of natural activity which is essential to normal functioning. If we transfer so many of our physical activities to mechanical devices that our internal as well as external muscles become weakened and flabby, we should not be surprised when our digestive and eliminate functions begin to deteriorate.

The tea and coffee habit, as well as tobacco smoking and the drinking of alcohol, has its toxic effect upon the intestinal tract. Added to these are the poisons of numerous medications. Consider the thousands of remedies for constipation alone.

Mental influences also are very important. When we analyze intestinal disorders or any other disturbances in the body, we should consider the effects of excitement, nervous tension, anxiety, fear and worry. These can throw the nervous mechanism of defaction out of balance.

The Principal Disorders

CONSTIPATION.—More than 45,00 laxatives and cathartics are used in this country today. It has been calculated that Americans spend a hundred million dollars a year in their effort to overcome constipation.. These laxative and cathartic products contain harsh and poisonous substances so that the colon will react and eliminate them as quickly as possible—and the fecal material along with them.

The foods we eat normally do not remain very long in either the stomach or the small intestine. And the length of time required for passage through the large intestine is important. The slower the movement of waste material through the colon, the greater the bacterial content and the greater the possibility of putrefaction. A certain amount of time is required for the bacterial break-down of some of the cellulose and coarse fibres, but in many persons the passage is too slow. Accumulated matter in any disposal system, decays and omits foul odors when allowed to become stagnant. It is said that normal human feces consists chiefly of dead bacteria,—millions being exreted daily.

Quite frequently we see magazine and newspaper articles by writers who contend that indefinite retention of intestinal contents is not harmful to the body. This lulls some constipated individuals into the false belief that although they are accumulating waste day after day, it really does not matter. They might be surprised at what their iris would show to the contrary.* Other individuals are deceived into believing they are not constipated because they do have

*All bodily conditions are reflected in the iris of the eye.

frequent movements, but altogether they may be eliminating only a small portion of the bowel contents instead of about four-fifths of it as they should.

While attending the National College in Chicago many years ago, autopsies were performed on 300 persons. According to the history of these persons, 285 had claimed they were not constipated and had normal movements, and only fifteen had admitted they were constipated. The autopsies showed the opposite to be the case, however, and only fifteen were found not to have been constipated, while 285 were found to have been constipated. Some of the histories of these 285 persons stated they had had as many as five or six bowel movements daily, yet autopsies revealed that in some of them the bowels were 12 inches in diameter. The bowel walls were encrusted with material (in one case peanuts) which had been lodged there for a very long time. Thus we see that the average patient coming to a doctor's office does not know whether or not he is constipated.

Some of my patients believe that if they have three bowel movements a day they have diarrhea, and that a couple of movements a week is normal. An example of the latter was a lady patient I had who assured me that she had normal movements; that her bowels moved regularly, every Tuesday and Friday morning. Most people have not been properly educated in their childhood to realize the importance of adequate daily elimination and to heed nature's call to evacuate the rectum. This indifference to the natural urge to evacuate the bowels may be the beginning of constipation.

Doctor John Harvey Kellogg, who gave us so much of his philosophy and practical experience, lived to the age of ninety-one. Since he did more work in connection with intestinal sanitation than anyone in this country, his advice should be worth listening to. It was his opinion that we should eliminate the residue of each meal fifteen to eighteen hours after eating it. Babies, savages, birds and animals evacuate a short time after each meal. Some of the patients who came to us for colonic treatments were far from this ideal; some of them passed the seeds of grapes they had eaten nine months before the colonics were given them; others passed such things as popcorn and barium meal they had been retaining in the colon for years. Those segments of the bowel where there are such encrustations are the sources of disturbances behind reflex symptoms in remote parts of the body.

Observe from the following statistics published by the Register General of England that no group has contributed more to the death rate from intestinal diseases than doctors.

"Comparative Mortality from Diseases of the Digestive System.

Physicians, surgeons	50
Inn-keepers	45
Barristers, solicitors	44
Seamen	43
Clergymen, priests, ministers	34
Butchers	30
Carmen, carriers	28
Farmers	25
Gardeners	22
Railway guards, porters	20
Agricultural labourers	19
Average among all workers	28

As shown by the above statistics, the death rate of doctors is 31 points higher than that of agricultural laborers, and 22 points higher than that of the average death rate of all workers who die of diseases of the digestive system.

The necessity for the removal of waste was proved by the embryo chicken heart experiment of Dr. Alexis Carrel in 1912 at the Rockefeller Institute for Medical Research. This isolated tissue was kept alive and growing for some thirty years. It was fed by the nutrient solution in which it was kept, but it was necessary that waste end-products not be allowed to accumulate. When not fed the tissue did not grow, but one time after the doctor had retired an assistant forgot to remove the waste. The tissue died.

I am convinced that the person who suffers from bowel constipation also has a type of tissue constipation and encumbrance in other parts of his body such as the eyes, gall bladder, liver, kidneys, lungs, etc. Constipation increases the work of other organs of excretion and may result in their depletion. As cellular processes are interfered with, they become inactive. With such constipation throughout, what body could remain well?

I do not wish to give the impression that I have become one-sided in my emphasis upon the importance of a healthy, clean intestinal tract, but evidence has been coming to me for a long time which indicates that people do not realize that constipation is at the root of most of our diseases today. I feel that people are not regarding poor health as seriously as they should. They place their health problems secondary to all their other problems—financial, domestic, real and invented,—while the health of an individual or a nation should at all times have first place on the list of duties and responsibilities. Without health there is little that one can truly enjoy.

Recently I received a letter from a patient I once examined in the Middle West, whose case is *apropos* and so typical that I mention it here. After telling me incidentally about the hemorrhoids which are bothering her and which are secondary to a number of disorders, she seriously requests that I advise her what type of floor covering in their new dwelling would be easiest for her to walk on and therefore be easiest on the hemorrhoidal condition. Like those persons referred to who do not realize the basic importance of a healthy intestinal tract, she is requesting advice about end-results rather than about the causes underlying her symptoms. If she got rid of all her basic troubles, she would be able to walk comfortably on the floor whether it was covered with linoleum or carpet. I cannot help believing that had this wo-

man's intestinal tract been cleansed and rejuvenated in the first place, most of her difficulties could have been avoided.

Other doctors also may have noticed that it is typical of patients to minimize the importance of adequate bowel elimination and try to call attention to other factors, such as the type of shoes they find the most comfortable, or the kind of floor they must stand upon, as in the above mentioned case. Constipation can be corrected by eliminative diet, by normalizing the intestinal flora, by slanting board exercises (see Mechanical Corrective Measures), and by health education. Other disorders which may occur when the body has become devitalized and laden with toxins are colitis, prolapsus, worms, piles and hemorrhoids.

Remedial Measures

It is difficult to make rules on how to handle the various intestinal disorders, but first of all we must consider that the colon is only one part of the body and depends upon the proper activity of every other organ for normal function. The mind, for instance, can sometimes cause more intestinal disturbances than the worst diet. There are times when a sedentary occupation can be a direct cause of a bowel disturbance. Anyone who is enervated, tired or depleted, does not have full power to eliminate and such a person may develop habits of delayed movement. There is the distended bowel, the irritated and spastic bowel. There is the bowel that produces pressure symptoms and there is the sluggish and pocketed bowel. There is the bowel that is suffering from the effects of drugs, hard waters, and devitalized foods. There is the bowel that is subjected to putrefaction and fermentation.

With all of these conditions, it might be well to consider an *eliminative program* to begin with. See the chapters on The Theory of the Healing Crisis and Fasting and Eliminative Diets.

Just as faulty habits have contributed to the development of constipation, so can desirable habits help to overcome it. As we have stated, it is very important to allow the bowels to move whenever they give the impulse.

Rest after meals is desirable.

Hydrotherapy when intelligently applied is powerful in its therapeutic effects. Just the drinking of pure water is beneficial in the correction of intestinal disorders, especially if one drinks one or two glasses immediately upon arising.

Sitz baths are very helpful in overcoming constipation. Every other day one should sit for two to five minutes with the hips in cold water (60°F.), followed by sitting in warm water (100°F.) for five to ten minutes, and ending with cold water for two minutes.

Persons who are troubled with intestinal *gas* may be greatly relieved by a wet pack applied to the abdomen. Wring a hand towel from cold water and fold it the size to cover the abdomen. After this wet towel has been placed on the abdomen, cover it completely with a heavy Turkish towel that will extend at least an inch beyond the wet towel. Wind the Turkish towel all the way around the body, in corset fashion, so as to hold the wet towel securely in place and to prevent the entrance of any air. This pack should be left on over night and repeated until relief is obtained.

Along with the use of these wet packs, very stubborn cases of intestinal gas have been quickly relieved by taking no food for two or three days and drinking only buttermilk when hungry and water when thirsty.

In cases of *colitis,* also, cold water packs on the abdomen are beneficial. A relaxed mind, free from fear, hatred and resentment, will help any case of colitis. Although in most instances a person should have in his diet plenty of fresh fruits and vegetables and some whole grains, it may be necessary for patients with colitis to eliminate raw foods from the diet, at least temporarily, and also fibrous and bulky foods such as stems, peelings, and seeds. The best food in the world may cause disturbance in the intestinal tract of a nervous person. In correcting spastic conditions, we use a bland diet to begin with, proper exercise, mental hygiene, and eventually a full health-building program.

In all cases of intestinal disturbance, a *diet* which is balanced, varied, and in proper combination is necessary. Some persons are food drunkards; they crave the effects of certain foods to which they have become accustomed, and they sometimes go on "binges" of chocolate, starchy foods, etc. There must be some knowledge and regulation about the food that goes into the stomach. Abnormal cravings that have developed through excessive acid accumulations in the body should not be indulged.

In persons with intestinal disorders, the *intestinal flora needs normalizing,* and we are going to discuss this presently. In addition to fresh vegetables and fruits, these individuals are particularly in need of such foods as yogurt and other sour milk products. Yogurt is a cultured milk product which originated in Europe. When I was in Switzerland I noticed that yogurt was considered the most important item in the dairy store. They use a combination there of yogurt with apple juice or a small quantity of apple concentrate, which is wonderful for the intestine. Persons who consider milk to be constipating usually will have no difficulty when using milk in the raw state and in combination with fruits and vegetables. Foods that are high in B vitamins, such as yeast, assist normal intestinal functioning.

Fermented milks have been used as beverages and as food for many centuries. The souring of milk is a spontaneous change due to the action of the *bacillus acidi lactiti* (which means acid-loving, acid-producing, acid-resisting). When these bacilli have converted the milk sugar into lactic acid, the milk becomes sour. After milk has soured, the growth of disease-producing bacteria ceases, and the milk proteins change into more digestible form.

Fig. 197. This photograph taken in Switzerland shows how a herder in the morning calls the goats belonging to various families in a town, after which he guides them to pastures in the hills during the day. When the goats are returned in the evening, they are ready to supply their owners with fresh milk.

Professor Metchnikoff became famous for his recommended use of fermented milk as the best neutralizer of putrefaction in the colon. He felt convinced that abnormal conditions in the bowels caused disease, premature aging and death. Presence of the proper acid-loving bacteria in the colon of the infant makes him immune to many diseases. These can be present only so long as he receives breast milk, which enables the colon to be normally acid in reaction. After a child begins to eat adult foods, unfriendly bacteria begin to grow in the colon. There may be fermentation of carbohydrate foods and putrefaction of protein foods, and the formation of numerous toxins such as indol, skatol, phenol, ammonia, ptomaine, cadaverin, etc.

In "New Dietetics," Doctor John Harvey Kellogg records that in 1907 he began an experiment to test the ability of lactic acid forming organisms to suppress putrefaction. "A pound of beefsteak was immersed in a two-quart jar of buttermilk. Although the flesh was slightly tainted when purchased, after a few days in the buttermilk, it was found to be entirely free from taint." The buttermilk was changed each week and at the time this account was written, 1927, bacteriological examination showed that no putrefactive bacteria were present in the beefsteak.

Since unfriendly, disease-producing bacteria do not thrive in an acid medium, a change of intestinal flora to contain a preponderance of acidophilus bacilli is desirable. As previously stated, in most patients the ratio of unfriendly bacteria is 80-85 per cent to only 15-20 per cent of acidophilus bacilli. This ratio should be reversed in order to destroy the cause of constipation, auto-intoxication, and other intestinal disorders.

There are several good acidophilus cultures which can be obtained, such as those put out by the Battle Creek Sanitarium at Battle Creek, Michigan and the Kovac Laboratories in Los Angeles. We have found that the acidophilus bacteria can be increased in the colon by the use of daily retention enemas of whey. Whey by mouth also is helpful.

Fig. 198. Note the prominent place given to yogurt in the Swiss dairy store pictured above.

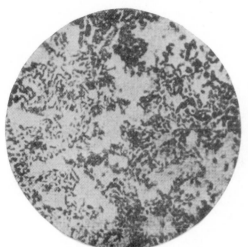 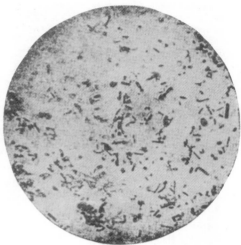

FIG. 199 (a). This micro-photograph (taken at Cornell University Medical College) shows the fecal flora of a patient before the feeding of an acid-ophilus culture.

FIG. 199 (b). This micro-photograph shows the changes in the flora of the same patient 48 hours after adminis-tration of acidophilus culture. Spores and anerobic bacilli (B. Welchii) have been eliminated by the substitution of aciduric bacilli (B. Acidophilus).

When is the intestinal flora changed? According to Doctor Kellogg it is changed "when the stools are soft, frequent (three times a day), and free from putrid or ran-cid odor. Examination by a bacteriologist should show 80 per cent of the acid form-ers and 20 per cent of other bacteria . . . Old troubles may still continue, perhaps somewhat modified. But when the change reaches 75-25, marked improvement will be evident, and the more complete the change of flora, the more decided will be the change for the better in the patient's symptoms."

The presence of *worms* in the intestinal tract is more frequent than we might sus-pect. They are sometimes taken into the body with foods not thoroughly washed, especially foods that have been grown on soil fertilized with manure or sludge not properly composted. At times it is diffi-cult to get worms out of the body without giving vermifuge. In cases of *tape worm*, extreme measures may be necessary. A method I have used successfully is the garlic treatment, which is given as follows. The patient must eat nothing but garlic or onions for two days. Then a powerful herbal laxative is given, and when it is time for the bowel to evacuate, the patient sits in a vessel of warm milk. Since cold air usually keeps the worm from leaving the body, the warm milk is a favorable means of getting it to pass out of the lower bowel.

In acute cases of *piles* or *hemorrhoids,* the warm sitz-bath will usually give tem-porary relief, and permanent correction if persistently used along with other thera-peutic measures. A cupful of flaxseed tea placed in the rectum with a large bulb syringe each night upon retiring, will al-so give relief. When the rectum and anus are tightly contracted, we use Doctor Young's rectal dilators, which are cylin-ders in graduated sizes designed to gradu-ally stretch and relax the muscles in this area. These are also quite helpful in cases of hemorrhoids, as is finger massage also. Since hemorrhoids result from improper

FIG. 200. This photograph shows Mrs. Anderson, champion figure skater, leading a group at the sanitarium in exercises intended particularly to develop the intestinal muscles. The importance of intestinal management was stressed at the sanitarium.

functioning or disease of the liver, we work toward cleansing of the whole system in order to correct the condition. We use the slanting board in these cases. When at stool, it is well to hold the hands above the head as this keeps the rectal tissues from protruding during defecation. Papaya tablets taken with meals are very effective in all digestive disturbances.

To soften the bowel contents we use *flaxseed meal*. A tablespoonful mixed in a glass of water should be taken three times a day. A tablespoon of blackstrap molasses three times a day is also a wonderful laxative for most people. When the bowel tissues are irritated or inflamed, a cupful of flaxseed tea ten minutes before each meal will have a soothing effect. Flaxseed tea is made as follows: Simmer for ten minutes one tablespoon of whole flaxseed in one pint of water. Strain, and drink the liquid only. Flaxseed tea can also be used

for enemas of the lower bowel where there is an irritation.

While we do not approve of the regular use of laxatives, for persons who must have a laxative of some kind, we use a *food laxative* that helps to evacuate the bowel contents because of the bulk which it provides. In time this natural food laxative should help to rebuild the bowel wall, as it is nourishing. It is made as follows: Grind together one-third pound each of raisins, dates and prunes. Then add 8 tablespoons of whey, 6 tablespoons of flaxseed meal, 8 tablespoons of blackstrap molasses, and mix well together. If more liquid is needed to mix the ingredients well, use a little flaxseed tea. An amount the size of a golf ball should be taken before each meal. When taken with acidophilus culture, bowel activity will eventually improve.

While I do not believe that any of these measures alone will cure, they are helpful as relief measures that can be used along with our right-living program.

When we have succeeded in correcting intestinal disorders, we are on the surest road to health. Alexis Carrel has said, "The cell is immortal. It is merely the fluid in which it floats which degenerates. Renew this fluid at intervals, give the cell something upon which to feed and, so far as we know, the pulsation of life may go on forever."

INDEX

— F —

— G —

— T —

ORDER FORM

Please Ship My Order To:

Name _____

Street _____

City _____ State _____ Zip ____

	Quantity	Amount

BLENDING MAGIC — 3.95

Blend your way to health and happiness. 650 prize winning recipes. A must for those interested in preparing meals, drinks and special food combinations by way of blending.

CREATING A MAGIC HEALTH KITCHEN — 1.95

A doctor's manual for his patient. Clear directions and lists for the best proteins, starches, vegetables, etc. Start your life and health the right way in a revised kitchen prepared by a nutritionist.

HEALTH MAGIC THROUGH CHLOROPHYLL — 3.95

Gives the true value of greens and how to use. Many case histories and remedies are presented. The most definitive text on greens, grasses and sprouts. First in the series of Survival Books. Following this will be BERRIES AND YOUTH FOODS and SEEDS AND SPROUTS (enlarged edition).

HEALTH TIP BOOKS

All include recipes along with practical advice:

1. HONEY—The natural sweet. Ancient and modern usage. Types of honey for beauty and health. · · · · · · 1.00
2. SEEDS AND SPROUTS FOR LIFE— How to grow and use these vital foods. Recent discoveries, descriptions. · · · · · · 1.50
3. YOUR LIFE IN YOGURT — Special benefit to the intestinal tract. Used by oldest men in the world. How to make yogurt at home. · · · · · · 1.00
4. CHEESE IT! — How to make, buy, prepare, serve. Advantage of raw milk cheese. 1.50
5. SOUP'S ON! — Special ingredients. Thermos soups. Blended soups. · · · · · · 1.00
6. CANDY FOR YOUR SWEET TOOTH — Natural candy making for all ages. · · 1.00
7. PROTEIN — What is the best? How much protein do you really need? · · · · 1.00
8. DRIED FRUIT—A natural way of preservation. Sun drying, storing, reviving. · 1.00
9. SALADS AROUND THE WORLD — Gathered from Dr. Jensen's travels. New twists for serving. How to select around the seasons. · · · · · · 1.50
10. NUTS FOR YOU — Nuts in their natural state. Nut Milk Drinks. Growing, planting, Descriptions. · · · · · · 1.50
11. HEALTH DESSERTS — Tasty and nourishing for your family. · · · · · · 1.00
12. HOME FREEZING — Another natural method of preservation. Learn how to retain vitamins and minerals with proper freezing. · · · · · · 1.50

DR. JENSEN'S HOME STUDY COURSE

Health encyclopedia in 56 lessons. This complete course in healthy living covers the physical, mental and spiritual aspects of life.

Individual Lessons · · · · · · · 1.50
Complete Encyclopedia · · · · · · · 75.00

Volume I	Lessons 1 — 10	14.00
Volume II	Lessons 11 — 20	14.00
Volume III	Lessons 21 — 30	14.00
Volume IV	Lessons 31 — 40	14.00
Volume V	Lessons 41 — 50	14.00
Volume VI	Lessons 51 — 56	8.50

SEND FOR FREE OUTLINE AND INDEX

DR. JENSEN'S LECTURES on CASSETTE TAPES

1. Chemical Story
2. Building a Way to Eat
3. Replacement Therapy
4. Regularity Management
5. Divine Order

6. Seeds
7. Natural Healing
8. Key to Inner Calm
9. Breathing Exercises

$6.95 EACH!

IRIDOLOGY, The Science and Practice of
Full-color Photographs, $18.50
Wall Chart, 27"x22", 2 color photos *$5.00*
Plastic Desk Chart, 4"x8" plastic cover *$3.00*

Subtotal _____

Ask For FREE Folder ☐

6% CA Sales Tax _____

TOTAL _____

BERNARD JENSEN PRODUCTS
PUBLISHING DIVISION
P.O. Box 8, Solana Beach, California 92075

LECTURE REPRINTS

YOU CAN FEEL WONDERFUL, ENJOY IT NOW! $3.95
An all around book for the whole family and one that will
make a wonderful gift.

JOY OF LIVING AND HOW TO ATTAIN IT 4.75
This will get you started on the Royal Road to Health.

VITAL FOODS FOR TOTAL HEALTH 4.50
Know the foods you can get well with by using the Science of
Nutrition. Know your "ONIONS", know the berries, know
how to make sandwiches, salads, soups and broths. A book
dedicated to changing your kitchen to a health kitchen where
the whole family can start the healthy body everybody wants.

YOU CAN MASTER DISEASE 4.75
This gives all the work used at the Health Ranch. Illustrates
and gives the treatments and the philosophy used.

BEAUTY & CHARM AT A GLANCE 2.00
This book helps you to do many things for yourself to raise
your health level. Reducing diets — a complete plan for
Health and Beauty.

OVERCOMING ARTHRITIS OR RHEUMATISM 3.00
Water treatments, fasting, elimination, diets, sunbathing and
the natural phases of the Nature Healing Arts discussed.

Buy them at your health food store, or if not available, order direct from:

BERNARD JENSEN PRODUCTS
PUBLISHING DIVISION
P.O. Box 8, Solana Beach, California 92075

TO BE PUBLISHED

CHEMICAL STORY
Know how chemicals build your body. All diseases and symptoms can be a chemical shortage.

COOK BOOK
365 days of menus and recipes. Information on setting up a health kitchen and how to build a disease free body through the proper nutrition. Available in early 1974.

EXERCISE BOOK
An exercise for every organ in the body. Explanation of what each exercise does for you.

NOW TIL LONGEVITY
Goes through 34 countries giving 30 keys to long-life, health and happiness. Dr. Jensen's travels to the old people of Hunza, Russia, South America, New Zealand. Well-illustrated.

JOURNEY INTO COLOR
Secrets of the finer forces of nature. Has to be seen to be appreciated. Body and soul building. Beautifully illustrated.

ENCYCLOPEDIA OF FOODS
Description of all foods and how to use. Where they originated. Vitamin and mineral values. How to use as remedies, packs, drinks and recipes. For health and beauty.

READY FOR THE PRESS

MAGIC EYE BUILDING
ARISE AND SHINE
A spiritual book made up of Sunday morning lectures at the Ranch.
NATURAL REMEDIES FOR NATURAL PEOPLE

IRIDOLOGY EQUIPMENT

1. SCIENCE AND PRACTICE OF IRIDOLOGY. Text for the study of Iridology. Color photos, 360 pages. $18.50
2. JENSEN'S IRIGOLOGY MANUAL. Explanation of lesions with 36 slides to study. 20.00
3. PATIENT ANALYSIS. Given by Dr. Jensen to one of his patients. Complete explanation of lesions; slides includes; 10 pages. 5.00
4. NOTES FOR CLASS. Chart included. Best when giving classes. 2.00
5. WALL CHART. Colored photographs. Iridology wall chart. Suitable for framing. 16 x 20. 7.50
6. DESK CHART. Laminated, 3 x 5, chart of the eyes. 3.50
7. MAGNIFYING LENS. Four power 4.25

World Iridology Fellowship: Memberships and Journals are handled by Dr. John Arnold, 3763 Glenfeliz, Los Angeles, CA 90039.

Write for Complete List of Books and Tapes.
California Residents add 6% Sales Tax.
ORDER DIRECTLY FROM:
DR. BERNARD JENSEN
Route 6, Box 811, Escondido, California 92025